THE BEST TEEN

WRITING OF 2010

FOREWORD BY DAVY ROTHBART

EDITED BY JARED DUMMITT

2009 PORTFOLIO GOLD SCHOLASTIC AWARDS RECIPIENT

THE SCHOLASTIC ART & WRITING AWARDS

Alliance for Young Artists **&** Writers

Cover Image: **Xavier Donnelly,** Crop from *Green City,* Drawing, Age 17, VT

For information or permission, contact:
Alliance for Young Artists & Writers
557 Broadway
New York, NY 10012
212-343-6892
www.artandwriting.org

Copy editor: Adrienne Onofri

Copyright © 2010 Alliance for Young Artists & Writers
All rights reserved. Printed in the United States of America
Anthology printing, October 2010
ISBN-978-545-32793-0
ISBN-0-545-32793-8

The Best Teen Writing of 2010 is dedicated to former Associate Executive Director Bryan Doerries. In his tenure at the Alliance, Bryan was the organization's best salesman and theorist, a bottomless source of energy and imagination. He balanced a fascination for the lore and legacy of The Scholastic Art & Writing Awards with a practical eye for innovative ways to spread the ideals of The Awards and their founder, Maurice R. Robinson. Bryan was instrumental in streamlining the submission process, exploding the potential of our website, and embracing video games as a new medium for self-expression. Under his guidance, the Alliance, our partners, and the young artists and writers we serve have learned how powerful creative energy can be when it is nurtured and shared.

About The Best Teen Writing of 2010

The works featured in *The Best Teen Writing of 2010* are selected from this year's Scholastic Art & Writing Awards, a national program presented by the Alliance for Young Artists & Writers, which recognizes talented teenagers in the visual and literary arts. The Awards were founded in 1923 to celebrate the accomplishments of creative students and to extend to them opportunities for recognition, exhibition, publication, and scholarships.

In 2010, more than 165,000 artworks and manuscripts were submitted in 30 categories to regional affiliates across the country. Professionals reviewed the works for excellence in three core criteria: technical skill, originality, and the emergence of a personal vision or voice.

More than 1,300 students received National Awards and joined the ranks of such luminaries as Richard Avedon, Truman Capote, Bernard Malamud, Carolyn Forché, Sylvia Plath, Joyce Carol Oates, Robert Redford, Andy Warhol, and many others who won Scholastic Awards when they were teenagers.

This year, 395 teens were recognized as the best young writers in the country. The works selected for this publication represent the diversity of the National Award winners, including age and grade, gender, genre, geography, and subject matter. They also present a spectrum of the insight and creative intellect that informs many award-winning pieces.

A complete listing of National Award winners and examples of winning works of art and writing can be found on our website at **www.artandwriting.org.** There, you will also find information about how to enter the 2011 Scholastic Art & Writing Awards, a list of our scholarship partners, and ways that you can partner with the Alliance to support young artists and writers in your community.

National Jurors

We are grateful to this year's panel of jurors for their commitment to finding compelling young voices:

American Voices
Ekiwah Adler-Beléndez
Ruth Culham
Ellen Freudenheim
Jacob Lewis
Zoë Pagnamenta
Patricia Smith

Dramatic Script
KJ Sanchez
Tim Sanford
Joanna Settle
Ted Sod

Humor
Alfred Gingold
Patricia Marx
Paula Poundstone

Journalism
James Marcus
Peggy Noonan
Lesley Stahl

Personal Essay/Memoir
Julie Holland
Phyllis Kaufman
Ned Vizzini

Persuasive Essay
Roger Cohen
Candace Sandy
Alfred Tatum

Poetry
Major Jackson
Christopher Luna
Alice Quinn

Science Fiction/Fantasy
Alex Carr
Paul Melko
Greg van Eekhout

Short Story
Colin Harrison
Davy Rothbart
Jill Sobule

Short Short Story
Madison Smartt Bell
Rebecca Bondor
Louise Crawford

General Writing Portfolio
Carolyn Forché-Mattison
Tony Kushner
Walter Dean Myers

Nonfiction Writing Portfolio
Lauren Keane
John Leland
Luc Sante

THE ALLIANCE FOR YOUNG ARTISTS & WRITERS

CONTENTS

GOLD, SILVER, AND AMERICAN VOICES MEDALS POETRY

PERSONAL ESSAY/MEMOIR

SHORT SHORT STORY

HUMOR

SHORT STORY

Editor's Introduction

The book that you hold in your hands is about 300 pages long. This is a bit deceptive, in the way that a 200-ton iceberg is a bit deceptive: What you see is a tiny fraction of the hulking mass that lurks just beneath the surface. I think that the phrase "hulking mass" is a fitting bridge between icebergs and essays written by teenagers, because it perfectly describes the quantity of writing from which the pieces in this anthology have been selected.

The Best Teen Writing of 2010 probably weighs a little less than a pound. The collective weight of the National Award-winning pieces that were considered for publication is 22 pounds. (I know this because, overwhelmed by the size of the three manuscript boxes that arrived on my doorstep for editing, I felt compelled to create a teen writing tower on my bathroom scale.) Of course, only about one-hundredth of one percent of all 20,000 entries wins an award. If *The Best Teen Writing of 2010* is the size of a guinea pig, then it was selected from a body of work the size of a walrus.

The point is not to awe you with numbers, or to shame you with the quantity of trees that must have perished to make this book a reality. Rather, it speaks to the fact that the works here are the best of the best, the cream that has risen all the way to the top of a very deep barrel. It has been my pleasure to see them through that ascension. I have read through a foot and a half of personal essays, fished through hundreds of poems, and became caught in the twists and turns of a stack of short stories that easily outweighed my 2-year-old cousin. It took 10 hours of reading a day for three weeks, but I can truly say that it was a labor of love.

The emotional range of these pieces is extraordinary, and their capacity to touch and move far outstrips the ages of their authors. In the end, the challenge was not reading through my 22-pound pile—it was choosing. For every piece that could be printed in the anthology, several authors vied for position. It has been both a struggle and an honor to select these pieces from such impressive company, and I hope that you enjoy reading them as much as I have.

In his short story "The Library of Babel," Jorge Luis Borges describes a universe composed of an infinite library. The endless shelves hold every book that has been and ever will be written. In Borges' world, some believe that there is one final, unfindable book, and on its pages are written the truth. If all writing seeks to emulate that unspeakable text, then these pieces grasp at it with remarkable skill and tenacity. For years to come, we will rely on these young visionaries to navigate those dusty bookshelves, to bring us closer to understanding ourselves, one other, and the relationships that bind us to the world.

I'd like to stop here to thank those who have helped me along the way in my own journey. First, I wish to thank the Alliance for Young Artists & Writers for providing me such a rich variety of opportunities over the years, both as an individual and an author. In particular, I owe a debt of gratitude to Alex Tapnio for his trust and professionalism; to Lisa Feder-Feitel for her willingness and ability to be helpful; and to Matt Boyd, without whose patience and constant assistance I could not have succeeded. I'd also like to thank Mr. Eric Grossman of Stuyvesant High School, who got me started on this whole process several years ago. Finally and most deeply, my gratitude goes out to my friends and especially my family: to my parents for their unbounded love and support; to my older siblings Joanna and David, for their guidance, loyalty, and amazing capacity for giving good advice; and to my twin brother, Morgan, for being the best and most reliable friend and partner I could ask for. I owe each of you in ways I cannot put into words.

It only takes the very tip of an iceberg to create beauty, shape the environment, and change history. In spite of its size, this book has the same awesome power. This sampling of writing is the small—perhaps too small—portion that has reached the surface and found its way to you. I invite you to sail fearlessly straight toward it, to follow these young men and women into that uncertain library. Be careful, remember what lurks beneath the surface, and allow your breath to be taken away.

—Jared Dummitt

FOREWORD

A few winters ago, I developed an excruciating crush on a red-haired girl named Chelsie who worked at the coffee shop near my house. A few times a week, I'd stop by, hoping to see her. Sometimes she'd flash me a smile, and I'd leave the place soaring; other times, she handed over my change without even meeting my gaze, and I'd trail out, lost and hopeless. I knew I had to find a way to engage her and start a conversation, but there was always an impatient crowd stacked behind me in line, and it was hard to get many words in beyond "Hey, how's your day going?"

One afternoon, I saw an opening—Chelsie was alone, wiping down tables in the back of the place. I gathered my courage, went over, and introduced myself, then made my awkward pitch: "OK, so I know you don't really know me or anything, you just sell me bananas and juice, but it always brightens my day to see you, and I was just wondering if you might be down to hang out sometime?"

I expected to be rejected, I just wasn't sure what tack she'd take—most likely, she'd say that she was already seeing someone, or that as a rule she didn't date customers. Still, I'd made a pledge to myself to always risk rejection in life on the chance (however small) that things would work out. Her response was gleefully stunning: "I'd love to hang out. In fact, I just read your book."

Yes, a book of my short stories had come out a couple of years before, but nothing like this had ever happened. Chelsie explained that she often sifted through the dumpster in the alley behind the coffee shop, which was shared with the chain bookstore next door, to pick out unsold magazines and remaindered books the store had discarded. The magazine covers were always ripped off and the books torn in half, but at least she had a constant, fresh source of reading material for her lunch breaks. A couple of months earlier, she'd rescued my book from the dumpster and read the half that was there. I couldn't believe my ridiculous luck.

We hear all the time about the supposed death of publishing and how the simple act of reading has been crowded out in a cacophonous world of Xbox games and YouTube clips. But if a beautiful, kind, and curious-minded girl like Chelsie is willing to sift through garbage to extract half of a book, I declare that reading is alive and well. As an author, to be published means that anyone might bump into one of my books at a bookstore or a library—and that even if one gets tossed out, somebody might find it in a dumpster and give it a whirl. When someone reads a book I've written, I feel like I've communicated myself to them in a deep and profound way. I cherish every e-mail and Facebook message I receive from people who let me know what my book has meant to them. It's truly thrilling to have your writing out there in the world for anyone to discover.

The book you're holding in your hands right this second contains a rich mix of short stories, poetry, journalism, and humor pieces by our country's finest young writers. To the authors included in this book: Thank you for sharing your funny, moving, and absorbing voices. Thank you for having the courage to put your ideas, emotions, and stories into words and the skill to transmit them in such captivating fashion. To publish for the first time, as many of you are doing here, is worthy of great fanfare and congratulations. I look forward to reading much more of your writing in the years to come.

To all those young writers who may have hoped to be included in this book and were not, or who might hope to publish here or elsewhere one day, I say this: Keep writing. Keep finding ways to get your work out there into the world, whether you staple together your own zine and pass it out in the hallways at school or send poems and stories to your favorite magazines and book publishers. Writing, in itself, is a noble and meaningful pursuit, but putting yourself out there and allowing others into the worlds you've created is truly a gift. It's never easy to risk rejection—whether it's entering contests, submitting work to your school's literary journal, or asking out someone you have a crush on—but it's essential. We make our own luck, through hard work, passion, and determination. It was awfully lucky that Chelsie stumbled upon my book, but it was my dedication to writing that brought the book to life in the first place. Keep writing, and your writing will find a home.

Finally, to those holding this book in your hands, about to dive in: You're in for a scrumptious treat. I know you'll enjoy the writing inside as much as I have. All you haters out there decrying the future of literature? Crack this book open and shut your traps. Here's to a new generation of writers, readers, and American storytelling!

—Davy Rothbart

PORTFOLIO GOLD MEDALS

Graduating high school seniors may submit a portfolio of three to eight works for review by authors, educators, and literary professionals. Winners of the General Writing Portfolio and Nonfiction Portfolio Gold Medals each receive a $10,000 scholarship.

Rita Feinstein, 17
Homeschool
Glorieta, NM
Teacher: Margaret Peters

*Rita Feinstein will attend Wells College in Aurora, New York. She finds
that she is most often inspired by people she has barely met and places she has
just passed through. Aside from writing, she loves to draw and study tarot
cards. Her favorite subjects are foxes, although she can't quite say why.*

TOMATO TOUCH
Short Story

Her name is Roma, like the tomato. Pale as salt, too thin, with a
cavity below her ribs—the perfect size for a baby's head. She stands
like a question mark, hips thrust forward, spine slung back. Those hips.
Her most prominent feature, they are awkward and jutting like a roast
chicken in tight plastic. She has a potato nose that is only noticeable
from profile. That may be why she doesn't have a boy. Everything goes
swimmingly until he catches her at the wrong angle, excuses himself,
and finds someone he can kiss without her beak jabbing his eye.

Tomato belongs to the nightshade family. Woody nightshade
has flat white petals and lustrous berries the color of dragon breath.
Each berry resembles a little Roma tomato—each cluster of berries,
a noxious constellation. Roma herself looks in her mirror, pulls
beneath her eyes to make herself a specter. Poisonous. Lethal.

Roma is pretty and polite, the kind of girl whose mouth you
want to stitch into a smile so she can join your doll collection. You
look at her and know she donated all her Christmas money to the
Save the Red Pandas! campaign. She's a global thinker, someone who
replants her peach pits and has a pen pal in Mumbai.

She has legs from here to heaven. She looks foxy in short shorts.

Grandmothers try to stroke her hair. Boys try to pinch her rear.
Children try to tag her *it*. She jerks away every time, has grown
accustomed to their hurt expressions. If they had touched, though,
they would have been hurt much worse.

Her name is Roma and she has seen a pickled heart. It was on that new hospital show, *411 on 911*, that's on every Thursday at 3. A jar of formaldehyde seems like a safe place for a heart, Roma thinks. She knows they bloat into plaque-yellow sea creatures with lacy tentacles, but she can't stop believing that a preserved heart is as sturdy as a Roma tomato encasing a trove of seeds.

Roma watches the program with her neighbor, whose hair curlers seem about to uproot her face. The neighbor says "Botox" so often it becomes subconscious, the way Roma says "like" and "wow." Her face is a plastic mask. She says Botox changed her life, says with a face like this, you can't lose at poker.

The neighbor pokes the place between Roma's eyebrows, where the muscle bunches. She pushes and pushes, trying to lock it into smoothness, but it pops up again. She tuts and says, "That muscle is always the first to go. I'm taking you to Doctor What's-His-Face on your 18th birthday, hear? Goddamn it, what *is* his face? It was such a nice face, too…"

Roma goes to the kitchen for water. Sand always gushes from the spout and the glasses are soapy. She leans against the counter, views her reflection in the toaster, pushes the muscle. She doesn't want trenches, but she doesn't want Botox either. She doesn't know what she wants, except maybe to eat a lot of tomatoes and therefore gain some identity. And some weight.

Her name is Roma and whatever she touches dies.

She once had a plastic barn. When unlatched, it split in half to reveal rows of stalls with stick-on nameplates, molded hay bales glued to the floor, and a cat painted accidental purple. Roma stuffed her horse collection in the barn and latched it. Then she shook with all her might. And opened the barn. A toothpick jumble of legs, shattered at the thigh, poured into her lap, followed by 15 legless horses, smooth as hot dogs. "Mom!" Roma howled.

Her mother looked away from the chicken skin she was picking from the dish drain. "Christ, honey, what did you expect to happen?" she said, which to Roma's ears meant "Don't you realize you destroy everything you touch?"

Her name is Roma and she had a mule named Samson. Samson had eyes like Russian jewel boxes or fudgy mirrors thick with lacquer. He bore the humiliation of Roma's dress-up box—conical princess hats, polyester eye patches, hot pink lipstick, clip-on earrings.

She mummified him in toilet paper for Halloween. They got lost on a spidery, forested driveway and arrived at an outhouse instead of a chocolate-filled cauldron, though Roma's mother would later ask what the difference was. Red berries sprang from the spongy earth, gripping serrated leaves as blood grips a network of veins. Maybe they were jellybeans. Maybe this was the new fad. After all, there is nothing spookier than a portable toilet.

Roma began loading her pockets with berries, relishing the dark energy seeping through her fingers. Dry leaves bit her ankles. The cheddar moon buttered the sky to a higher gloss.

Roma's imp costume stopped scratching her armpits and became like a second skin. She felt ritualistic, and because a witch must nourish her familiar, she fed Samson a handful of berries. Just then, her name was called. She grabbed Samson's reins and rushed back to her mother.

The next morning, flies paraded in front of Samson's eyes.

Roma emptied her pockets of what was apparently woody nightshade, swallowed wrong, started coughing, and ran behind a tree to puke up a pound of Snickers bars and Twizzlers.

Her name is Roma and she is helping her neighbor. The neighbor recently received Botox injections in her hands and cannot cook until the bandages are removed. She watches *411 on 911* and drinks raspberry iced tea. Her buns, steely from workout videos and liposuction, sit like perfectly packed snowballs on the couch. "Can you believe that?" she cries, banging a mummy hand on the armrest. "People wouldn't smoke if they had X-ray vision. Look at that goddamn lung! Looks like a rice cake covered in tar, goddamn it!"

Roma is making lasagna. The kitchen is hot and the air quivers like bacon fat. Roma wipes her hairline, dries her hands on a duckling-patterned dishtowel. She slices tomatoes and rubs in the salt, groans and drizzles cold water on her neck.

She gave up watching the hospital program several weeks ago, when it featured her old biology teacher. He was in for a severe head injury. While driving his European car down a dark road, looking for the right address, he stuck his head out the window. The steering wheel was on the right side of the vehicle. So was his head. It smashed into a mailbox. His nose was crushed, his frontal lobe mangled, and his neck snapped.

By the end of the program, the male nurse was reapplying cologne so that when he told the man's wife the sad news, she'd let him take her out to dinner.

Roma's knife cuts deep. She remembers handing in her homework, her cold fingers brushing his callused ones. A curse bloomed between them, invisible but fatal, and entered his bloodstream like millions of ravenous centipedes. Roma's touch. Roma's fault.

She reaches a hand to block the sun. Her fingers extinguish its light.

THE IMMIGRATION OF GUINEA PIGS
Poetry

I drew guinea pigs on your demonstrative
speech outline. You crossed them out,
a fat **X** of Sharpie, a stamp of rejection
denying guinea pig orphans safe passage
into America.

Their noses run and crust over.
Bitten with mange,
they scratch their seashell ears into flame raisins.

They have not had fresh salad
since the blight seized their homeland.

And you, the dictator, the Stalin of rodents,
make the mark darker and larger than necessary
as if the **X** could become the pig.

Mama Guinea Pig breaks a yogurt pellet
into 31 pieces for her 31 adorable children:
Miles, Matachovich, Metaphizzle, Marina,
Shimmer, Tango, Flamenco, Inderbitzen,
Czar Marco, Adina, Cellophane, Belle,
Carbonatrix, Twinklefoot, Sh'Shyra,
Brunhilda, Sandy, Peter, Nichole, Natalie,
Wolfgang, Fluzzy, Fuzzy, Foofy, Fuffy,
Mookie, Muffcake, Ginger, Eddie, Freddie,
and Jemima.

All in mourning dresses the color of the
fat black **X**s on their foreheads: ACCESS DENIED.
You do not want guinea pigs on your homework,
the poor sweet immigrants anxiously nibbling the pink

webbing of their toes.
Four months on a sewer-smelling ship,
blinking tears into the face of the wind.
Their teakettle voices wail dreams overboard
into the vast tantrum of the Atlantic—

Mama is an honest pig who wants honest pay.

Peter wants to eat nachos before riding the Cyclone
so he can experience the thrill of vomiting in a foreign country.

Ginger wants to inhale Mama's bank account and
cough it back up in a chic Soho boutique.

Eddie and Freddie want to go coin diving in Bethesda Fountain.

And little Jemima blows her nose into her black calico dress,
letting her one dream—that she might purchase a Tiffany
necklace for the Statue of Liberty—fall into the sea.

Alexandra Franklin, 18
Jackson Preparatory School
Jackson, MS
Teacher: Paul Smith

Alexandra Franklin will head to the University of Alabama and plans to major in poetry and creative writing. She grew up in Mississippi and feels inspired by her home state's long history of subtle, tragic literature. She would like to thank her parents, particularly her mother, for supporting and encouraging her throughout her life.

CHEATING AT CARDS
Short Story

I cut myself shaving this morning. I wasn't paying attention, and I let the razor slide sideways, and it opened up a deep, narrow seam in my shin. I didn't even notice it until I stepped out of the shower and the blood ran in diluted pink rivulets between my toes. Now, already, the skin is just beginning to meet and weave together again.

I paid $400 for a roundtrip ticket home. I cannot begin to calculate how far behind I am in paying the rent, but I paid $400 to come home, to sit on the bed I slept in until I was 17, and to play gin rummy with Mary Elizabeth. We've been playing cards like this for as long as I can remember, and I don't think either of us knows how to play without cheating.

"I've taken her to doctors," Mary whispers. Our conversation started at normal volume but has gradually slipped until we are inexplicably whispering. Neither of us wants to be the first to speak up. It reminds me of when we were small and staying up too late, holding hands across the gap between our matching twin beds. "I've taken her to doctors and I've even made doctors come here to see her. They all say nothing is wrong."

"If she says she's sick…" I shuffle the deck flashily, Vegas-style, and pull out 10 cards for each of us. I rifle shamelessly through hers before presenting them with a flourish.

"I don't know what to do anymore."

"I'm glad you called me."

Mary sizes me up. "I'll pay you back for the ticket."

"Yeah," I say, humoring her.

"Maybe I should go check on her."

"She's fine, she's asleep." My sister worries too much. "Just sit. Play this hand."

But she's distracted now, her baby-fine, corn-silk hair swaying back and forth over her shoulder. Her narrow body is curved tensely over her lap, and her fingers hover above the cards like a tarot reader's. I remember when I could pull her against me, rub her shoulders, and calm her down. Now I sit and watch her, motionless and dreamlike, only half-invested in this particular scene.

Mary is flipping through cards now without strategy or purpose. She presses two kings together, turns a queen's back on both of them. She spins a jack away from the pile, and several mundane subjects—a three of hearts, a seven of clubs—slide haplessly under the bed. I feel terrible for leaving her here to cope with our mother's compulsions. My fingers drift to the cut on my shin. "You're enabling her."

"I'm taking care of her," Mary maintains. She obscures her face with a curtain of hair, but her back stiffens dangerously. When she was 8 and I was 12, I told her what I knew about the legitimacy of the Santa Claus story. I haven't thought about it until now, but I remember that her reaction was the same. Regret tastes salty in my mouth. I always know the right thing to say, but I can never bring myself to say it.

She sighs and collapses onto the pillows, reaching up to turn off the lamp. I push a dozen teddy bears to the floor and curl up beside her. Our hips nearly touch; our fingers are so close I can feel the static between them. The green plastic stars that we stuck to the ceiling 10 years ago glow dimly.

"Do you know," Mary slurs sleepily, "that the stars we see are just old light from stars that died centuries ago?"

Within minutes, her breathing becomes deep and long. I slip out of bed and down the hall to our mother's room. The door is ajar. A long, thin slice of light falls across the carpet.

I creep into the room and stand beside her bed. The sheets are tangled and twisted; she is not a silent sleeper like Mary. Instead,

8

she thrashes and groans and cries. Her hair is already damp and curling around her forehead. I can feel the heat rising from her bulky form. I am still stinging from the criticism she offered during dinner—shouldn't I be head editor at the *Tribune* by now? After all the time I've put in? After all the tuition she paid? The truth is that I have forgotten what it would mean to advance a career. Like scuba divers who become disoriented and swim away from the surface when their oxygen is low, I am sure that one day I will advance myself right out of the copy-editing cubicle and onto the street.

Something is crawling up my leg. No, down my leg. *Jesus!* I swear silently, which feels wrong to do in my mother's room, even though I am an adult and she is asleep. I am bleeding, but it takes a moment for me to realize that I have been scratching the razor cut on my leg.

I cannot imagine where my mother keeps the Band-Aids. For a hypochondriac, she keeps her first aid kit woefully bare. It consists of a bandage for sprains, syrup of ipecac, and a pair of tweezers. I sit on the bathroom counter pressing a fistful of Kleenex to my cut and feeling sorry for myself. When the bleeding has slowed, I rummage through her medicine cabinet. She has stocked it like a drugstore. I pull down dozens of bottles of pills for depression and pain and insomnia. There are no Band-Aids. Wearily, I wrap the sprain bandage around my shin and reach up to the tiny window near the ceiling. It's painted shut, but I force it open and take long drags of the cold air. The lights from the city reflect against the clouds, projecting a smoky cap over the horizon. They drown out the stars that traveled for centuries just to be seen tonight.

AT A DINNER PARTY THE NIGHT BEFORE THE DIVORCE IS FINALIZED
Poetry

In crowded rooms I stand alone,
leaning on my whittled bones.
Their brittle laughter spears me through,
as biting as your cheap cologne.

Last fall we needed something new.
You bought six pints of robin blue;
we painted through a week of nights
and hung red drapes to block the view.

We thought the paint would make it right,
and though we tried, it wasn't quite
enough to seal the growing split
that led us here. You're so polite

and calm. You kill them with your wit.
You're charismatic, I admit—
you charmed me once. God, what a sin;
I once thought I could shrink to fit

your standards. I was lovely then.
Tonight they press my icy skin
and whisper that this poor girl's grown
as hollow as a violin.

ANNE BOLEYN TO HER NEWBORN
Poetry

I know how to weave daisy chains,
splitting the wet living stem
with my half-moon thumbnail,
threading them together like lovers' arms.
I taught my sister when we were
children. It was days—no,
weeks ago—months, maybe
(not years, surely?)

I clutch that memory between my teeth
like a bullet, now, while you split me sideways,
turn me in on myself, around and over
again.

We made them for our mother.
That doesn't mean anything,
except I wonder if you will
ever bring me flowers.

You stretch, bloom—darling bud,
rose and blue, strangely silent
until you wake to a world that wanted you
to be someone else. Daughter,
daughter—
the word feels like blood on my tongue,
steel in my throat,
blame on my lips.
I can hardly separate your rattling cry from my own.

What right do you have to cry for fear of living?
I am afraid of dying, and the bitterness
of my tears wanes slowly
as you draw me bone dry.

I am reminded that
my mother wore the daisy chains
in her hair, proudly, even after
they turned brittle and brown.

Jake Ross, 17
South Carolina Governor's School for the Arts and Humanities
Greenville, SC
Teacher: Scott Gould

Jake Ross will attend the University of South Carolina Honors Program. He would like to thank his mother for fostering his creative development and for encouraging him in his craft. The teachers at his school were also instrumental in steering him toward writing well by demanding hard work.

LOVE AND LOATHING IN THE WAFFLE HOUSE
Personal Essay/Memoir

"Is that flannel?" The waitress reaches over the counter and gropes at my arm until she's holding only the fabric of my sleeve. She slides her fingers over it. "Ooh," she moans. She quivers and brings her hand back to the pen and pad. "You're just too sexy for me."

I must not have heard her right. "I'm sorry?"

"Too sexy. I said, 'You're just too sexy for me.' My first husband used to wear flannel."

"Oh." I put my menu down. It's midnight by now, or close to it.

"I wear flannel to bed every night. I come in the bedroom and my boyfriend says, 'Ah, shit, here she comes wearing that sack.' I know he hates it. But I just can't get enough. He don't know why."

I'm not sure if I'm being invited to respond. Probably not. "I think I'll have—"

"You know how some people talk about Christmas in July? That's what it's like for me, wearing flannel, even on a hot night like this. I used to think all that business was silly, but I think I understand it now. Some people just want to keep the feeling going, you know? Even though it's gone, and don't come back often."

I am silent now. She looks at me expectantly. Her irises are pale blue but the whites of her eyes are a veiny yellow. Porcupine hair, throaty voice, skin like peeling stucco.

She takes my order and walks away.

I used to hate this place. The first thing I remember is finding a human tooth stuck to my menu, slightly yellowed and casting a shadow over the breakfast specials. Can you imagine that? The contents of someone's mouth, a tiny little thing once kept alive by wet tissue and grazed by hot breath. I scrunched up my face and flicked it so hard that my mother looked up and asked me what was wrong.

"Nothing," I said, though I heard it faintly clicking across the tile and grout.

The bell clinks pitifully when two guys my age walk in. I recognize them. I used to go to school with them. One plays the drums. The other plays bass. They look but do not quite recognize me. They head to a booth in the corner.

That booth they picked, that's where most of the kids sat after the eighth-grade dance. Not me; there hadn't quite been room for me. Which was convenient, seeing as how I had just admitted to a year-long crush on Stephanie Morgan. I sat at the counter with the castaways and watched her pluck bits of scrambled egg from her pink and blue braces.

The hash browns were a little late that night. Our short-order cook was arrested. I was the first one to spot the men in black vests slinking around outside, signaling each other to cover the back and side doors. Finally one came in through the front, and the bell clinked, and he said, "Crystal, it's time to go," and as Crystal was dragged away, her dyed-pink bangs fell down between her eyes, eyes with that dead look that results from someone thinking *I'll never get what I want.*

My eyes skim over the slim bodies of the musicians I recognize. Pants like a second skin, vinyl high-tops, trendy shirts with collars that plunge past pale clavicles. Hair like they just rolled out of bed. A perfected look. From across the restaurant I think, *This is what people want.* Some people are born with it, this assurance. Some people aren't.

They pry packs from their pockets and wrap their lips around cigarettes.

I could go over, ask for a smoke, and see if it jogs their memory.

I don't, though. I've never been able to smoke right. Nothing comes out on the exhale, nothing ever has. It stays in my chest, like it's trying to fill a gap. Can't be healthy.

The waitress is back now. She asks if I want more coffee. She doesn't look at me, she doesn't look down. She looks out the window while she pours. There's really nothing to see. Traffic. Her own reflection, maybe. Even without looking, she knows exactly when to stop pouring.

The waitress has been on a slippery slope ever since I reminded her of her first husband. The cook snaps at her for making him pull too much bacon. She walks tiredly over to the booth with the musicians. It takes her some time to understand their order. She apologizes. She asks them please not to get smart with her.

A few minutes later, she presents tickets to a handful of customers in one deft pass of the counter. She slaps down my own grease-stained slip with a sigh and keeps walking. I look over the shoulder of a nearby man. He has flipped his ticket over to reveal our server's name, printed legibly. Laura. I flip mine and find a chaotic scrawl in the same space: loops colliding with loops, letters becoming unrecognizable hills and valleys. Like the readout on a heart monitor. It's as if Laura put her pen to this paper and felt an overwhelming urge to get home, to sink into a fabric more forgiving than her black nylon apron.

For a tip, I leave everything in my pocket. A loose dollar, 12 or so coins, a movie ticket stub. I go to the cash register to pay. On the way out, I almost, but not quite, leave her the $5 bill she has given me for change.

I am leaving, and the bell clinks, and I am in my car, and the engine is starting. I'm on the road now. I do not like driving by myself at night. *Scared* isn't necessarily the right word. I've never wrecked before. I just don't like how my headlights gesture toward the darkness.

I put my foot to the floor, and the car kicks and presses me back into the seat. Because sometimes you do this; sometimes you want to hear the engine rev up and fill that silence.

PORTALS
Short Story

The deal is on, yes, the deal is on, yes. Runs through closing time today, which makes it Darrel's lucky day, and that is good. Because Darrel needs luck—luck, and many other things.

The customer service man stares down at Darrel over his thick nose, and Darrel's eyes have trouble making it all the way back to the man's, have trouble making contact. That schnoz, that gargantuan honker is in the way. This doesn't bother Darrel all that much—even if he can't see the man's eyes, he can at least look to the walls for consolation. Lining them are glossy, blown-up photographs of people with their devices pressed to their ears. All of them are young and very attractive. Most of them have their heads thrown back in a joyous cackle.

Darrel can't see the man's eyes, but he can see the teeth of the people in the photographs, and Darrel likes their teeth, trusts their teeth, takes comfort in their whiteness and straightness. No hint of decay in their mouths.

"After I've switched to your company, will I be able to keep my phone number?" Darrel strings his words together self-consciously, as if trying out a foreign language. Really, he should have been keeping up with these types of things, but Trina had always handled the phones, the bills, the insurance; with her gone, Darrel feels as though he's walking around the Grand Canyon in the dark. Perhaps he's at the bottom of the gorge, and that's why everything sounds so echoey. Or maybe he's on top of a plateau, the cliff just a few blind steps away. Who's to tell?

The man snorts at the stupidity of Darrel's question, and again Darrel isn't so much offended as scared the exhalation will blow him away. *After all,* Darrel thinks, *the bigger the nose, the greater the air intake. Or is that the way that works?* For a few moments, Darrel imagines a microscopic version of himself riding the brisk stream of air as it flows into the man's right nostril, imagines watching the dark bristles— swaying like trees—remove imperfections from the flow, imagines following the sweet oxygen all the way down to the capillaries of the man's lungs.

Darrel imagines the gift of life, reenacted at the rate of 20 times per minute.

Noses are good. Breathing is good.

"Yes," moans the man. He clicks away at his keyboard with long, pale fingers that form harsh angles at the knuckles. The computers are arranged in a cordoned-off circle at the center of the store, with another sign swinging over them: a giant, glossy, satisfied customer confined to two dimensions.

"There are *laws* that protect your right to *keep* your cell phone *number*," the man continues. Darrel is up in years, sure, but not old enough to be addressed like the mentally handicapped. "*You* just fill out the *paperwork*, and then we'll wait for *your number* to come through the *portal*."

What in the hell is the portal? Darrel thinks. He doesn't like the sound of it. Portal, to him, means something like a miniature black hole, swirling and fuming and ominous. Distortion, irrevocable transportation to another place. Someone who is there and then not.

Darrel takes his old cell phone out of his pocket, cradles it in his palm like an injured bird.

"How long will it take?" he asks.

The man stops clicking around on his computer. "*What?*" he groans. "How long will *what* take?"

"The…the switch. Or transfer. You know, how long before… how long until you are in charge? Of my phone?"

The man abandons his computer altogether and turns his entire body toward Darrel, who is momentarily intimidated by the man's khakis, his logo-emblazoned black polo, his silver pen hanging onto his breast pocket with one gleaming claw. Darrel finds the man's sharp, protruding Adam's apple off-putting. Darrel reads something in the man's face (or, at least, the disgusted twitching of his nose)— something that says *The customers have reached a new low.*

"*Sir*," the man drawls in the general direction of Darrel. "*Your* old phone won't work with *our* service. The *chip* isn't *compatible*. You're going to need a *new* phone. Now *you* look around the store and try to find one while *I* draw up the paperwork. *Okay?*"

Darrel says nothing.

"*Sir?* I assume you still want to take advantage of our *deal?* No registration fees for *new* customers if *you* join *before* the store closes tonight? *Discount* for the first year of your *contract?* Remember? Isn't that why you're *switching?*"

Darrel nods meekly. The man exits the round altar of computers, heads for a printer in the back. Darrel looks down at his old phone. He must have bought it, what, five years ago? Six? He can barely remember. Trina was with him, the driving force behind the purchase. They needed to join the 21st century, she had said—the kids were always trying to call.

Darrel looks down at his phone. It's a solid, sturdy, standard-looking thing—shaped like a tiny casket—bought before they could flip or even slide open. Its plastic antenna is bent and sad-looking, its buttons are worn and gummy. The tiny screen below the earpiece is scratched from being dropped and chewed on by the cat. Sometimes it lights up, sometimes it doesn't. Even when it does, displaying the time, date, and numbers he dials is the extent of its ability—blocky black letters on a dim green background.

It is nothing like the phones Darrel sees as he makes a halfhearted lap around the cellular store. There are phones with $100 pricetags, phones with $200 pricetags, phones with $500 pricetags. They take pictures, they record videos, they play music and have games and can get on the Internet. Some of them have little keyboards. Some of them have no buttons at all but large screens instead.

I need a phone, Darrel thinks. *Not a tiny television.*

A girl in a similar polo as the man asks if Darrel needs any help, and Darrel laughs dejectedly and says, "Yes, I need help affording them." (Why hadn't they planned better? Where had the money gone?) The girl nods somewhat assuredly and escorts him to the back corner of the store, to a shelf full of phones that look basic in a way not unlike his own.

"You pay for these as you use them," says the girl.

"What about the reception? As good as my old one?" asks Darrel. Darrel had seen his children performing borderline-surgical procedures on the fancy phones they bought with leftover scholarship money, but not his—never a problem, not in all those years. He could always hear, clear as day, his son complaining about the job market, his daughter complaining about her boyfriend. He could hear Trina's sweet voice, and could keep track of her even when he couldn't see her—the shuffling of papers on the kitchen table as she looked for a receipt, the opening and closing of cabinet doors as she looked for a prescription.

"Depends on the towers in your area," says the girl. She hands him a ratty-looking box. "There's a test phone in here," she says. "You can use it tonight, make sure you're satisfied with the reception. Bring it back tomorrow."

Darrel thanks the girl. He tells her he has to sign a contract tonight, but he'll run outside and use the test phone if he has time. "One more question," he says. "Say I'd like to keep the voicemail greeting I have now. How would I go about making sure I still have it?"

The girl looks confused. "You can't just rerecord it?"

Darrel searches for his words carefully, then settles for full disclosure. "Sentimental value," he says under his breath.

"Oh," the girl frowns. "Well, we certainly can't get your own service provider to send it to us. Things just aren't open like that. It took enough bloodshed to get the portal up and running. A world where two competing companies shared more customer info would make our jobs a lot easier, but it just doesn't work that way." Here the girl laughs. "Two companies who share voicemail systems! Can you imagine?" she slaps Darrel playfully on the arm.

Darrel is petrified. "What about the chip?" he asks. "Can't you take it off the chip?"

The girl frowns slightly. "Your voicemail greeting isn't saved on your chip," she says. "It's saved in some server at the headquarters of your old service provider, millions of miles away. You could maybe pay some sort of specialist to rip it from somewhere," she hesitates, "but—"

"But I don't have that kind of money," Darrel finishes for her. She nods sympathetically.

"Hey," she smiles. "Just think of the deal you're getting! It's a new day."

A woman sits at the counter next to Darrel screaming as he tries to fill out his paperwork. She wears an unbecoming pink velour tracksuit and tennis shoes. Her eyes are red and puffy from angry sobs. She's yelling about something—her contract? They won't let her out of her contract. Her cries are shrill; her blond hair is crazed—parts of it appear curly, parts of it appear straight, parts of it are pinned down, and others bounce freely with her ranting.

It occurs to Darrel that the fight between the woman and the man, from far off, would look like a battle between a blond mop and a giant nose.

How is he supposed to finish his paperwork here, with this ruckus? How can he remember his social security number with the woman screaming about trust and loyalty and fair business practice, about the money she doesn't have, about the money nobody has?

The woman asks to speak to the manager. The man informs her he is the manager.

The woman would still like for him to get someone on the phone. The man, after snorting and groaning a bit, leaves to do so.

The woman covers her face with her hands and turns to Darrel. She says she knows she looks like a mess and apologizes. Then she drops her hands and weeps, not angry this time but helpless, and a few tears splatter onto the dark, plastic counter.

Between sobs, she tells Darrel that "sometimes it's just us versus them."

Almost immediately, Darrel is scared to stay in the cell phone store—scared that the woman's hysteria will enter and fester in him through osmosis. He sets the clipboard down on the counter and turns to leave. He takes his old phone and his test phone with him.

"I need to go eat dinner," Darrel tells the man, who has returned to the counter and is holding a receiver out to the woman. She grabs it with a sticky hand, brings it slowly to her ear, as if she expects the words to fall on her like axes.

"The *deal*!" the man calls after Darrel. "Store *closes* soon! Don't *forget* about *the deal*!"

"I won't. I'll be back," Darrel tells him, but he isn't so sure.

There's a hole-in-the-wall Mexican restaurant down the street that Trina found on her drive home one night and insisted they try. They had gone here at least once every two weeks ever since.

The waitress asks Darrel where Trina is, and Darrel says she's in bed, not feeling well.

The waitress suggests he order a carryout, bring some chips and salsa home to Trina. "They're to die for," says the waitress.

"I know," smiles Darrel.

He orders his quesadilla and chimichangas. He eats them.

He orders a flan. Not his favorite dessert, but Trina always loved it, right down to the caramel sauce left at the bottom of the saucer.

The way the whipped cream blooms out of the flan reminds him of the baby's breath in Trina's casket spray.

The way the whipped cream disappears into the portal of his mouth reminds him of the way Trina sank into the portal dug in the ground.

The whipped cream is not coming back.

Darrel takes out his test phone and calls his old phone.

His old phone rings too happily, clashes with the music in the Mexican restaurant. The voicemail kicks in. Trina's voice.

"Hello, you've reached Darrel and Trina's cell phone—"

I've reached you? I'll never reach you again. I reach and reach and reach and feel nothing. I am walking blind in the Grand Canyon, and you are a star in the dark sky, and the light that reaches me is an image of the way you were then, and I won't feel you blink out until years after the fact, and this rift in time, this portal that sucks away all of our minutes and hours, it kills me.

"—please leave us a message after the tone—"

If I speak into this, store a recording for you in a server millions of miles away, will you hear it? Where is your answering service? How is your reception up there? Down there? Can you hear me it all? All that time spent together and now it's the chips that will rob me of the last part of you, the chips and so much else will separate us, the chips and millions of miles and people smiling in posters, the people who aren't really customers at all but models who don't know the misery they're smiling at with approval. Why are they smiling? Why are they laughing at the clouds? Do they look up and see you? Are they talking to you and are you talking back and are you paying-as-you-go? Can I?

"—and we'll get back to you as soon as possible."

Get back, get back, get back.

The tone sounds, and echoes through Darrel's head in a deafening way that could last forever, but it's gone again before he can miss it, and Darrel hears nothing.

Loretta López, 18
American School Foundation of Guadalajara
Guadalajara, Mexico
Teacher: Leonardo Díaz

A native of Guadalajara, Mexico, Loretta López will attend Bard College in New York's Hudson Valley. Her work is inspired by the culture and people of her hometown. Her favorite authors include Junot Díaz, Gabriel García Márquez, and Isabel Allende. She would like to pursue a career in teaching or writing.

SWAMP
Short Story

She always liked to mention it when we were together in a group or when we met someone new. She said it loudly, in a matter-of-fact way, and then she would press her body against mine, push my head sideways with a passionate force and twist her lips with a squealing sound that made my head buzz.

It made her extremely proud that we had known each other since forever and our mothers' swollen bellies had bumped together 17 years ago. With my cold hands in her warm chubby fingers, she named me without my consent her confidant, her pet, her sister, her best friend, stroking my curls that used to fall down to my waist and making me swear that nothing would ever change.

And it didn't for a while.

Hot summer afternoons were spent in her unkempt backyard. We would dive into her cold pool that really was more of a swamp, with its green mossy edges and floating bugs, and make ourselves mermaids. She made us search for a treasure at the bottom of the world that, once discovered, would eliminate the deep sea of evils.

But we never found the treasure.

Whenever I came out of the water, my ears aching from the lack of air and from struggling to press my body against the bottom of the pool, to exclaim breathlessly that I had found a wooden treasure trunk, she would disappoint me. "The treasure is not in a wooden trunk, sister mermaid. The evil octopus has disguised it again. Keep looking." Then her short stubby legs, tired from spinning in bicycle circles, would come to a halt and she'd let herself sink.

Tedious hours spent in a useless search exhausted me but eventually the rain ended the sessions. As warm drops fell, we got out of the pool, our blue scales fading to reveal the light hairs on our girl legs.

Maria. La Virgen Maria. La pura, la inocente.

Her parents named her proudly, like any good Mexican Catholic. They hoped that their youngest daughter would resemble a woman they placed in their living room with flashing Christmas lights hovering above her holy head.

Maria wears the name with indifference. "Why are there so many Marias?" she complained when put in a classroom with two girls who shared her name.

Maria wishes she were named Roxanne. Not a name that makes her another brown girl in a crowd.

But Maria is not just another girl in a crowd. She has a gift or a burden like her Holy Mother. She has more love in her than I have ever seen in anyone else. She expresses it preposterously, giving it out in overwhelming amounts, never measuring, and it's always too late when she realizes she has given more than anyone could ever give back.

I still do not know where this hollow pool of blind love she let spill on so many came from. As much as she seems like someone who says everything that comes to her mind and yells it out inappropriately across hallways and in restaurants, Maria keeps her secrets, she has her sadness. On gray days they bind her to warm sheets. It's only after several hours that she learns to pull herself back together, shake it off, and wake up. When she untangles herself from a sea of blankets, she lights up a cheap cigarette and pours herself a glass of her mother's wine and sits on a balcony that looks out over her swamp pool.

Heavy eyelashes and red lipstick disguise her pain well. When she finishes covering up swollen eyes, she goes out with one of her many friends. Maria laughs herself to sleep. She wakes up again in admirable resilience, ready to love the world once more. She skims past imperfections, viewing them as personality quirks and amusing contraptions of human existence, not something she ever has to protect herself from.

And this I envy.

Dios te salve, Maria.
Llena eres de gracia:
El Señor es contigo.
Bendita tú eres entre todas las mujeres.

She lost her virginity young. At 13, I did not really understand why she felt proud of herself. I hadn't even kissed a boy. Holding hands with someone was a distant wish that made me nervous, that made my palms moist. Maria had just gotten out of her Pokémon phase and I had just begun keeping a journal. We were young.

Maria persisted in telling me more than I wanted to know, with her sly red grin. The way she described the whole ordeal made me nauseous. I disliked the thought of a young man I had never seen in my life breathing heavily upon her, caressing the slight curves of her bursting breasts, threading sweet webs inside her mouth with this tongue, while dragging his heavy hands across her. She said he had made her feel important.

Maria adored him.

Daniel, a tall, strong 18-year-old with dark eyes and a mustache, marked the beginning of our separation. He became the first in a long list of men and boys who tore her away from me. Maria would invite me to tag along with Daniel and his friends. "Daniel has a car," Maria would squeal through the phone. "We can come and get you." But I made up excuses. Hundreds of them. I felt like a girl, my breasts had just begun to ache, and I hated it when Maria would grab my hand and make me touch hers, soft and round. Like a woman's, she said.

Our daily telephone conversations died when Maria got kicked out of school. She had always hated doing homework and then she started to fall asleep in half the classes, bored out of her mind with equations and stories about people who lived long ago. She looked beautiful when sleeping. Her red lips looked fuller and her eyelashes longer. It was a shame to wake her up but I did anyway, getting out of my seat and pretending to blow my nose while giving her hair a tug. She always woke giggling.

Guiltily, I came to the conclusion that my efforts in creating our bond had been minimal. After she got kicked out of school, I only saw her on weekends. Each time, she looked older and there was something new to her: a pink streak in her hair, a hole in her ear. But then our outings diminished to scarce crowded nights where she would place her chubby, soft hand in mine to resuscitate our past. And then, in a whisper, she asked a question we both knew how I should answer. "How long have we been best friends?"

"*Desde siempre.*"

Daniel days did not last for long. They slowly morphed into days of names I would hear Maria mention only once, lovers saved for the darkness.

At 15, Maria's short body, overwhelmed with curves, shaped her into a girl who seemed mature and womanly. She carried herself well, thick black waves of hair against round breasts, her cat eyes honey yellow, and her bronze skin glimmering. Maria only kept her long hair and silver tongue-piercing throughout the years, giving her an ethereal gypsy look. Everything else about her matched whomever she shared a bed with.

By then I looked different. I stopped being scared of my body, and I let go of being a girl. Maria smiled every time she saw me and, like a proud Mexican mother, she praised my hips, my discrete curves, my long hair.

I do not think Maria really fell in love for a long time. She loved everyone, flirting with every gender, any age. She tried to be liked by all. With her intense nature she drove several away. But that didn't bother Maria because, even though not for long, people enjoyed her everywhere.

I knew Andres from school. He got good grades and liked to read, even though he pretended he didn't. He never brushed his hair but he always kept his sneakers clean. Maria had become his friend the year she got kicked out. He was not her type.

"Andres? Really?"

"You know I have always had a thing for him."

"No, I thought you were friends, not…I don't know, something else."

"When are you going to realize you only get one best friend, and for me that's always been you?"

Maria did not fall in love until she was 16. Andres was different. She did not cheat on him and he did not cheat on her. He wasn't like the others, who were always much older, much larger, holding Maria in their thick hands as she pressed herself against chest hair. Andres was still a boy, skinny, naive, but not innocent. He had had his share of girls, of one-night stands, of *putas*, but he never took advantage of Maria. They were equals.

They fell in love quickly, spoke to each other all the time. When Maria took a bath, she would put him on speakerphone and tell him how her razor was rising up her thighs and how soap had gotten into her eyes. Romance. Andres listened to all of it, maybe not to what she said but definitely to her voice.

Chiquita hermosa: No sabes cuanto te adoro y te amo. Gracias por ser mi mujer algo que para mí siempre serás. Quiero que sepas que haría cualquier cosa por ti porque eres la niña por la que siempre he soñado. Eres perfecta aunque tu lo niegues. Me haces la persona más feliz del mundo.

Maria shoved his love letter into my hand on one of those crowded nights. "Isn't it really corny?" she said, giggling in amusement. "He's like that. He likes to whisper things in my ear, when we are…"

I smiled, shaking my head while pressing my finger to her red lips. Maria put her mouth against my ear, indifferent to my expression of discomfort. I gently pushed her little body away from mine but then pulled her back in a hug. "Just remember to be careful."

Maria responded in a sudden storm of laughter, "You know I'm not, but don't you worry about me." She paused and looked at me in her usual flirtatious manner. "Plus, you'll rescue me if anything happens."

I let go of her and tried to give a serious look, as I had many times before. "Maria, I mean it." But she had already turned away, putting her hands into one of her friend's long blond ponytails, twisting the strands around her finger.

The summer it started to go wrong with Andres, the calls began again. I couldn't help but wonder why it was me and not one of her other friends, the ones like her, those wild night girls. We hadn't spoken for more than a couple of minutes on the phone for years, because really we had nothing to talk about. Nothing that tied our worlds together. We just called about the important news, the new boyfriends, my dead cat, her parents' divorce, stuff you might tell a relative out of obligation, out of politeness. But Andres was breaking her heart, and she was too proud to admit it to anyone in her world.

Maria clung to his presence. She had sacrificed other relationships to dedicate herself solely to him.

In her presence, Andres looked exhausted. Maria clutched his bony hand in hers, making his fingers numb and purple from holding on too tight. She manipulated his blood circulation, his breath, his time.

Maria foreshadowed their end with vague comments. He would get tired of her mood swings and uncontrollable anger. She realized she frightened him with some fits where she allowed herself to throw furniture and scream in excruciating sobs.

I didn't know what to say, so I told her that everything was going to be fine and that things happened for reason. But I didn't understand the reasons. I didn't know about her anger, her sobs, where they came from, why they emerged. She had named me her best friend with pride and I didn't know her at all. I saw what I wanted to: the superficial, shimmering blue surface, not mucky green corners and the dirty square tile at the bottom.

It was the only time I have witnessed her tears. The catharsis lasted a few minutes. Her tears, short and quick, never trickled down her small face because she brought her chubby child fingers up to her eyes every time a teardrop merged to fall.

I hugged her in a corner. She disliked the idea of anyone watching her weak.

Maria confessed to me in whispers that she had never felt so alone. She longed for simplicity, childhood, for the days I couldn't find that stupid treasure because there just wasn't one. She told me there was no one else anymore, I was what she had. Everything else seemed fleeting and fake.

She wrapped her brown arms around me, holding on as if I would float away if she changed position. "Invite me to sleep over. I don't want to sleep in an empty bed tonight."

I look at my room to realize she has invaded it. Maria functions like a heavy storm coming every once in a while in a sudden swirl, moving conventional objects out of their place. No invitation, no warning, just thick wind shaking glass windows, making them tremble with riotous laughter.

Her clean blue sneakers lay uninhabited among my pile of dirty shoes. Her plugged-in curling iron heats up against my plastic beads, her crumpled T-shirt is on my carpet, and her drippy fuchsia nail polish lies on my desk. She will soon complain in forgetfulness that she has lost these things.

My toothbrush stained with red lipstick serves as a sign of our sisterhood, your saliva is my saliva, "who gives a shit?"

You are back, Maria, probably for sheer convenience and for a limited amount of time, but I don't care because I need you too.

I need you to love me the way that only you do. Ignorant of imperfections and ready to forgive. The way that I love you. We are willfully ignorant.

PIEDRA
Short Story

My father never wears pajamas. He's been in his underwear forever, walking barefoot on the cold tile, indifferent to my complaints that normal fathers wear plaid flannel.

But my father, my *papi*, doesn't even put on a sweater when the rain becomes violent. When it transforms into hail. When my patio is a cold cemetery encrusted with round diamonds and his car's window has cracked.

His bare shoulders make me cold. But he doesn't care about the rain and the ice. He likes the sound and he can feel it better without all those clothes on.

"I'm not cold, I'm never cold, and I never get sick. *Yo estoy hecho de piedra.*"

My brown *papi*. My *papi* made of stone.

My *papi* is tangled in passion, in sounds, in five lines and museums of round notes. Invisible moons floating black and whole. Stored everywhere. Stored in the rain. Stored in traffic. When I am with him, the world is a place too beautiful to understand. So I listen to a language that he interprets for me. A language he makes a song.

My *papi* has a mind with little room for conventions. He never wears pajamas and he never finds his keys. He is obsessive. He believes in the power of stars and aliens. He is afraid of death but he never says so because he keeps many of his thoughts silent.

"I'm like a stone," he says, "like a stone."

But with him I learn to listen in different ways.

I find his voice is stored in sighs and glances and in the way he takes a deep breath when the rain has stopped.

Mackenzie Jacoby, 18
Walden School
Provo, UT
Teacher: Lara Candland Asplund

Mackenzie Jacoby has lived in London, Iowa, Brazil, and Utah, and traveled to Spain, Guatemala, Turkey, and several other places. Her experiences, both in faraway countries and in the Midwest, deeply impact her writing and provide her with subject material. She'd like to thank her parents for helping her develop as a writer.

El Cuarto de Julio
Personal Essay/Memoir

The summer I was 15, I spent three weeks in a tiny apartment in Barcelona, the heart of Catalonia, Spain. As important as space-time markers are in personal narratives, the real key to the previous sentence is the word "tiny." Allow me to elaborate. I shared a room with my sister, Taylor. Though actually considered small for humans, we do not fit in a breadbox, being of rather notable heft. We slept on a double foldout bed that, tiny though it was, hindered the movement of the door when extended. By "hindered," I mean "prevented the door from opening." In order to leave (or enter) the room, you had to lift up one end of the bed, open (and swiftly close) the door, and not think about re-creating the process again for at least a couple of hours. Going to bed had a certain tone of finality to it.

We had been gone from the United States for seven months, and Europe had taken its toll on us. We began just as excited as can be to immerse ourselves in European culture, history, romance, cooking with wine, but now, seven months in, we were soaked to the bone. We were soggy with savvy. Every night, when our bed was folded out and our door wedged shut, visions danced through our minds of the friends that we had left behind taunting us with containers of Nesquik and Jif peanut butter. I had been going strong for seven months, but now with three weeks left, I was losing it. I was the marathon runner lying down on the last leg to dream about Taco

Bell and anything-but-compact cars. The amount of time I spent in dreams about home surpassed the amount of time I spent living in Spain. It was a very tiring existence. I even lost weight, not enough that Taylor and I comfortably fit in the bed, but enough that it became visibly clear that I was burning more calories than I was taking in to keep up with my double life. And then, on the horizon, I saw the Fourth of July. We all saw it. It was coming at us with amazing speed. We calculated that when it arrived, we would still be here in Spain, cherubs mocking us from bedazzling architecture, the yawning language barrier rendering incomprehensible the chatter that surrounded us.

In Idaho, we have this cabin in the woods. Of course, that statement harbors in its diction a rather enormous reservoir of irony. Woods and cabin. Truer words have never been spoken; however, our own little Walden Pond it is not. Owned by my grandparents (on my mother's side) and built by the paid labor of my dad and his hooligan brother, the cabin sits, with its seven bedrooms and fully equipped kitchen, a cushy 75-minute drive from Boise. It is built of roughly hewn logs in true Lincoln Log fashion. The roof is made of red metal. Solemn carved bears and tall aspen trees guard the front. Somewhere between a cabin and a McMansion, our cabin is sort of rustic-plus: We've got both a water pump and a ping-pong table. Above all, every necessary aspect of a good cabin is present.

So we needed a celebration. Obviously, my first inclination was to find fireworks, though that thought was never verbalized. Being impossible, it would have made me look foolish. Food was the next best option. When being fed, people automatically assume they are having a great time. The trick works on people in even the dullest of circumstances in the most cogent of states. I've tested it out on myself on several occasions, and each time I've been fully convinced that while eating fun hors d'oeuvres, I was experiencing real hard-earned joy. So food was a must. A barbecue we would call it. We were on our way.

It's a six-hour drive to the cabin. We say we go up to water-ski, to four-wheel, to swim and fish, and even to see our family. These explanations vary in levels of ludicrousness, from the believable to the laughable. But most family members find solace in one or two of the above reasons. The following insight is one that few of us have consciously noted, but is the true mantra of each of our souls: We go there to eat. In particular, we go there to eat Grandma Terry's trifle. Trifle is a curious thing, though curious is a word altogether too negative. Strange though it may be, trifle is perhaps the least offensive food known to man (the British don't like peanut butter and jelly sandwiches—go figure). Trifle is creamy, soft, silky, soggy, but never chewy, layers and chunks of different ingredients that, though eager to please, always complement and never bully their fellow tastes. It is a dish that bridges gaps, represents unity, and is easily digested.

It had to be made. We didn't have a copy of the recipe—it's likely that none exists. We didn't have to get Grandma on the phone either. We knew what we needed. This is almost absolutely the first time that the following recipe has been written down because, more than a recipe, it is something that lives in our minds, something our taste buds yearn for. Writing it down for any purpose would have been fruitless anyway, as our hands would disregard the rigid instructions in favor of what they know is right.

GRANDMA TERRY'S TRIFLE
INGREDIENTS:
ONE ANGEL FOOD CAKE
ONE PACKAGE OF STRAWBERRY JUNKET
ONE PACKAGE OF VANILLA PUDDING (JELL-O BRAND, NATURALLY)
BLUEBERRIES
STRAWBERRIES
RASPBERRIES
ONE PINT OF WHIPPED CREAM

PROCEDURE:
TAKE A BIG, GLASS CYLINDRICAL DISH, FOR WHICH I KNOW NO NAME. BREATHE EASY FOR A FEW MOMENTS AND GATHER THE CONFIDENCE YOU NEED, BUT JUST KNOW THAT SCARCE LITTLE CAN BE DONE TO RUIN THE DESSERT AT THIS POINT. START PLOPPING IN THE VARIOUS INGREDIENTS; STRUCTURE IS YOUR ONLY BARRIER. FIND A SONG AND TO ITS BEAT BUILD YOUR MASTERPIECE. CHOOSE SOMETHING SOULFUL, BUT WHOSE LYRICS WILL NOT REQUIRE ANALYSIS. DO NOT ACCEPT OUTSIDE HELP AND, IF POSSIBLE, TUNE

OUT ALL NOISE AROUND YOU. YOUR EYES ARE YOUR
BIGGEST ASSETS. LOOK AT THE COLORS. HAVE A GOOD
TIME.

Grocery shopping was an epic journey. My mind wandered
off toward America, indulging in memories, getting its hopes up,
and visualizing a flawless outcome. My feet, still based in Spain,
struggled to keep up. The public transportation system exhausted
us. As we sat waiting for the metro to take us to the store, "Costco"
was mentioned and saliva welled up in my mouth, an unavoidable
Pavlovian response. We couldn't figure out the Spanish word for
blueberry, and the literal translation got less-than-coherent responses.
And then the brightness attacked. The Spanish Sunshine Armada.
That glaring sun that, up until this point, I had been puzzled by and
was certainly at the mercy of but could happily coexist with. But now
it was conniving. The sun didn't beat or blaze—it was much more
subtle. Its heavy rays slowly seeped in through the top of my skull.
By the time I realized what was happening, my ankles and calves
had already been pushed down, submerged in the cement. I trudged
along, dragging the sidewalk with me. Three hours and four grocery
stores later, not one ingredient had been found in its intended form,
and our standards were dropping quickly. Strawberries and bananas
were chosen as the fruit. A packaged but suitable substitute for angel
food cake had been found.

But none of us wanted to think about what came next: strawberry
junket.

*I had never realized how patchy my foundation for tradition and culture
was until I had to analyze what exactly junket is and what might make a suitable replacement. Strawberry junket is kind of like Jell-O. My mother tells
me it's more of a glaze. The package tells me it's ever so versatile and can be
served with almost anything in want of a gelatinous coating, but as far as I
know, none of these claims has ever been tested. Also, as far as I know, ours
is the only family that uses it. It holds berries together and it holds our family
together. Few powders on the modern market can honestly claim to do that—
perhaps just junket and Kraft Mac & Cheese. In any case, neither powdered
life-form could be found in Spanish grocery stores.*

It's easy to see where prejudice comes from. Upon hearing that a huge population of the world lives without the words "bake" and "sprinkles," and to just assume that they don't have the same capacity for happiness. It's incredibly easy, almost unavoidable, to—after having tasted trifle with junket and trifle with jelly—condemn a whole country for their lack of variety in the gelatin aisle. I'm not saying we did, I'm just saying it would have been easy…

If one thing can be said for certain, it's that Europeans screw around with their dairy products. Granted, once the grocery store is navigated and the correct white liquids are identified, the final product tends to be tastier that any American equivalent, but the trauma of differentiating between heavy, double, clotted, and pouring cream always gives your creation a bittersweet twinge. So we decided on spray whipped cream. It didn't even feel like settling anymore. At least we recognized it.

TRIFLE DE CATALONIA
INGREDIENTS:
PACKAGED MADELEINES (A LITTLE FRENCH PASTRY,
   STALE IN THIS CASE)
ONE PACKAGE OF FLAN MIX
BANANAS
STRAWBERRIES
STRAWBERRY JELLY
ONE CAN OF SPRAYABLE WHIPPED CREAM (BETTER
   SAFE THAN SHELF MILK)

PROCEDURE:
   ARRANGE AS ABOVE, BUT WITH EYES HALF-SQUINTED AND PARTIALLY FOCUSED ELSEWHERE. REFRIGERATE BEFORE SERVING.

Traveling is one of those things that'll just linger. It will sit there in your bloodstream, fogging everything up, coloring everything with its biased hue, waiting to cling to something of importance. Traveling introduces you to totally new things. You read them on museum plaques and meet them in church and order them by accident in restaurants. Sometimes there's no place for the new things in your old life. Sometimes you have to search for a place for them and give them meaning, you have to be firm and say to them: *You there! You give context to this part of my life.* Otherwise, these foreign experiences just run wild in your system, tainting everything with significance until you can't remember what you're supposed to enjoy and what you aren't. I've still got some free radicals, memories acquired before I learned how to store them—images of suns setting and no mental junk drawer to put them in. If you travel without thinking, combining, synthesizing, your sensory inputters get all in a jumble. You can feel it happening when someone hands you a glowstick and immediately you sense an obligation to be having a great time. Undigested experiences and memories congregate in a haze around certain things, like Push Pops and Sixlets, things that reek of a sentimentality that is not at all personal. They half-connect themselves—the song that makes you sad and you can't remember why, or the face that reminds you of someone and you can't remember who. But not this memory. This one knows exactly where it belongs.

We ate the trifle like fiends. Disoriented by effort and heat, we forgot to reduce the portion sizes and, for our family of five, prepared for a family of 20. With every day, the leftovers grew better, the whipped cream broke down, softening the flan mix, the stale angel food cake steeped in jelly became entirely compliant. The Fourth of July came and went, as did the three weeks that separated us from our transatlantic flight home. We stayed in Utah long enough (three days) to realize it was too hot before we made the six-hour drive to the cabin. Grandma brought trifle. As I looked at it, it began to pulsate, fuzzy sunlight formed a halo around it, a flamenco beat oozed from its insides. Nobody else noticed.

EGG DROP SOUP
Personal Essay/Memoir

*I am from Utah, where we take our mountains rocky and our politicians red.
At dawn, rays of sunshine pour in from behind the peaks, filling up the valley
like a bowl of sun soup. When the sun sets again, the sky ignites like the head
of a great celestial troll doll. From our porch my grandmother contemplates the
sky and we listen: "Where else can you look out the window and see a pterodactyl
fly by?" she asks, admiring the golden cloud formations. We are cosmopolitan
folk cradled in the loving embrace of the Wild West. The mountains back us
up, surround us from all sides—as do our neighbors, who within the first week,
bearing Christmas carols and cream cheese frosting, crossed what in Iowa would
have been the appropriate neighbor boundaries.*

*They support and frighten us, those mountains and neighbors. We've
managed to settle in (though as staunch liberals in a Mormon community, my
mother has had to constantly improve her cinnamon roll recipe to keep our
reputation afloat). To be fair, my parents are Westerners. My dad's roots lie in a
small farm in western Washington, where his father still commands an army of
beagles 23 strong. My mom hails from the suburbs of Boise, where all backyards
have water features. But still, my family stretches the mold (careful not to break
it). We've lived abroad in London, Germany, and Spain, picking up quirks ever
harder to integrate. Remaining dogmatically open-minded. We come back loving
Utah more. What I mean is that I'm not the geographically unglued American
whom, say, traditional Italian families in Tuscan villages have pity for. I have
roots too. I am a Utahan.*

More parts of my body have been on the floor of my church
building than on any other floor in the world. I remember wondering
at the way the carpet didn't stop at the edge of the floor but turned
up onto the wall, continuing for a few inches before the painted
white brick took over. You could hear something inside, or on the
other side of those big cement blocks, and we'd press our faces up
against them to listen and because we liked the way the coldness felt.
I guess I just assumed that they carpeted that strip of wall for the
ants. Ants were the only things I ever saw walking on walls.

The prevalence of ants explained maybe 50 percent of the

confusing phenomena that I observed in my young life in Iowa. In elementary school, when I was sick of thinking, I would lay my head down on the wooden desk and listen to the family of ants inside scotching things around and making a real ant-level racket. They were getting ready for the moving trucks to come, I reasoned, moving from my desk to another. There was a quick turnover rate, but my desk was clearly prime real estate because every time I lay my head down, I could hear ants down there, scooting furniture about.

I couldn't understand the kind of people who believed that you could fit the whole ocean in a conch shell just so that it could whisper back at you. I invented my own, superior superstitions. The idea that there might be an ant conversation going on back in those curlicues made a lot of sense to me.

Potluck Sundays were the *best*. We would run around giving ourselves rug burns while the parents busied themselves with less important things. The dads set up the tables, folding the metal legs into place, while the moms arranged green bean casserole and Jell-O salad on top. Rug burns were the *best*. They were the one injury that nobody could give to you. The carpet would offer them up, but you had to reach out and take them. You had to earn them for yourself. And then you could eat your green bean casserole with Funyuns on top. Being a kid in Iowa is the *best*. You really do feel like an ant. I mean, adults are always going to be bigger than kids, but adults in Iowa are a physically daunting crew. And kids in Iowa are therefore fearless.

I got used to being an ant. And then all of the sudden I was big, and my dad didn't want to carry me in from the car anymore after the long ride home. I had to pretend to be asleep so that he had no choice. But sometimes I would only realize how close we were getting when we turned onto our street, at which point I'd conk over, dropping onto the lap of whoever was nearest, loosening every muscle in my body except my eyelids—which were squeezed shut to demonstrate how asleep I was. Sometimes I did this mid-sentence. My dad always carried me in. He never knew the difference.

Very occasionally we'd stop at the Chinese restaurant on the way home. Whining wasn't really *whining* when you were *that* hungry. It was just a natural reaction. In fact, I didn't blame myself at all; it was just that when I opened my mouth, all of the ants in my tummy started screaming at once about the dire lack of treats inside of me. I didn't know at the time that you weren't supposed to spend money on Sundays, but I did know that that egg drop soup tasted way too good to be holy. The bowl was only about the size of my fist but it was bottomless. I would fish around in there with my forefinger and my thumb, trying to catch one of those little pieces of egg confetti. But they were always too slippery. Those little egg bits never integrated. The soup resisted homogeneity. It was so delicious. Eventually I would collapse in a food coma and we would continue the drive home. My belly felt like a hot water bottle, as my brain whirred away trying to imagine the machine that could turn an egg into those little bits of paper.

We always used to go to the Dairy Barn. There were so many choices. And I loved the way that "Chunky Monkey" sounded. But how anyone got anything besides vanilla soft serve with triple sprinkles was a complete mystery to me. The sheer beauty of the thing was enough to bring me to tears. We would sit in the giant tractor tires of the John Deere dealership next door and eat. I would steer around the sprinkles so that the last couple of spoonfuls were *just* sprinkles with a little bit of melted ice cream holding them together. My dad ordered something small. I always suspected that he didn't really *understand* ice cream. He just loved potato chips.

I never heard the word "modesty" until I came to Utah, where it meant long shorts and T-shirts. Now there were all of these things that you had to believe in and have opinions about because we were Mormons. And the lines were so fine: Hot chocolate was good, mochas were bad. Cap sleeves were good, tank tops were bad.

Up until then, religion had been an entirely concrete thing for me. Everyone else's religions could be described in one word: Jewish, dreidels; Catholic, communion. Mine could be described in a couple: three hours of church, singing, egg drop soup. Suddenly, in Utah, there were all of these abstractions. What was "modesty," and what did it have to do with my swimsuit?

I didn't see a lot of ants in Utah. And maybe that was because there wasn't as much to explain. Unexplained phenomena rarely survived the one-way road trip to the Wild West. These people, these Utahans, certainly had strange practices, but they also loved to explain them. They would talk about simple things until they became complex—like not allowing ear piercings or sleepovers for children under 12. And church was three hours long, so most of the truly complex things they already had answers to. Maybe the ants just didn't like the desert.

At first, I didn't like the desert either. There was far too much sheetrock in Utah for my taste, and those Rocky Mountains didn't look all that stable to me. But then we moved out of the apartment and into our new house and the Realtor sent by cookies decorated like flowers on popsicle sticks, and I was pretty sure everything was going to be OK. Anyway, I was 8; it was my job to be brave.

But things did get undeniably more complicated. In Iowa, the two popular girls were the daughter of the only car salesman and the daughter of the only dentist. In Iowa, my best friend and I had both been professors' children: not the top of the social ladder, but also not to be picked on, lest we throw back a scathing, intellectual, two-syllable insult. In Iowa, we sort of knew how things worked and where they fit. Provo was more complex. Provo had lots of car dealerships.

And a giant elementary school full of social interaction. I wasn't necessarily a social being when I moved to Utah. There had been too much tactile input to be had to bother with developing emotions. I arrived in the third grade just interested in having a good time. Most of my new friends didn't really do cartwheels, so I had to teach them. They taught me about drama. Drama is when you *want* to know something, but instead of finding out, you just imagine the possible outcomes. It was pretty fun, but kind of tricky too because I had to ignore my rational instinct to just ask boys if they liked me or kiss them when I liked them.

Soon, my forwardness earned me the awe of my fifth-grade peers. I turned the back of the bus into a confessional. I convinced the boys to give the girls flowers on Valentine's Day. Apparently, this was all new stuff to them. I felt like a revolutionary, but I missed softball. In Iowa, the whole city came down for the little girls' softball games. We got matching socks. We had real logos that we didn't have to pay licensing fees on because our town was too small for Major League Baseball to check up on. In Utah, we had to combine six elementary schools to scrape together one team. In Utah, all people cared about was who brought the juice boxes after the game.

Grinnell, Iowa, didn't have a Starbucks, so I only ever knew the place as a battleground. Most Mormons don't drink coffee, some don't drink tea, some don't drink caffeine. It's one of those rules that everyone feels everyone else is interpreting wrong. So every hot drink had a meaning. Black coffee was blatant disregard, espressos were just asking for attention, mochas were rebels whose hearts were in the right place, hot chocolate was a goody two-shoes. It was all fascinating to me, the way they assigned meaning to meaningless things. And it was hard to blame ants for any of it. Once I moved to the city, the ants all but disappeared. The paving stones fit together too snuggly and the windows closed too tight.

I always just suspected that we would leave like we'd left Boston and Germany and California and Iowa. But somewhere along the line, Utah became home. My parents must've chosen Utah, at least in part, because it's such an impressive place to fly into. My family went to Europe a lot for my dad's job, and we'd fly back to Utah because that was where our stuff was: our clothes, our bikes, our little sister. I remember once returning to Utah after spending the semester in London. The first time I looked down on Utah from above and saw all of the little people down below, they looked like ants. I laughed when I realized that the ants had been causing the inexplicable all along.

You can't swoop in over the Rocky Mountains dry-eyed. As the altitude drops, the tears well up. And nobody likes to cry without knowing why, so we turn to the stranger sharing a row with us and explain that we are coming home. We are the egg bits that float around Utah. We never fully integrated, never lost our shape or slipperiness, but we eventually realized how fabulous it was. And we are proud to be a part of it.

Margaret Nietfeld, 17
Interlochen Arts Academy
Interlochen, MI
Teacher: Michael Delp

Margaret Nietfeld is taking a year off from school to work as an intern for Walt Disney Imagineering. The following year, she will attend Harvard University. She feels that she has lived thousands of different lives and wrote the pieces in her portfolio to capture the images and memories they have produced and left behind.

SPEEDBIRD
Personal Essay/Memoir

The first time I took Adderall, I whacked a boy over the head with *Allez, viens!* Our real French teacher was pregnant, and under the care of a substitute who spoke halting Spanish, we were not doing our crossword puzzles. Instead, an eighth-grade boy stood over a sixth grader, his hands wrapped around her neck. My muscles twitched. "Stop!" I screamed, but not loudly enough for the sub to hear over his acid jazz. But he heard when I wonked the book down.

My mother picked me up from Northeast Junior High in her Buick.

"What's wrong, honey?" My mother said, rubbing my shoulder.

I explained the story, sobbing. And I continued crying, clutching my heart all week, smearing the ink on the Peanuts strip that I read during Saturday detention.

Finally, as we drove to Domino's, my mother called the HMO. "Hello," she said. "My daughter's member number is 03-174-584. She started taking Adderall last week and now she can't stop crying."

She dropped me off outside Walgreens. I sat on the curb of Lowry Avenue, pizza box on my lap, sobbing. "Here," my mother said, sitting down next to me. She offered me a diet cream soda and half a Xanax. I dug my face into the faded floral shirt covering her belly.

When I rubbed my eyes again, everything was calm and drenched in light.

Two years later, writing a paper on "Harrison Bergeron" at 11 p.m., I should have considered why I stopped taking Adderall in seventh grade and switched to Prozac. I did not. Instead, I remembered an article in the Strib about the speed market in Dinkytown. University kids took it to study.

I remembered briefly the *Allez, viens!* incident, but I wrote it off, thinking: I was 11, and now I'm almost 14. I'm practically a university kid. I can handle this.

After 45 minutes, it didn't seem to work, so I took another. And another three hours later when the first seemed to wear off. Then one after Popular Song Writing at the water fountain in front of Algebra II.

For the next month, I continued in this fashion.

I loved my life on Adderall. I constantly felt blessed: at lunch, as I drank a plastic bottle of Coke Zero and ate pickles and carrots with mustard from the salad bar and joyously read about Mesopotamia; during the night, as I shot pictures of myself in my underwear and found those pictures on thinspiration sites; after school, when I sat in the glass library downtown. Every moment save for those on Thursday mornings when I had to abstain. My mother drove me out to the Eating Disorders Institute in St. Louis Park. They would draw blood and I had to come up clear for amphetamines.

"God, mom," I said, "this is ridiculous. I do not have an eating disorder." I took the swig that finished my Diet Coke and cracked open another.

"Yeah, well, tell that to Dr. Reeve," she said, taking a bite of her peanut butter sandwich. We drove opposite rush hour.

"Even so, why do we have to go all the way out to *St. Louis Park*? They're a bunch of suburban bourgeoisies."

Unlike the Regions Hospital, where my psychiatrist worked, Methodist Hospital smelled like salmon. I strolled through the automatic doors, drinking my third can of Diet Coke, and into a purple box. On the floor, purple carpet; on the walls, purple wallpaper; on the elevator door, a purple sign asking in Helvetica "Do you binge eat?"

We rode to the fourth floor, where only the wallpaper was

purple. I crushed my can and stuck it in a potted palm.

"Oh, Emi," my mother said. "Take it out."

"I'm just storing it there, Ma."

I sat in the reception area of the Eating Disorders Institute. The EDI is a place of tapping feet, sagging pants, and Citizen watches swinging loose on thin arms. It hadn't occurred to me that having an "eating disorder" would allow me to schmooze with the rich. Instead, I—wearing a skullcap to hide my greasy hair—resented them and resented the fact that I was there. While I may have been losing seven pounds a week, the impulse definitely seemed different between the girls in Juicy sweats and myself. I had never started out on a diet. I had set out on a mission to destroy myself. I probably would have managed without the Adderall, but I blame it anyway.

"Margaret Nietfeld?" a nursing assistant in kitty-printed scrubs called from the doorway. "Can we get your weight today?"

"Hell no," I said.

Nights, I wrote. I tried to analyze "The Rime of the Ancient Mariner." At 3 a.m. I gave up and began writing my "true work": namely, horrible poems. I titled each of them "Ode to Speed."

And I paint my body (in the metaphysic actions)
I am a canvas, and it hurts,
but I am a sail.
And speed, speed, my albatross.

For my mood at the time, "albatross" was grossly inaccurate. I loved Adderall. I had done nothing wrong; I was not ashamed. In fact, I felt pretty badass: As I lost weight, my Levi's hung off my ass. Every day I wore the same pair of 504s and the same XXL black cashmere sweater. Strands of blond hair clumped to it and hung from my shoulders in alarming clumps. I didn't wash my hair, save for the evenings when I ate cookies at readings at the library and then threw up in the shower.

The albatross image never occurred to me as an omen, despite my weekly appointments at Methodist. Now it seems painfully ironic and I seem painfully ignorant. I just liked the way "albatross" sounded, the way it rolled off my tongue after flicking all day the word "speed, speed, speed, speed."

"Wow, Emi," Dr. Reeve—my real psychiatrist said—as she opened her office door, "you look like shit today."

"Thank you," I said, sitting down in my black parka.

"You're not supposed to be happy about that," she said, standing up. "Take off your coat." She cleared plastic dinosaurs from underneath the other padded chair and pulled out a scale.

She worked at Regions, not the eating disorder hospital. I stood in my black sweater and Levi's 504s. "Take off your sweater, too."

"But I'm cold," I said.

"Do I look like I give a shit?" Reeve said, aiming her dark eyes at me. "You come in here, skinnier than last week, with greasy hair. You obviously don't care that I get any sleep at night, so why should I care if you're cold? Take off your other sweaters, too."

So I pulled them all off, threw them on the chair. "I washed my hair last night, Reeve," I said.

"Wash it in the mornings from now on. 109." She plopped into her swivel chair, her bob and the venetian blinds casting shadows over her face. "109. Do you still think you're fat?"

I pulled my sweaters back on. "I never thought I was all that fat. I just started losing weight." I sat down and wriggled my arms into my parka. I wanted to tell her about the anorexic I met with a bloated stomach and thin legs, how I thought—delusional—that starvation would be a beautiful way to die.

Dr. Reeve stood up and brushed a lock of her blond bob behind her head. "Well, we can get all Freudian and shit about the deep issues behind your eating disorder once you stop losing weight. But for now I'm going to tell you the opposite of what I tell my obese patients." She drew a pyramid on her white board with "Fruits and Veggies" at the "Hungry Man, etc." in the middle and "Haagen-Dazs" at the bottom. She'd been a French poetry major as an undergrad.

"Do you think you can do this?" she said.

"I already do eat cookies," I said. Although I wanted to, I didn't mention that I only ate the chocolate chips, to supplement my diet of Coke Zero and Adderall. I picked my nails and pretended that I didn't understand how sick I had made myself. My heart jerked and thrashed, my head throbbed despite ibuprofen and Imitrex. I had reduced my personality to sweat-stained T-shirts, coffee, and silence.

She was the only person who seemed to care about me as a person. I trusted her but I wouldn't tell her anything. She would lock me up and put a note in my chart: "Do NOT prescribe stimulants."

"So, Dr. Reeve," I said, looking up at her, "I'm having a hard time concentrating."

"It's because you're *starving*," she said.

"No, I don't think so. I think Adderall would help."

Her face hardened into a grimace.

"There's no way in hell I'm giving you amphetamines." She stood up and walked to the door. "I hope you know that I go home at night and cry because you won't gain weight," she smiled. "And now you think I'm joking. Schedule an hour again next week."

I wanted to tell her that I wasn't losing weight to hurt her, that was merely incidental.

One afternoon in the beginning of November, I found myself with $2—bus fare or coffee. I was at Patrick Henry in north Minneapolis, three miles from home, five miles from downtown. I walked downtown. Snow blew. It was minus-4 outside. I felt blessed, chosen by God. I stopped next to 94 at a SuperAmerica and bought a giant Styrofoam cup of coffee and an M&M cookie. My hands were so cold; they didn't want to grip the cup. I stood in the doorway of the bar. Trying to drink, back to the street, snow whipping in my hair. By the time I reached the library the streets were dark. I stood in the bathroom and rubbed my purple hands under the heater.

The next day, I went into Methodist Hospital drinking a can of Diet Coke, with my feet up on the dashboard. I rode the elevator up to the fourth floor, where—for the first time—I did as I was told. I put on the gauze gown, I peed in a cup, I offered my vein.

I sat down on the exam table. A fat nursing assistant took my pulse (42), my reclining blood pressure (90/60), my standing blood pressure (90/40).

The doctor came in. "So, Margaret," she said, "are you still going to deny that you have an eating disorder?"

I looked out the window. Outside, the sun shined on the parking lots and haze draped the office parks and skyscrapers far, far out in Minneapolis. "Yeah," I said finally, "I don't really know what happened." I wanted, suddenly, to tell her about the Adderall, to throw my hands up and say, *It wasn't my fault!* And maybe, if I had, I would have followed the 12 steps and not a meal plan. But probably not.

"Well, Margaret, at this point it doesn't really matter. We're admitting you."

I pulled my sweaters on over my furry back. I went back outside. I told my mother. I went to see Dr. Reeve in St. Paul.

"You asked for it." She folded her arms over her chest. "I told you to gain weight and you wouldn't. Do you think I'm going to advocate for you at this point? Get on the scale."

I kicked the dinosaurs away with my sneakers. Sweaters and all, she read off, "Ninety-four pounds. Look, Emi, you have two options at this point. You're smart; you can do whatever you want. Either you can go to Methodist among the prissy suburban girls, wanting to get better, and stay for six to eight weeks. Or you can go, wanting to be sick, and get locked up for a nice long time."

I folded my arms over my chest and briefly considered crying. "I'm sorry," I said. "I didn't do this to hurt you."

"Of course not, you're sick," she said, her face softening. "Don't apologize."

I wanted to explain what happened with metaphoric significance. *I found a golden feather*, I wanted to say, *I followed it to the Firebird and my whole life lit*. But I knew that would have just sounded psychotic.

"Anyway," she stood, "it's up to you now. I'm triple-booked." She led me to the door. "Congratulations, you're my sickest patient."

Wearing a white wool sweater with the left sleeve blackened, burnt from sitting too close to the heater, I rode with my overnight bag back to the Eating Disorders Institute. Tired and cold, I watched nightfall over 94E at 4 in the afternoon and drank my last Diet Coke.

It began to drizzle and I listened to the windshield wipers.

With ketones in my blood, urine with a specific gravity of 1.04, low blood pressure, with bradycardia and arrhythmia, and a BMI of 14.7, I walked through the automatic doors into the lobby of Methodist. I surrendered myself to reality, to chicken noodle soup, to blind weights and vitals at 5 a.m., to shut curtains at 5 p.m. We were not allowed to look out after dusk because we could see ourselves in the reflections.

After a week, 14 viewings of *Elf* and a tripled dose of Abilify, an atypical antipsychotic, I knit in the dark box of the dayroom. A giant TV lit the room. Our faces glowed green and red in the colors of Christmas.

Around me, the girls of Edina, Lakeville, Eden Prairie, and Minnetonka wore sweatpants printed "Pink" or "Juicy" down the left leg. They tapped their feet as they knit tight rows of afghans. I wore my Levi's and my black cashmere sweater. My hair hung limp over my face. The only person from Minneapolis, I would have fit in better in rehab.

But during the day, through the fog outside the window, I could see Minneapolis. At night, I snuck out of bed and pushed my head under the curtain. All I could see were lights and I clung to them, the last reminders of the life I had left, burning.

SCRAMBLED EGGS
Personal Essay/Memoir

Jaundiced and coated in amniotic fluid, I was born female. I weighed 9 pounds, 8 ounces, stretched to 24 inches, and had an ovarian cyst the size of a chicken egg. As one obstetrician stitched up my mother's episiotomy, the doctors on call filed in to poke my belly in awe. By the time I could walk, the cyst would dissolve, along with its simple declaration of biological sex. Already I was trying to nurse through my father's shirt.

My mother, quickly approaching 40, had wanted a blond daughter to name Honey. She met my father, a blond RN without a place to stay. They married a month later. When she told him she was pregnant, he didn't believe her. And then he said, "I think I'll move back in with my mother." Before he could leave, he pushed a patient in a wheelchair down a flight of stairs, killing him. He lost his nursing home job and, with it, his patient's drugs. But when my father held me, "he fell in love," my mother said. I slept on his shoulder as he dissected motherboards, watched *Jeopardy!*, and shopped Best Buy. My mother couldn't stand being at home with him, so after six weeks of a six-month maternity leave, she went back to work, processing film at the state crime lab.

For all the importance my father placed on having a daughter and not a son (my father abhorred Grason, my mother's son from her first marriage), I was not distinctly feminine. I wore my brother's "ideally unisex" sweatpants and flannel pajamas and a purple and yellow Barney pullover. My brother, who is 12 years older than me, taught me how to do karate and build Lego rockets. He took me by my ankles and swung while I giggled and screamed, spinning. I ate Chunky Beef Sirloin and staged fire-rescue crime scenes. I have a picture of myself at 13 months, blond-haired in my Barney sweater, inserting a CD into my computer. Instead of ballet or gymnastics or soccer, I played kickball in the street and soccer in the alley with a group of kids from the block, their heads swarming with lice.

I hadn't realized any distinction between the sexes until I was pulling on the mandatory skirt for my first day of school. I had known, theoretically, that I had "girl parts" and that my brother had "boy parts," and that's why he was a boy and I was a girl. At Fourth Baptist Christian School, wearing a skirt was necessary to qualify as a girl. I had imagined "school" as a warehouse with a kidney-shaped pool surrounded by desks, where I would learn how to be a firefighter. Or a medical missionary, or a Christian comedian, or a defense attorney. Instead, I learned that instead of saving lives, I should save myself for marriage and follow the gender roles inscribed on the back of the Ten Commandments.

My teachers, concerned with my "unfeminine behavior," called my parents almost daily about my uncombed hair, dirty or mismatched socks, and skirt that flew up on the jungle gym. And by second grade, my floral skirt was too short. Every few weeks, I knelt on the floor in front of the class to test whether my skirt was long enough. The hem never touched the ground; I was tall.

One day, my teacher sent me to have a heart-to-heart with the principal. "Knees," he said, "are fundamentally sexy. We can't allow you to have them show." When I figured out what sexy meant, I didn't understand how legs could fit the bill. But I hadn't watched professional volleyball, either.

My norms for marriage and relationships didn't come from my parents, but from *Leave It to Beaver*, which I watched with my mother while eating Moose Tracks ice cream. Unlike June Cleaver, neither of my parents cooked besides my father's occasional bratwurst on the propane grill or my mother's Pillsbury brownies.

"Mom," I asked, "why don't you cook?"

"I don't have time," she said, sighing. "I work. Why don't you ask your father why he doesn't cook? He's here all day."

"Women cook," my father said. We ate rotisserie chicken and bagged salad on the bed, again.

In front of the television, my mother explained chromosomes and, with them, sex. I was surprised but unshaken. "Sperm cells are tiny," she said. "They don't contain much and they don't have any mitochondrial DNA. The X chromosome is so powerful that only one is activated." The strength of the egg compared to the slithering sperm was clear. "More boys are conceived than girls," she explained.

"But more girls are born. The boys die off before they're born."

I pitied boys. Their testosterone-severed corpus callosum made mental math excruciating, their Y chromosomes made reading herculean. I adored my father but knew he had to compensate. Unlike my mom, he lacked a job, biceps, and two X chromosomes. I believed him when he said, "Nail polish is too sexy" and "The Girl Scouts are filled with lesbians." Even more than I was missing out, he was too.

When I was in fourth grade, riding home to watch *ER* at 4, he told me, "I'm changing my name to Theresa." His thin blond hair hung down to his shoulders and nubs of breasts stuck out from his shirt because he was so fat. "I was thinking about just changing it to Terry, but I thought I'd just be direct."

"Oh, that's cool," I said.

At Northern Sun, a leftist store downtown, we chose a purple embroidered purse. He bought Birkenstocks. I picked out "Siren" 10-Hour Lipcolor that painted his thin lips orange in our bathroom.

"What do you think?"

"It looks pretty good," I said. I smeared some decade-old lilac eye shadow on his lids. Then he rubbed it off with peach cold cream.

Finally, my father, who had been ordering estrogen online from India, got an estinyl prescription and a lesbian therapist whose parrots imitated the answering machine.

"Ring, ring, ring," one parrot said. I looked up from Stephen King.

"Hello, you've reached the private, confidential line of Karol Jenson," the other parrot cooed. "If this is an emergency, please call 911. Please leave a message after the tone." Sometimes it was not the parrots and a client would begin to speak. So much for "private, confidential."

Karol was the first lesbian I met. She was tall with short hair, although not as tall as Ellen, my father's 6'5" role model. Ellen was curator of the electricity museum in Minneapolis. She transitioned into a woman at 50. Her wife, Mary (who writes Embroidery murder mysteries), stayed with her even after the surgery. At dinner at Olive Garden she explained, "The trick is to find the ending first." My father smiled.

"Rosella's butch, anyway. She'll stay."

But three weeks later, after my mother delivered the papers, my father broke into sobs at the McDonald's drive-thru. "I can't believe she's leaving me!" he wailed, pounding the steering wheel. I wrapped my arms around him. "That bitch!"

Before the first of endless psychological assessments, my mother, my father, and I went to Perkins. My father wore a skirt.

"What would you ladies like to eat today?" the waitress asked.

"Scrambled eggs." My mother shut her menu.

My father left a $10 tip. I was never together with them again.

Logistics eroded all of my father's relationships. Because my mother wouldn't call him anything but Tom, their lawyers sent their kids to private schools. My father sobbed when I mentioned "my mom," or when his mother forgot he was now a woman. I started calling my mother "R" and he stopped seeing his mother.

Others tried to help work out the worms of the situation. Annalisa down the block gave me a VHS of a transsexual on *Oprah*. My cousin Jessica, who is 6-foot-5 and works for Planned Parenthood, brought my father garbage bags filled with her old clothes. "Have you ever watched *Oprah*?" she asked me. "They had a show on transsexuals. One of the kids said he calls his father 'Maddy.' It's a cross between 'Mommy' and 'Daddy.' Maybe you could call Theresa that." I started calling him "Mom." He just loved that.

In the middle of fifth grade, my father's girlfriend Susan moved in. I spent Wednesday nights and Sundays with my mom, digging through the Walgreens clearance and watching *Passport to Paris*, while my father and Susan cruised gay bars and bought cocaine. In the basement, while they shot methadone, I watched *But I'm a Cheerleader* and *My Summer of Love*. *Whoa, that could be me*, I thought, watching the young lesbians kiss. And then I went back to my scrambled-egg quesadilla.

I was everything my father wanted to be. At the Unitarian church's "women's night," complete with hotdish and drums, he whispered to me across the table, "When you menstruate, I'm going to throw a party and buy you a monkey." I didn't think it was *that* big of a deal.

As my parents' day in court approached, the promises grew.

"If you come with me, I'll let you get a belly-button ring when you turn 13," he said. "We'll do it together. We're going to have a pool in Arizona." But when my mother won custody, we knew that an AMBER Alert would meet me at the state line.

So we hauled the mattress from the basement, unscrewed the bookshelves from the walls, tore down the kitchen table. My father smashed my piano with a Slugger. I carried the pieces out to the firepit. He lit up a cigarette and then the edge of my mattress, whose flowers melted into its wire springs.

We watched from the patio, drinking white wine and vodka in Squirt, as the flames climbed, catching on the lowest leaves of our oak tree. I packed up the leftovers of my room into a garbage bag.

When the trees turned golden, my father and Susan picked me up from Marcy Open School in their red Ford F-150. With the sunroof open, my father raced me around the block at 80, 85, 90, seeing how fast we could go. We ate falafel on the tailgate. We hugged goodbye. "I love you, Mom," I said.

There were no drums for my first blood, no dances, just a trip to Rainbow Foods for pads. The June air distilled into beads on my skin. I stuck my feet out the window. It was Father's Day.

Rachel Rothenberg, 18
Pittsburgh CAPA 6–12
Pittsburgh, PA
Teacher: Mara Cregan

Rachel Rothenberg admires authors like Ernest Hemingway who are able to tell stories with very few words, as well as Southern Gothic writers such as Flannery O'Connor. She will attend the College of Wooster in Ohio and one day would like to write full-time, or teach at a high school or post-secondary level.

EULOGY FOR ANDY
Poetry

"I had to do it," she said.
"He had too much control over my life."
But even that couldn't kill you, fingering your battle wounds,
art for art's sake.
Not even the women who floated through your silver rooms,
lovely and quiet as breath on the back of your neck,
who faded into nothingness and black-and-white and it was all
    your fault
could do it.
What got you,
finally,
was your own fear
of fear.
You were your world's own negative,
sad and smoky with the Slavic dreariness of everyone who breathes
the air of this last coal town.
We examine your pictures, your photographs,
the giant women in red lipstick,
plastic clouds,
the sting of our own
mortality. In this picture,
between the red-yellow lights of your fame,
you're standing with the children

drunk on their own desire, but you say nothing.
In another, we see the screen goddess,
her eyes glazed over, frozen by your hand,
and she's telling us that you have left the building.
We walk to Mass hand-in-hand,
light candles for you, whisper your name in a language
no one speaks anymore over and over, believing
in God and Mary and the saints and your hot-pink ghost
rapturing us body and soul into Times Square.
Half-lit in the smoke we see you as you were
in life, pale and silvermoon and yet,
so much brighter.

THE INCORRUPT BODY (FROM UTOPIA)
Short Story

For five days during the summer I was born, my father was the most famous man in America. Years later he would remark, "I went into the mine a poor son of a bitch and came up again a mill-ion-aire." He was proud that he had survived the mine collapse, proud that he had gotten to give an interview to CNN. People crowded around him as he emerged from the dark hole, struggling to touch him. Like Jesus. My mother sobbed and wiped her eyes with the sleeve of her dress before clinging to him, her clawlike fingernails scratching the thin fabric of his work shirt. The day after he came out of the mine, she went into labor with me, and was overwhelmed with flowers, some of which came from, she later found out, the president of the United States. My parents spoke fondly of those days, and after a while, the abject terror my father felt while he had been trapped in the mine was replaced by a faint sense of nostalgia. He reminisced about it, joked about it with his buddies. Very early on I was aware that I had arrived into the world at a miraculous time.

When I was 10, after the money from the *The John De La Barre Story* had run out, Dad decided to run for mayor of our town, Utopia. West Virginia is a state where you get elected both for looking like John Kennedy and for being a good union man, and Dad had both those qualities. I went with him in my pink Sunday dress to the Nu-Way Bakery, to the First State Bank of Utopia, to the Carraway Theater, its bleached paint peeling. I held a sign with the UMWA logo and the phrase "De La Barre Raises the Bar." Dad was young and handsome and he waved a lot, brushing his hair back from his head. I fell in love with him as much as every other constituent did, breathless with the thought of some new blood in Utopia at last.

When CNN heard that John De La Barre, the mining miracle, was running for mayor, they sent someone down from the office in Charleston to interview him. It was an election year, and one of those election years where suddenly everything anyone says becomes a comment on their patriotism. I would like to think that my father knew this, that he said what he said because he wanted to be radical, just for once. Even at the age of 10, reading his quote over and over again in the newspaper, I didn't want my father to say what he said because he actually *believed* it, and still think he'd get elected. I didn't want for him to be that stupid.

What he said was "Personally, I don't think the president could give two shits about the people of Utopia *or* the people of West Virginia."

The president was a Republican, so it was dangerous in itself, but I think it was the "shit" that really got to them. The man they had envisioned on his knees in the blinding dark, begging God to relieve him of his labors, had said "shit." About the *president.* When he lost, Dad merely shrugged his shoulders, said, "Well, I didn't want the goddamn responsibility anyway," and went back into the mine.

I thought about the quote years later, when my brother, Elijah, called me from Morgantown and said, "You've got to do something about Dad."

I was in Lexington, standing at my kitchen counter, watching coffee drip into the pot.

"He went to work today," he said.

"He goes to work every day."

"Yeah, well, that's the problem, Cara." I could almost see him rolling his eyes. "Just drive back to Utopia this weekend and tell him he's an old man and he can't work."

It went like this: Elijah had driven down one Friday afternoon and had witnessed my father pass out upon stepping out of his truck. The blackouts were, according to my mother, something fairly common in recent months and had something to do with the fact that my father refused to use his inhaler for his work-induced asthma.

Elijah said, "He's got to stop working. Let him live off the movie residuals and the mine pension. He's not dumb. He's doing this because he's a mean son of a bitch who's afraid to die."

I saw his point. But I didn't want to drive to Utopia. "You do it."

"Aw, Cara. He loves you. He doesn't love me."

This is Elijah's thing. He avoids any family responsibility by claiming that Mom and Dad have never shown affection toward him, and so he owes them nothing. I imagined him sitting in a half-drunk stupor up in Morgantown with his WVU buddies (all unemployed), whining at me to "do something about Dad."

"I mean it," he said. "There is absolutely no affection there."

"Elijah," I said, "are you drunk?"

"Yes, ma'am, I am," he said. "I surely am a little bit drunk."

"I'm hanging up now, Elijah."

As I put the phone back on its cradle, I looked at the Post-it note of my parents' phone number I kept on the wall. I hadn't called them in ages. I wondered, vaguely, whether my father still thought the president—any president—didn't give two shits about Utopia.

I called him.

Driving into Utopia feels like driving onto the surface of the moon. You turn off the interstate and go over an old industrial bridge bruised with soot, while under you the muddy Guyandotte trickles its way to the Ohio. The town itself juts up into the hills, and the roads sharpen into points and dangle over the dusty downtown streets, casting shadows over the Nazarene church and the Utopia Society for Crippled Children and Bob Barker's Income Tax Service and West Virginia Gift Shop. At 2 o'clock in the afternoon, downtown Utopia is silent, except for the occasional thundering *chucka-chucka-chucka* of the CSX coal train as it roars its way to Tennessee. Not long after my father came out of the mine a hero, Utopia began to go silent. I could actually hear it as I grew up, walking to the Kroger to get something for my mother. Quietly, the voices of my neighbors drifted away into the dark rooms of their houses, and emerged only on Sundays, when they would sit on their porches and glare at one another.

"A ghost town," I would sometimes say to my friends in Lexington. "I come from a ghost town."

My family lived on Miller Road, at the head of the Hatfield-McCoy Trail. Miller Road was a good street to live on, because it wasn't on a cliff and no one sold drugs on it and it wasn't a far walk to the Kroger. So we lived well enough, but we were still poor. Everyone in Utopia is poor. But growing up, I never thought of my family as such. We lived in a white clapboard house with a sunroom where Elijah and I would sleep in the summer, sharing knockoff

Oreos from the Kroger and whispering late into the night. When I left West Virginia, I sometimes thought back on the house fondly, especially the little creek that ran at the bottom of the hill that crested off the back porch. The Old Regular Baptists would baptize their faithful there, and even though we were plain old Southern Baptists and therefore weren't supposed to associate with them, we would open the windows on Sunday afternoons, listening to their strange and beautiful singing piercing through the heavy air with their foreign melodies.

"*Guide me, o thou great Je-ho-vy*," Dad would sing, throwing his head back. "*Pil-grim in this barren la-a-a-nd.*"

But I had heard the Old Regular Baptists had moved their operation down to the Guyandotte, and as I turned onto Miller Road it was silent, except for the occasional barking of a dog in someone's distant yard. I pulled into the makeshift driveway, the tires crunching on the gravel, and I saw that the white paint on the outside had begun to peel, that my mother's flowers were shriveled and dry. My feet were sweating in my boots, and, as I put my hand up against the side of the house and paint flaked into my hands, I felt a thick sense of shame.

I rang the bell hard, because I knew Mom wouldn't have her hearing aids in, then knocked twice for good measure. Someone was watching *The 700 Club* deep within the house. She appeared at the screen door. Mom was a strikingly beautiful woman, Miss Utopia 1970, and she still had all of her hair and her teeth and her good figure. When I was very young, I thought she was Barbie. But now she looked hard and careworn, a Dorothea Lange photograph come to life.

"Hello, Mama," I said.

"Oh, Cara." Her embrace felt bony and forced. "Oh, Cara. You've got to do something about your father."

He was plopped in front of the old Naugahyde lounger in the living room, watching the TV. This was always my image of him from about the age of 10 onward, after he lost the election. He would come home, and, without even showering, he would sit down in his lounger and flip on the news and call for Elijah or me to bring him a beer. Around 9:30 he would fall asleep, and the three of us would tiptoe around, trying not to disturb his sacred rest.

"Goddamn politicians wouldn't even bother coming to Utopia," he muttered, as I put my bag down in the doorway. "I don't trust either of those slick-talking snake-oil salesmen as far as I can throw 'em."

"Don't listen to that *700 Club* Bible news, Daddy," I said.

He turned himself around in the lounger slowly, and broke into a fit of coughs before thumping his chest soundly.

"Sorry," he said. "Feelin' a little under the weather lately."

"Daddy," I said, "we need to talk."

"Did Elijah call you from Morgantown?" he asked.

I nodded.

"Aw, Jesus," he said.

"Daddy," I said, "how big is your mine pension now?"

"Hell, Carrie."

"I'm just saying, you could retire real nice. Maybe you could even move out of Utopia."

He reached for the remote and shut off the TV. Obama's picture died into black.

"Girl," he said, "I'd advise you to shut your mouth."

He took dinner in his room. Mama and I ate split pea soup standing over the sink, in silence. The soup looked and tasted like baby food. She told me that ever since the collapse, Daddy couldn't stand to eat much else. Then she yawned, said she was going to bed. I slept in my old room, my old posters peeling off the wall. The bed was too short for my legs, and my feet poked out of the blankets, icy-cold even in summer. My room was right next to my parents', and because I couldn't sleep I stayed up all night, staring at the ceiling at my glow-in-the-dark stars forming the constellation of Orion, listening to Dad cough and then sigh.

It was almost 5 in the morning when Dad poked his head into my room, fully dressed.

"Get up, Carrie," he said. "I wanna show you something you'll never see again in all the days of your life."

I made coffee on the stove—they didn't have a coffeemaker—and we drank it, black and bitter. Sometime in the night, my mother had gotten up from their bed and settled down on the couch. The blanket was drawn up around her, over her head. She looked like a corpse. I shuddered.

"Let's not dilly-dally any longer," Dad said, tossing the rest of his coffee in the sink. "Got a long drive to Aracoma."

The Aracoma mine was named for Princess Aracoma, the daughter of the Mingo chief whom the English first made contact with in these hills. Every summer, my family would make the pilgrimage to Logan to hear the story of her love for Boling Baker, the Englishman, and her subsequent death. It was amateur theater, but it always left me breathless and full of admiration of their love. When I got older, I found it amusing that they had given the Aracoma mine such a romantic name. It belched up black smoke and foul-smelling fire, and the people who staggered through it looked like ghosts caked in ash. After the collapse, the UMWA had managed to get it closed down, and a few years later it reopened, and it looked much better—at least on the outside. Mines bothered me. They possessed all kinds of spiritual questions about whether humans were meant to go so deep into the earth. If you dug far enough, would you eventually hit something?

It was 7:30 when we reached the mine. It was Saturday, but there seemed to be an unnaturally large amount of people around. Getting out the car, I noticed Lyman McKenna right away. He was a friend of my father's, and used to come over to sit on our front porch, drink beer, and watch the WVU games with my father. I always had considered him a man who kind of surpassed joviality and was more boorish than anything, but today he seemed nervous, jumpy. Suddenly it was cold, and I vaguely wished that I'd remembered to bring a sweater.

"Johnny," he said, "Miss Cara. When'd you come in from Kentucky?"

"Yesterday afternoon," I said. "Been trying to convince this one here to give up this fire and brimstone."

I said it cheerfully, as if to be funny. Neither of them laughed.

McKenna invited us into the manager's office and poured us more cups of coffee. Then he and Dad retreated into the backroom and shut the door. I drank my coffee and flipped through the copy of *Newsweek* someone had left on the manager's desk. There were lots of articles about the election and how each candidate would do in each state, but they'd apparently forgotten West Virginia. It was so predictable I didn't even roll my eyes.

After a while, Dad and McKenna came back in, both rubbing at their temples as if they had terrible headaches.

"You own a handgun, Miss Cara?" McKenna asked.

Dad laughed and shook his head. "Naw," he said, "she ain't got no gun. She's one of those liberals who don't *believe* in guns."

McKenna pursed his lips in distaste and shrugged. "Well," he said, "she can do what she wants."

There were voices coming from outside the office, voices I couldn't easily identify. Dad went to the window.

"Lordy," he said. "Oh, Lordy, Lordy."

I got up to follow him, but McKenna put his hand on my arm. "Now, Miss Cara," he said, "you don't want to see about that."

"What's going on?" I said. "Dad?"

Dad turned away from the window and stuck his hands in his pockets.

"Well," he said, "it seems a bunch of folks from up north got wind of the fact that this mine ain't exactly up to *snuff* when it comes to the standards of the Environmental Protection Agency up in Washington."

I looked at him blankly. "What are you talking about? They fixed it up a while ago. I thought it was fine."

Dad shook his head. "No, not that."

"Then what?"

McKenna wrung his hands together. "This ain't a standard mine anymore," he said. "This mine is a *strip* mine now."

Strip mining. Since I didn't live in mine country anymore, mining issues were very rarely on my mind, but I *did* know that in Utopia it was something of a black-and-white issue.

"People need to eat," McKenna said. "Strip mines feed 'em."

"Goddamn Yankees," Dad said. "What the hell they know about West Virginia?"

"They know it's beautiful," I said. "They don't want to lose the mountain."

Dad's eyes rolled so far up into his head I thought they might get stuck there.

"What the hell I care about the mountain? They could pave

over the mountain tomorrow if it was gonna give my kids a better meal at night." McKenna's voice was sharp and angry. "The mountain is for people who can *afford* the mountain."

The door opened, and several more men came in, wearing UMWA jackets.

"Nina Floyd's out there," one of them said, "and she's half-naked in front of God and everyone."

"Nina Floyd?" I asked, perhaps a little too breathlessly. Nina Floyd had won an Oscar the year before for her role in a dark comedy that had been shot in Lexington. I'd served her coffee, and she'd tossed her long red hair over her shoulder and said "*Thank* you-u-u," in such a way that I had tried to emulate it for weeks after. All it had done was make my boyfriend ask me if I had a cold.

"Yeah," said Dad, with a little suspicion in his voice. "Nina Floyd. She's been poking around here for months." He shook his head.

One of the men who had come inside reached into his jacket and pulled out his handgun. Handguns were a fact of life in Utopia —you saw them everywhere—but still, the nonchalance with which he handled it unnerved me.

"Why do you boys have to have your guns out all the time?" I asked. "They're just protesting."

"We protect what's ours," said McKenna darkly.

After a while, it was decided that we would go out and face the protesters head-on, block the entrance so they couldn't get into the mine and engage in what McKenna called "their fool tricks." They opened the door and filed out, one by one. In the parking lot there were dozens of others—men, women, and children, most of whom I recognized. But I didn't want to talk to them, so I kept my head down and walked along silently, like a ghost.

The protesters had gathered outside the mine gates, now padlocked shut and guarded by the state police. They were all young and white and thin. Actually, they all looked a lot like Nina Floyd. And *clean*. The first thing that struck me was how clean they were. Living in Utopia gives you a kind of unwashable grit in your hair and nails, as much a part of you as your teeth and eyes. They were all chanting, wild, loud chants I couldn't pick out. And at the front was Nina Floyd, her shirt showing her midriff toned by the best hands in

Los Angeles. And she ran her hands through her hair the same way she did in the coffee shop.

I pushed past Dad and McKenna, ignoring their cries of protest until I was as close to the gate as I could possibly get. I wanted to see Nina Floyd again, in the flesh, her body incorrupt by ashes.

Someone behind me turned on their car radio.

You're so condescending,
your gall is never-ending,
we don't want nothin', not a thing from you...

Dad worked his way up to the front, beside me. He was panting now, gripping his chest in pain.

We're not gonna take it,
we ain't gonna take it,
oh, we're not gonna take it anymore...

Nina saw him. She held up her hand.

"Mr. De La Barre," she said. Her voice drifted smooth and unctuous through the gate. "I wonder if you'd like to come outside and address the crowd. About the dangers of mining."

"To *hell* with you!" he shouted, and the crowd outside erupted in boos as the crowd behind us erupted in cheers and hollering.

She smiled, the kind of smile my mother used to give me. "But," she said, "it was mines like these that almost killed you."

"Only thing that killed me was you goddamn hippies chaining yourselves to the equipment for the last 20 years," he spat.

"Fuck the mine!" someone behind Nina shouted, and they cheered again.

Dad stuck his finger through the iron bars of the gate.

"I would just like to know," he shouted hoarsely, "just how many of you folks are from the mountains?"

"You don't have to be from the mountains," Nina said, "to care about them."

"Sure," said Dad, shrugging, "but you don't know nothin' about what it means to *live* here."

Nina reached into the loose canvas bag hanging at her side. "Let me give you the card of the Southern Appalachia Conservancy Group…"

"Where's that group headed up, Miss Floyd?"

Nina tossed her hair again. "Charlotte, North Carolina."

"Wouldn't hardly call that *rural*, would you?"

She ignored him. "Mountaintop removal is hazardous to the environment. Mountaintop removal is when—"

"I know what it is, Miss Floyd. I do it every day."

He said this with an air of exasperation. You get used to it after a while, especially when you're from where we are from. People assume you live and die by the mine, that you're either illiterate or just unwilling to read the literature the environmental groups from the North send down.

"And you're destroying the Earth!" a boy in a stocking cap next to Nina shouted.

Dad held up his hand. "Folks, I don't pretend like I don't know what strip mining does to the mountain in the *geographical* sense. But the fact is, people gotta eat. And if strip mining's gonna save our economy, then I think the good people of Utopia and of Appalachia are gonna be doing it for a long goddamn time."

Nina turned her nose up in the air. "We don't want you making money," she said, "at the expense of *our* future."

A surge of white-hot rage shot through me. It was her voice, her perfect unaccented *voice*, with the hint of self-absorption a person of her caliber earns. Us and them, us and them. What did she know about us?

In the days and weeks that followed, I thought long and hard about what happened next. About how I might have taken her slender, pale, clean neck between my two fists and shook, hard, until Dad and McKenna dragged me off of her, how she fell to the ground clutching at her breastbone, coughing. About how Dad coughed harder on the drive back from the police station. About how Nina Floyd had her article in *People* about her savage attack by West Virginia miners, too dumb to know what was best for them, showing off the purple bruises around her neck.

"Some girl did it to me," she said. "Some girl who just didn't know any better."

And, most of all, I remember how much my father looked like John Kennedy in the coffin, the cheap powder scaling his cheeks and nose, and, when they opened him up, they found everything in perfect order except his lungs, which were black as night. From the mine or from the cigarettes? We would never know.

Dad *did* live and die by the mine, in a way. His was the Utopia success story—a man can get rich through faith in God and hard work. His American dream. It might have killed him. But hell, it kept me fed and sent me to college and made him proud. We have so little in our lives, don't we? And maybe it made me mad that Nina Floyd, with her muchness, with her money and her talent and her car, would try to take that away.

We protect what's ours. We live and die by it.

GOLD, SILVER, AND AMERICAN VOICES MEDALS

Students in grades 7–12 submit works in 11 writing categories. This year more than 20,000 writing submissions were reviewed by the authors, educators, and literary professionals. Gold, silver, and American Voices medals were awarded to works that demonstrated originality, technical skill, and emergence of a personal voice.

Victoria Sharpe, 16
South Carolina Governor's School for the Arts and Humanities
Greenville, SC
Teacher: Mamie Morgan

Victoria Sharpe looks up to the poets Billy Collins and Stephen Dunn and feels inspired to write by the people she has met in her native town of Greenville, South Carolina. In addition to writing, she is an avid whitewater kayaker. She hopes to keep writing and one day earn a master's degree in creative writing.

MAPS
Poetry

An aged atlas, skin-wrinkled pages
laced with boyish scrawls, childhood
sketched out in ink. I study the names of distant,
sand-covered cities: Tripoli and Pretoria.

The shores that a child aches for. Maybe
as the roundness of your cheeks melts away,
you forget there is life beyond your front door.
You forget how the rivers in India

look like the veins in a hand, how the men
and women on an island in the Pacific scar their backs
with seashell pieces to say *We are not children anymore.*

The tides of the Atlantic stop ebbing
at your brain, and the Andes peaks become
no more than a flowering of triangles on a map.

Elise Lockwood, 18
University High School
Carmel, IN
Teacher: Alicia Lamagdeleine

Elise Lockwood will attend Indiana's DePauw University, where she plans to major in English and biology. She is inspired by Kurt Vonnegut's biting satire and ability to challenge long-held assumptions. In the future, she'd like to write seriously while living in a tent on the Amazon River.

EVE
Poetry

I don't remember being that single, bloody rib.

The stark white bones sprouting like bald, jointed trees. Breasts,
flabby knolls erupting from muscle striped like plowed fields.

Adam giggling in the corner, I'm sure, adjusting his single,
   well-positioned leaf,
startled at the sight of something so strange and different,
at me.

I started remembering at the time of the skin rippling
over everything,
from head downwards, toes upwards, meeting to connect at the
   bottom of the pelvic
bone, then a nauseating shuddering and rolling like
a boulder about to topple off a cliff, teetering at the tip, then—
"Good enough," God said,
and my skin went zipping together, inwards instead of out.

There was a hole.

Where Adam had a summit, I had
nothing. Raw, unfinished, air.

I asked Adam why. In his innocence,
there was only the vague sense that his leaf might be getting a
   bit tighter,
so I left.

I sat in the garden,
surrounded by so much beauty it was
commonplace, flowers as big as my head blooming beside me,
the pollen coating my skin like gold,
and I would wonder.

The animals Adam and I had named
Refused to answer my questions, or maybe they just
Didn't know.

The snake and I compared our bodies,
Looking for a similar
Incompleteness on her smooth underbelly,
Finding none.

I was alone. God had finished everyone else.

And then, the next time I visited the snake and her tree,
she told me
I could know why. I could know almost
as much as God knew.

"Eat this," she said, handing me a fig. I took a small, scared bite,
finding, even as I chewed, that it had needed to be done.
I tasted something pungent and strange,

Then I knew.

I expected a rift in the earth, thunder at least,
but all was silent as I looked down and saw what I had to be
   ashamed of.
Calling over Adam, I told him, "Eat, and get that thing away from me."

Flowers wilted under our feet as we took our last steps
out of the garden. Our sorrows multiplied under God's icy glare.

He was the master of the silent treatment.

With each step away, I felt a twinge
between my legs.

With each step,
a drop of blood,
leaving a trail
we could never follow back.

Clara Fannjiang, 15
Davis High School
Davis, CA
Teacher: Susan Pangelinan

Clara Fannjiang will be a junior at Davis High School in Davis, California. Although her primary interest is in the sciences, Clara enjoys reading and writing poetry as a means of escape from everyday problems. She looks up to such poets as Irving Feldman, Craig Arnold, and Karen Volkman.

A PERPETUAL SOUND
Poetry

the wise misters of our time
or even their sons, their half-head
coddlings who attend
bighead academies with names of
sour shaving cream, they ask

big things like what if,
let us say, see there's this
big tree and it falls
and suppose there's no one
in its respective forest

(firstly, we assume that every entity
of nature must – of course! – be defined
by some syllabic fetter or another,
earth air *riv* er *fi* re
au tumn *falls* from *sun*

so *ti* red)
does it make a sound?
[exclamation mark here]
give me thy sugar-spun heart
and i will give thee a lump of coal.

william once spent twenty-four entire seconds creaming a beetle
with his chair leg, stamping a discursive essay of bruise-colored juice
and bitty crackled legs across the bulletin of time,
the fleckly linoleum. it's nicer to think, *oh yes, for a damsel
in distress*, see of course karis thought bugs were *yucko* what is
thato, but william doesn't have swirly golden locks to flounce his
nonexistent
bravado and chivalry. he took his sweet honey love time,
grating his stiff little chair across the pitless floor
like it was a piece of finely aged mozzarella
with the curves of a finely aged woman.

a crowd was in the stiff little room
where william committed his stiff little murder.

it made no sound. within twenty-four hours the speckled
linoleum
was once again virgin, purged, and the beetle was no longer
a what to is thato. someone pulled out a baton and did not
hallmark
the time or day across the fluorescent walls, and hurried us
along,
snappy black funeral heels and all, into schubert's unfinished.
it made no sound.

a draught of ennui can leave us stoned
in perpetual motion
or perfectual stopping. old franz
was cursed with a roundhouse of
three-in-a-bar, and thus fell his

composing quill the way one
falls a big tree in a great *for* est.
his perpetual sound creates an asylum
for a well-forgotten beetle,
as it does for

the lost-of-mind, the washingtons
and einsteins who burned into ashes
that fell away with the clear
wind. there is no salvation for
a wronged beetle, there is no justice

for a poet who ridicules
wise men. were the weight of the world
balanced upon the undeath of
schrödinger's cat, would the death of
william's beetle be its accomplice? and say

there was nothing left to say
in our midst; would we call upon his beetle
to give the demagogues' words? perhaps all
was lost between the gorgons' fall
and the wretched anonymity

of the apple. over the lines of the waters
we will seek things greater than
creation, finer than the lingerings
of small minds, farther than a beetle's solstice
could bring us.

Matt Schultz, 15
Highlands High School
Fort Thomas, KY
Teacher: Teri Foltz

Matt Schultz was inspired to write his submission after reading Henry Rollins'
Solipsist, *which deals with the same themes of loneliness and pain that he*
touches on in his poem. He is an avid guitar player and hopes to be a professional
musician in the future.

DON'T
Poetry

Don't.
My skin will burn you.
I never want to hurt you
but I will,
and I won't stop.
I hate myself more
and more each day
because I know this.
I see the pain
you've lived through—
the scar tissues
obscuring your lips
and infecting your
fallopian tubes—
and it's nothing.

Don't.
You can't trust me.
I'm just like the others—
ignorant, stupid, selfish.
I will put your heart
in a bag and slam it
against the wall until

it's runny and frothy
and my anger is
completely
gone;
I can't help it
that I feel good
seeing you bleed—
the sight of blood
gets me high.

Don't.
If you want
human contact,
touch someone else—
fuck them,
kiss them,
give them
the most intense
orgasm you can because
I don't need it.
I can live off of
loneliness, indecision,
depression and repression,
hate and anger,
because those are comforting;
between them, I have nothing
to prove or be or strive for.
They say patience is a virtue.

Nicholas Vafiadis, 14
The Village School
Houston, TX
Teacher: Kate Ferguson

Nicholas Vafiadis is a Houston resident whose poems deal with themes of identity and philosophy. He wishes to create beautiful poetry so he can leave behind something that other people will be inspired by. In addition to writing, he plays several instruments, including the guitar, piano, and violin. One day he would like to be a doctor.

PEPPER SHAKER OF LIES
Poetry

The moment the soup touched my lips
I knew it could be the best I ever had
It just needed pepper
Three little shakes of pepper
Would forever engrave this soup
Into the glorious pantheon of all great soups
Three little shakes
And my taste buds would bask in a nirvana of flavor
And shake I did
Much to my surprise
This was not pepper
Rather than familiar black ashes
Fell cruel white hail
From this pepper shaker of lies

Nadra Mabrouk, 18
Dr. Michael M. Krop Senior High School
Miami, FL
Teacher: Jason Meyers

Nadra Mabrouk was born in Cairo, Egypt, and has lived in the U.S. half her life. She will attend Florida International University, where she hopes to study journalism and eventually earn a master's degree in fine arts. Her work focuses on her personality and the personalities that surround her every day.

UNTITLED
Poetry

I.
My father is a fraud.
He is afraid of losing his identity
and love.
So he stays up late,
watching televised stories
about the similarities between lovers and lies
as he fingers his collar
with the button on the middle of his throat
that my mother sewed in steady place
so she wouldn't be tempted to slit it.

He doesn't know about that, though.
He only knows his childhood
and how truthful he was.

Sometimes he wishes
when we're all asleep.

II.
My mother is a dreamer.
She stands on the windowsill
and cleans between the panes,

praying to the God
to distract her eyes
from the pale way her daughter's face shivers
in scared contortions late at night.

III.
My brother is a hero.
He keeps two guns in a cardboard box under his clothing
next to the books he will never have the time to read.
The day he got his uniform,
he was nowhere to be found.
And now he sits cross-legged staring wide-eyed
in front of all the doors I close and lock.
Because what he doesn't know
will almost certainly hurt him.

He doesn't know me.

IV.
My sister is confused.
She likes to put on little plays
She doesn't know are true stories
To make me laugh about my mistakes
until she holds me by the waist
And makes my hands shake from crying.

She will never see.

V.
My friend is depressed.
She calls me in the darkest of nights
To whisper on the phone and then grow silent
Because there isn't much we can do.
Little Benjamin draws her presents
of newborn frogs smiling
and suns with crudely painted rays
that reach out to all four corners

to make her stay in her too large bed at night.

She doesn't stay.

VI.
My love is alone.
He had another
until his car veered off
into the dying branches
and her breath
smelt of permanently crushed glass.
Now I beg him to keep holding my hand
whenever we go down long staircases
because they spiral down in unnatural patterns
and I'm scared his legs from the accident
would kill him on the way down
and his hot breath would smell of the cold concrete beneath.

VII.
I am a liar.
So I write until my fingers
smell like the tired hum
of the computer.
The letters fade off the keyboard and disappear
Because all my pencils are broken
Just like everything else I own

I am alive.
As I sing along to the voices
that always knew more than me
and try to look up meanings
Because I don't understand
And never will
But they all try to make me
keep going to feel the sad fate of my poetry
and read things
that would make them love

their own decrepit lives.

I am hope
Between 12:35 and 3 a.m.,
wondering if I can be as productive as my hands
that caress the drunk words my love slurs
between gasps of vomit
and uncomfortable sleep.
As I continue singing the meaning
of every song in my head to him
until it hurts enough to sleep
and dream of silent colors that don't have the courage to ever exist
and things so impossible to say
to the lies living with me.

Mimi Hamblin, 16
Karl G. Maeser Preparatory Academy
Lindon, UT
Teacher: Matt Kennington

Mimi Hamblin lives in Provo, Utah. Her work conveys her fascination with libraries, which she considers to be nearly sacred. She'd like to study psychology, creative writing, and biology in college and wants to become a certified masseuse in her spare time. Her hobbies include singing, sewing, and dog grooming.

EULOGY
Poetry

He died on the second floor of the public library
sometime after work on a Friday evening.
A blood clot hit his brain, and
he slumped forward into sonnet #133:
"Beshrew that heart that makes my heart to groan."

From the stained-glass window overhead
red evening light burned quiet on the page,
crossed the back of his hand,
singed tips of hair.

What grace can be said?

He lay there among stacks
of hard-backed friends,
disturbing no one.
There he lay, his back
arched up and over
into the valley
of the shadow
of words

where I let him lie
until closing time,
switched off the lamp,
let those fire-ribbons unravel
and the inked words
drip, drip, shadow.

Better to leave him undisturbed.
Better to be silent.
Because silence is nothing,
and nothing is so full of words.

Wesley Snell, 18
Charleston County School of the Arts
North Charleston, SC
Teacher: Rene Miles

Wesley Snell will attend Reed College in Portland, Oregon, and plans to major in anthropology. He grew up in South Carolina and his home state's socio-racial tensions are reflected in his writing. He is influenced by such authors as Milan Kundera, David Foster Wallace, and Pablo Neruda, as well as his travels to other places and countries.

STANDARD-BEARER
Poetry

Young Emmett Till,
fished out of a river at fourteen.
His line—barbed wire
wrapped tight around a hoarse throat,
the hook a hasty bullet,
the weight a cotton gin fan
that bore him all the way
to the bottom-feeders,
to the festering wound itself,
sent by those Southern boys
who grin with teeth the color of pus.

Young Emmett Till,
fished out of a river at fourteen.
Boiled in his mother's tears
and the bitter sweat of others like him,
he served cold, limp, and rotten
a world that had waited to see
what the South would cook up next.

Young Emmett Till,
fished out of my memory at fourteen
when I heard that racism was
a thing of the past,
a dwelling-point,
a trifle.

Young Emmett Till,
fished out of a river at fourteen,
your face
remains hidden beneath muddy waters,
stripped of honor,
screaming.

Elizabeth Gobbo, 15
Homeschool
Hood River, OR
Teacher: Laurel Armerding

Elizabeth Gobbo grew up in the Central Valley of California, and her piece is a reflection on the scorching summers she remembers from her hometown. She is inspired by the ancient poetry of Beowulf *and dabbles in theater and music as well as writing. She hopes one day to earn her living as a singer-songwriter.*

HEAT
Poetry

I seen the summer
He's nothin' but an old man—
He sits on a creaking maple wood chair,
Been too lazy to replace,
Grinnin' like some crazy stray cat stretched on a warm stone step,
Spinnin' a long yarn for a crowd of kids all clustered 'round,
And tapping the ash from his cigarette onto the ground,
Like nothin' else in the world matters,
'Cept the cool brush of long dry grass 'round his hairy ol' ankles
And the sweet taste of tobacco and the thick chocolate breeze.

I seen the summer
Lyin' down in the tall smooth stalks of corn,
Worn brown hands behind his head and feet crossed,
Listenin' to the honey-whispers,
Singin' with the creeping purple-gray belly of the dawn,
And watchin' the stars as they dance.

I seen the summer
Walkin' by the side of the river,
Steppin' soft so pebbles underfoot rustle like down pillows,
Skipping silky flat stones into the rippling mirror-water,
They leap and jump so fast,

Then sink to the bottom,
'Til the cloth spun current sweeps them to the shore,
And someone comes along,
To find one.

Ruth Prillaman, 15
Richard Montogmery High School
Rockville, MD
Teacher: Molly Clarkson

Ruth Prillaman wrote her piece in the margins of her French-class notebook and eventually rescued and revised it. She thinks that her drive to write came from her father, who always encouraged her. She admires Dylan Thomas and Sylvia Plath. One day, she'd like to write a novel or a musical.

FRENCH
Poetry

L'Académie française strives to preserve the virtue of the
   French language.
Well, I don't find that dreadful *mademoiselle* very virtuous.
In fact, she's almost sinful.
Beautiful on the outside,
But sinister and mysterious.
She follows no patterns,
Abides by no rules,
And lives to seduce and mystify all mankind.
She twists this way and that,
Adorning herself with accents,
Trying on countless conjugations for size.
She does what she pleases, when she pleases
And we follow like eager puppies.
Why, you may ask?
C'est la vie.

Cameron Langford, 17
North Mecklenburg High School
Huntersville, NC
Teacher: Laura Taylor

Cameron Langford usually begins her creative process by writing dozens of pages, then isolates a good sentence and expands on it. Her parents are both doctors and she inherited their fascination with the human body, which plays heavily in her piece. She wants to be involved in the publishing business when she is older.

MEDITATION IN THE YOGA STUDIO MIRROR
Poetry

I forget why I am held in
so tightly
      by my skin. What if
my skin peeled   backwards
         in sheets
and bloomed
      like an upside-down flower, heaved
to the earth by gravity, tracing
      absentmindedly the loops of nervous bundles, pulling part
from part like tree branches sketched
        in the air,
and leaving bare
the broad sling of my   outstretched musculature,

muscles that are   tough
    and dry
and strong, tethering
my joints to my joints, encasing
my sockets with membranous tendons
and cartilage as smooth as sea glass,
the hodgepodge
I use to collage so many bits
together.

Gussie Roc, 15
Saint Ann's School
Brooklyn, NY
Teacher: Marty Skoble

Gussie Roc is a native of Brooklyn, New York. She often describes city life in her poetry. She wants her readers to take their own message away from her work, rather than prescribing a particular one for them. In addition to writing, she is interested in filmmaking, violin, viola, and ballet.

SHE WATCHED HER FEET...
Poetry

She watched her feet
Walk down the street
On a Saturday morning
Counting how many steps it took
To get from her front door
To the bagel shop on the corner
And when she got to number twenty-two
An old man shouted

I can control time
With my broken watch
And that's why we can all agree
That on wet, cloudy days
Time moves slower.

She looked at him puzzled.
Maybe it's just the dark dreary mood
Caused by the overcast she said.
But he just looked down and

Tapped his watch on his knee
And whispered
Do you know the hands don't move anymore?

She didn't say anything.
Did you know that I can't see the numbers anymore?
She was silent.

It's because I broke my glasses he said.
And slipped his watch
Back into his pocket.
When I cup my hands like this he said
I can see heaven
And the angels.
They don't do anything but play the harp all day
And eat grapes straight from the vine.

She said
Maybe you're just seeing into your head.
Like daydreaming.

He sighed.

My hands are cold he said.
But I lost my gloves
A very long time ago
And I drank the coffee I bought to keep them warm.
He stared at her for a while
And tucked his hands
Under his armpits
Rocking.
Why don't you speak? God gave you the gift of voice.
She shrugged.

Dance with me he said.
And she felt bad
Because his watch didn't tell time
And his hands weren't warm
And they were on a crowded street
But he was crazy and alone

So she joined him

And as they waltzed
In the middle of the sidewalk
He spun her around
Then joined the ranks of the people
That trudged along,
Keeping pace,
On a Saturday morning
And when she stopped spinning,
She stood there puzzled.
Then she bowed her head
Kept walking
And counted from twenty-two.

Sophie Obayashi, 15
St. Mary's Academy
Portland, OR
Teacher: Sara Salvi

Sophie Obayashi wrote her piece to communicate the subtleties of perception and complication. She hails from Portland, Oregon, an artistic community that shaped her as an artist and a person. She is inspired by Shel Silverstein, e.e. cummings, and Kelsey Rakes. One day, she'd like to study and experience many other cultures.

SOMETHING LIKE DECADENCE
Poetry

Last night I dreamt of buttons
    I was a man with harmonica lips
    you were the number six
    [six] cracks down your broken spine
I swam in Atlantis
and pulled the scales off the tender fish
    I plucked them like feathers
    one by one so I could hear each of them scream
I was watching the dirt collect under my fingernails
    and telling them thanks for the memories

but I was never one for lying

Last night I didn't dream of buttons
I dreamt of acid on cold pavement
    I was a man with love-handle hips
    you were the number nine
    [nine] cracks—no, bullets through my spine,
    through my heart
I was drowning
I was running
I was flying

and I was plucking feathers off the birds of paradise
    not one by one
    but dozen by dozen

Last night I didn't dream of birds
or numbers or acid
I dreamt of seashells
and colors and something iridescent

Last night I didn't dream at all

Well, I was never one for lying.

Darcy Tuttle, 16
Latin School of Chicago
Chicago, IL
Teacher: Frank Tempone

Darcy Tuttle attends high school in Chicago, Illinois. In addition to writing, she dances ballet, swims, and plays softball. In the future, she would like to be a classical archaeologist. Darcy would like to thank the teachers who inspired her to become a writer, as well as her mother and father for encouraging her.

RELICS AND DREAMS
Poetry

I am the god
of broken things,
Of birds that fly
but do not sing,
Of choking sighs
lingering,
And all the sorrows life can bring.

I am hidden cracks
in perfect hearts,
A festering wound
that burns and smarts,
An empty locket,
iron darts,
A million lost and pointless starts.

I breathe a lie,
I kiss a dream,
I lose my sanity
between,
I taste the sun—
my hope is keen,
But all's for naught and not as seen.

I am the god
who tastes of brine,
A friend of those
who love to pine,
My fate is fixed,
or I'd resign
And face the gods with better jobs than mine.

Aria

I sit alone on
Damp curb, watch condoms float
And I breathe the night.

Ouch

Splinter
my world
You know you want to.
Cast is clattering
convulsing
To shatter on your kitchen floor.
So you can sweep it all up,
smiling
So neatly.
And I'll watch your teeth
Harsh and artificial
they'll glint white
As I fade away.

Teen

I am an echo
Of tight jean conformity—
One dumb, endless laugh.

Noah Miller, 13
Hunter College High School
New York, NY
Teacher: Richard Roundy

Noah Miller attends Hunter College High School. His submission was inspired by Wallace Stevens. In addition to writing poetry, he enjoys animation and robotics engineering. He believes that growing up in art-oriented New York City has provided him with exposure to literature that's been essential to his growth as a writer.

THIRTEEN WAYS OF LOOKING AT A DACHSHUND
Poetry

1.
Like a curse
A dachshund will
Bite you if you
Stare too long
Into the black
Marbles in her skull.

2.
I am of three minds
Like three dachshunds
Under a bed not wanting
To go for a walk.

3.
A sharp shadow
Magnifies
The icicles
On a dachshund's
Spine.

4.
Life is moving.
The dachshund must
                    Bark.

5.
It was dark all morning.
The dachshund sleeps
Under the covers
                    on top of my legs.
                    I have woken up
Yet I am going to wake up.

6.
At the sight
Of a dachshund
Lying in green light
Even a dachshund
Would have trouble
Living in the moment.

7.
She walks low
On the ground with
Her head held
            high.
Why must you train
For a perfect dog
When you can have
            a dachshund?
She knows your thoughts
Before you think them
To get on your nerves
            a little more.

8.
Many cannot dream of dachshunds.
They are too real.
                    Dachshunds dream
Because they cannot live
Enough awake. A dachshund dreams
                    it is hungry.
When we yell our inner dachshund speaks.

9.
His heart
Leapt
When he thought
The shrill
Bell of the
Fire drill
Was a dachshund
Barking.

10.
The postcard from the dachshund
Says nothing.
That way it is easier to read.
The stamp is enough.

11.
The swan listens for the other
Part of herself and when
The dachshund barks she stops waiting.

12.
When a dachshund writes a poem
She makes sure to write as little
As possible so people won't get
Confused. Her favorite thing to do
Is to rhyme, so when she forgets how
To read she can remember it all again.

13.
Dumbo stole his ears
From a dachshund
But dachshunds don't
Mind. Dachshunds
Help the blackbirds
Help Dumbo.

Samantha Pellegrino, 17
Philips Exeter Academy
Exeter, NH
Teacher: Allison Hobbie

Samantha Pellegrino is a native of Andover, Massachusetts, who now attends high school at Philips Exeter Academy in Exeter, New Hampshire. She would like to travel the world, attend graduate school, and publish a book. She wants to thank her teacher Mr. Hearon for teaching her so much about writing.

FAIRY TALES
Personal Essay/Memoir

I. Battles

Once upon a time, there was a boy named Michele Angelo Petroccione, running across Luxembourg.

His feet are sore, so sore, from running what feels like thousands of miles, and his hands are smeared with dirt. Michele has not turned and looked back since he started to run. He cannot shake that ever-present sense that his pursuers are just behind him. He keeps running, trying to keep his gaze straight. The sunrise is his focus point.

He is already shivering, and with every distant shout and dog howl he shivers more. Michele picks up his pace. He wonders if they are close.

He stumbles, falls, and heaves himself off of the cold ground. He looks down at the German uniform he wears, now streaked with dirt. He is disgusted to even be wearing it, but he knows it is necessary to make it out of Germany alive. He remembers how clean it was when he first stole it, first beat the *crucco* down with his shoes, the only heavy objects he could find nearby. Michele stole the uniform, saving only the Italian insignia from his own bloody war clothes. He knew he would need it later, for France, when he escaped the prison.

The dirt is tinged with red, from garnet in the soil. It looks like blood.

Michele remembers his old uniform, stained with the blood of his fallen comrades. He takes a shaky breath, and memories surge forward once again. The plumes of gas on the battlefield. The peppered sound of gunshots. Blood. Blood on his hands. Blood on his shirt. Blood.

He stops to vomit.

He was stationed in Libya before the war began, and then called back to his homeland, to Caporetto, the name he can never forget. He was called to Kobarid to fight for his country in this "Great War."

He will never forget the day.

Blood. Blood everywhere. He pulls his canteen from beneath the uniform that is not his. He takes a hasty sip. Water spills over his trembling lips, the metallic taste making his tongue curl reflexively.

When he was a boy, he was terrified of dragons. As a man, he knows dragons are nowhere near as scary as what men do to other men in places like Caporetto.

Caporetto. The name he will never forget.

He wants to hold his mother just once more again. *Oh, Mama...* He fears he is lost, alone, and hungry and maybe near a land where they will shoot him down if they do not see his Italian insignia in time. Michele replaces his canteen, and runs again. *Oh, Mama...* Only a few more countries left to cross. Only a few more lines in the dirt to smudge. Then, he will be home again.

II. Princess Locked in a Tower

Once upon a time, there was a princess named Stella, locked away in a ship for 30 days.

"Papa!" she calls, but Peter does not answer. He is asleep, a trickle of spit gathered on the edge of his lip, for the first time in a week.

Stella sits beside him, head in her hands. The rocking is making her nauseated. With every minute that goes by, the ship lurches from side to side, rolling and roaring like a great beast. Stella feels sick, and does not know where to turn.

Swallowing her stomach, she pulls herself up and watches the sea through a dirt-stained mirror. Giant dragons made of water battle each other for dominance, blue-gray scales grinding against blue-green. There is no sun, only storm.

Stella closes her eyes, and sits again. Coughs echo through the cabin, and she covers her mouth and nose. *Everyone is sick here.* Their heaving and choking make a rhythm parallel to the pound of the waves against the boat's wooden sides.

It has been 27 days. Stella knows it will be over soon. Peter said it would take only 30. She wonders if she can stand any more. Stella curls up besides Peter, snuggling against her father's hard shoulders. His handlebar mustache twitches in his sleep.

America will be very different from Greece. She thinks of all the stories she has heard, of cobblestone streets where half the stones are pure gold nuggets, of money falling from the sky once a month. Stella wants everyone else to join her and Papa soon. She misses her mother already. *Oh, Mama...* Her arms would be so comforting.

Stella counts sheep as she tries to sleep, eno, thio, tessera, her long, chestnut waves spilling over her shoulders, and she thinks of home... *Three more days...*

III. Magic Potions

Once upon a time, there was a woman named Concetta, mixing magic on her porch steps.

Concetta takes a sip of her own creation, wiping the sweat from her brow. Massachusetts heat is fierce as any dragon this time of year, and she is exhausted from running back and forth between here and there, up and down, basement and porch.

This brew is good.

Concetta grew up watching her mother make *grappa* in Via Grande, Sicily, and remembers the recipe for it well. *Thank you, Mama.* Selling it is her better source of income. The mills pay nowhere near as well.

She fingers the scar on her index finger, a blessing compared to what could have been. *Spinners are blessed dually for each finger they have left*. She sometimes wonders why she left Sicily, why she came to *L'America*, land of the not-so-rich, home of the frequently greedy. She expected sidewalks made of solid gold. Instead, she finds herself sticking her fingers by day and making bottles of moonshine by night. She still thinks in her native, rough Italian but speaks in memorized phrases and idioms of English. She only talks to her family and neighbors in Italian, because others mock her everywhere else.

Concetta tells Anita, her eldest, to watch the roads when she is not in school. *The Prohibition makes no exceptions, even for the poor.* She gives Grazia spoonfuls of her grappa when she cries at night. It helps the little one sleep. They are 11 years apart in age, and Concetta wonders if they will ever be friends.

Tying a cloth around her head, she fills a bottle and places it by the rows of others. She has boiled birch bark in with this brew. It tastes faintly like the mint she used to grow in *L'Italia*. The bottles sit with crocheted blankets and dishtowels, stitched prayers, and embroidered handkerchiefs, piled high on the stairs.

But it is the magic Concetta brews in her basement, and flavors on her porch, that really draws in the money.

IV. The Loss of a Mother

Once upon a time, there was a girl named Tina who watched her mother wither away.

Irene had asked Tina when *Mana* would walk again, but Tina didn't know the answer. Rather, she knew the answer but was not about to share it with her younger sister—never. *Mana* would not stand again, nor braid her hair, nor cook them meals again. *Mana* was almost gone.

Tina drew her pictures, but *Mana*'s eyes could barely see them. Tina stopped drawing what she thought *Mana* wanted to see, and started drawing what she was feeling.

The dead infant. The chest of baby clothes upstairs that would never be emptied.

She had blocked Irene's ears when *Mana* was in labor, screaming as she pushed the flesh-colored lump into open air. It was dead before it had time to die. Tina was grateful.

She thought *Mana* would never stop crying, and kept Irene from her pain, until she realized how cruel it would be if Irene never had the chance to say goodbye. Tina could see the life ebbing from her.

It stared with parched lips, and moved to knobby fingers. Pale skin, forehead sweat, fever. Glassy eyes.

Tina watched and drew and waited for 26 days for her mother to die. "Infection," she heard the doctor mutter as she painted heaven in the kitchen. She would not know that word for a long time.

Glassy eyes became labored breathing. Became coughing, became wheezing. Became chills, became violent shakes. Tina waited for death.

When her shiny eyes could finally see no more, Tina took a lighter to her drawings, and the flames devoured the pictures with their dragon-like tongues. She planted a rose in their ashes. She and Irene carved wooden eggs and filled them with crafted geese and saints, and placed them in their mother's casket.

Tina traced her fingers over her mother's pencil letters, her name, Stella Dascolous, in her Greek Bible. She wrote hers underneath, and swore to keep it forever.

V. Sing, Dance, and Be Merry

Once upon a time, there was a grandfather named Anthony who knew he was dying.

He gave them all this psalm to read.

Psalm 30
The Blessedness of Answered Prayer
A Psalm. A Song at the dedication of the house of David.

I will extol You, O Lord, for You have lifted me up,
And have not let my foes rejoice over me.
O Lord my God, I cried out to You,

And You healed me.
O Lord, You brought my soul up from the grave;
You have kept me alive, that I should not go down to the pit.
Sing praise to the Lord, you saints of His,
And give thanks at the remembrance of His holy name.
For His anger is *but for* a moment,
His favor is *for* life;
Weeping may endure for a night,
But joy *comes* in the morning.

Now in my prosperity I said,
"I shall never be moved."
Lord, by Your favor You have made my mountain
stand strong;
You hid Your face, *and* I was troubled.

I cried out to You, O Lord;
And to the Lord I made supplication:
"What profit *is there* in my blood,
When I go down to the pit?
Will the dust praise You?
Will it declare Your truth?
Hear, O Lord, and have mercy on me;
Lord, be my helper!"

You have turned me for my mourning into dancing;
You have put off my sackcloth and clothed me with gladness,
To the end that *my* glory may sing praise to You and not
be silent.
O Lord my God, I will give thanks to
You forever.

Death's cancerous claws are no match for a drill sergeant's spirit.
No match for a baseball-loving, ham-and-cheese-sandwich-making,
all-around-rejoicing grandfather of three. No way in hell.

He knew that when he gave them the psalm. So they would
rejoice, instead of dismay. So they would celebrate how much of the

world he saw (Japan, Australia, Aruba, London), and how he spent his time in it. How he traveled where only dragons swam, and rode their backs in fierce pursuit of life.

Death may kill, but it does not conquer those who believe.

VI. Saints

Once upon a time, a different grandfather walked the streets of Boston hours before he died.

The last time I saw my grandfather, it was in Faneuil Hall. The Wood Hill Middle School bell choir was performing Christmas carols on December the 22nd, their music ringing through brisk winds and snowy breaths. I played B4 and C5, middle C, always the center of things.

Papou came to watch. He stood, with his newsboy hat and tweed jacket, brown shined shoes, and pleated pants. He wore a scarf that day.

He wished I hadn't been chewing gum "like a horse," as he put it to my mother two hours later. But he was proud of me, beaming as my hands danced through transitions and rhythms and a complicated solo during "Jingle Bell Rock." He hugged me, kissed me, and told me loved me. I did the same.

He left not long thereafter. I blew him a kiss and said "I love you" once again. He did the same.

Seven hours later, he was gone, dead at the wheel of a parked car. His giant heart had given out on a simple, snowy afternoon, two years after the triple bypass and forty after the Guillain-Barré that almost did him in. Three days before Christmas. Three days before a 12-pound prime rib and good holiday cheer.

His name was George, for St. George, slayer of the devil, slayer of the dragon.

VII. Bloodlines

Once upon a time, there was a man named Biaggio, who lived in the 1800s.

PERSONAL ESSAY/MEMOIR

Biaggio, who married a woman named Concetta, who gave birth to Gaetano, who married Grazia and gave birth to Concetta again.

Concetta, who married Rosario, son of Anna and Salvatore, son of Rosario and Rosaria. Concetta, who gave birth to Grazia and Anita, who married Antonio, son of Antonio and Dominica, who gave birth to another Antonio.

Antonio, who married Eileen, daughter of Santa Nicola, daughter of Pasquale and Dorotea. Eileen, daughter of Michele, son of Maria Teresa and Davide. Eileen, who gave birth to Anthony.

Anthony, who married Stephanie, daughter of Tina, daughter of Nicholas and Stella, daughter of Peter. Stephanie, daughter of George, son of Mary and James. Stephanie, who gave birth to Samantha.

Once upon a time, there was the blood of Italy, blood of Caporetto, blood of Naples and Sicily, blood of Sparta, and blood of Thessaly, all in the same girl at once.

Samantha.

Amen.

Domenic D'Andrea, 16
ACES Educational Center for the Arts
New Haven, CT
Teacher: Caroline Rosenstone

Domenic D'Andrea will be a senior in North Haven, Connecticut. He seeks to emulate the engaging, informal styles of Dave Eggers and David Foster Wallace. In ten years, he hopes to have a career as a high school English teacher. Domenic would like to dedicate this piece to Erin.

ALL LIGHTS COMING AT US FROM THE SOUND
Personal Essay/Memoir

And there is the wedding tonight on the beach, all the guests dressed up and it rains and I'm there to film, given a camera older than myself to hold and thank God it's a short ceremony because I almost drop it it's so heavy. Everyone looks up and the bride comes down from the big winding stairs in the reception hall, where the ceremony relocates during the storm. And she walks to where her husband stands, where I stand with my arms shaking under that heavy thing, recording this moment in sharp black and white. The camera drifts to Erin, her standing in the corner, pinned up, her blue dress, her face soft in all the light coming in through the windows— it's still sunny even though outside it thunders. The bride begins to speak and I focus back on her, and she says "I do" and she's kissed, and she and the groom have their first dance and they eat; Erin and I sneak out to the beach when we notice it stops raining. Now it's dark, two hours of wedding gone by the same way all weddings do. We take off our shoes and run out to the water, the sound lit up with the skyline of the city and all those apartments on the water.

A wedding arch is in the sand, this one cheap plastic, made to stay outside and get wet, and we walk over to it, cautious of the instinctive kiss these things provoke. But there isn't any tension, us three years apart, friends since elementary, Erin going off to college soon while I'm starting sophomore year.

This is what we share before she leaves for college: the simple beach, the same loud wedding songs drowned out by the tiny waves lapping at our feet, the bell-buoys.

Your mom said there's a lesbian wedding upstairs, she says.

Really? I say.

Yeah, she says. We should check it out.

So we walk to a gazebo and pluck the sand from our feet, carefully putting on our shoes. And we slip back in unnoticed, making for the doors to the hallway when my mom spots us. You! she says. We need you.

Us?

Yes, Mom says. The DJ won't let anyone dance till someone swing-dances first. And you're the only ones who know how.

Oh. We don't know that much, Erin says. Only a few steps. And we know different styles.

I'm Lindy Hop, I say.

I don't even know the name of mine, Erin says.

Well…practice for a few minutes, Mom says. And then go to the dance floor. Because I want to dance, goddammit.

So we slip out into the hall, standing there for a moment, laughing, thinking about summer. This is the first time we've seen each other in months, but here we are, we're making jokes, we're acting like we did when we were young. This is what we do, climb deep into the nostalgia of our roots. And now we teach each other our respective styles, humming what few swing songs we know to catch the beat. Rock-step, back, forward, and kick. You got it. Alright. You ready? Let's do this.

And the doors open and we walk onto the floor, all giddy with everyone watching, with everyone waiting to be dazzled with our flips and spins and jump-kicks, but we do none of those. We only know the simple stuff, the stuff they teach old married couples who go to dancing classes to add excitement to their lives. But here we are, look at us, alternating jumps and steps; I spin her out and in, her hair flying up like a second dress, and we just keep on, smiling, and it's good and simple and beautiful and I'm laughing, and she's laughing and people start to clap along. And we become a blur of brown and blue, we're improvising, making up moves. We're like marionettes with our clumsy feet, but it's good, and it's simple and beautiful and it's frustrating. And the song ends and we leave the floor with applause, sitting down, exhausted, us red in the face. I excuse myself for the bathroom, the door to the men's room slams when I walk in, checking under all the dirty stalls for shitting feet, and I curse.

This time last night it was just me and a phone and I lie on my bed in the dark, Elliott on the other end, us making small talk to keep from doing homework. What's the assignment again, for English? Uh…well, you had to read those two books over the summer. Well, yeah, I read those, of course. Oh…well, you have to write an essay about your best friend or something. Oh, yeah, right, who did you do? I did Erin…did you do yours yet?

No, Elliott says. I'm not sure who I should write about. Maybe I'll combine a few friends into one.

I did that a bit for my essay about Erin, I say. Just to be able to write more. I feel like a part of us was lost. She's been at summer camp so I haven't seen her in months. But we're going to a wedding tomorrow night, I say. And I can't wait.

Erin's the one who's old enough to be your mom, right? says Elliott.

Hah, no, I say. She's three years older. But we've known each other since we were kids.

A silence comes and then I can only hear his exhales coming in, distorted through the phone. I've only known this Elliott a year, but now every night there's always us on the phone, always us finding something to talk about: our friends and all the countries we'll never visit, all the places we'll never see.

A man walks into the bathroom while I stand so close to the mirror scowling and it fogs up from all that swearing. I see him and pretend to blow my nose, and I walk back out, walking back into the wedding room, and Erin comes up. Alright, let's check out that *other* wedding, she says.

So we're sneaking out again, down the hall into the elevator, feeling once more like we're young, making faces in the slick black of the reflective walls all around us, and we stick out our tongues and cross our eyes and laugh, and it's good, and Erin fixes her hair.

I'm still not sure if I should write about you or Mary or Greg, Elliott says. Too many to choose from.

I don't know what you'd be able to say about me, I say. I mean all we do is talk on the phone.

Yeah. You're boring, Elliott says, and he laughs. Maybe I'll write my essay about a friend of mine who's secretly gay, he says, and no one suspects but me.

Awesome, I say. Good luck with that.

The elevator opens and Erin and I step off and start down the hall, the music from the upstairs wedding room low and droning. Erin bites her lip, expecting strobe lights and erotic dancing. We turn the corner; outside the wedding room, two people sit on the floor, their heads hung, bored enough to look dead. But Erin walks right by, peeking into the room from the doorway to find everyone sitting, all those people quiet around round tables, conversation already exhausted. Drat, she says. This sucks.

Honestly, I'm surprised no one suspects, I say.

Because it's true? Elliott says.

No, I say.

Well, you *do* find a new girlfriend every two days, he says.

Yeah. I guess I'm just good like that, I say. But...I can't tell when girls flirt.

Yeah, same here, he says.

When they flirt I just think they're being nice, I say. And then, bam, they're my girlfriend. I don't know how it happens.

Yeah, he says. I mean, I like girls...pretty girls, but they do nothing for me.

So what does that mean? I say.

I don't know. What do you think it means?

I guess we're asexual.

Yes, he says. We're asexual.

And we laugh at this; we laugh at all the girlfriends we've had and their faces, and the way they kiss and the way we look at them with their eyes closed, leaning in.

But in all seriousness, he says. Are you?

Back down we take the stairs, Erin exaggerating disappointment to entertain me, to make me laugh. The stairs, big and winding, are almost too grand for this place on the beach; a chandelier hangs and it's so close it sways when we walk by, through the lobby, and we can hear music from our wedding hall again, all those same party songs muffled by big doors. That was so disappointing, Erin says. I wanted girls popping out of cakes.

Is that really what you want? I say. Because, you know, I can arrange that.

Well, I feel like we're both avoiding the question…, I say, now biting my lip in the dark. So are you, or are you not?

Am I asking or telling? Elliott says.

What?

I asked you first, he says.

No fun, I say.

I asked you first.

Well, I say, I mean it seems like we're both trying to say it without actually saying it, here. I feel like we're both too afraid, or something, like if we—

I'M FUCKING GAY.

And I stop. Elliott's words bring a silence and I'm sitting up now in my bed, breathing fast, hunched over, and he's breathing hard into the phone, I can feel it.

And he says, You don't have to respond to that.

No, it's okay, I say. Me too.

And Erin and I sit back down at our table, and it feels like it's the first time we've sat all night, so we pick up our forks and eat, and I'm thinking about her and the wedding and how—fuck—I want this, this is bullshit, I fucking want this. I want a wedding with a woman, with dancing, with swing dancing, and cake, and hair flying up, and I want a house and a kid and a yard and I want to build a treehouse. And Erin chews her food, and I'm just sitting there, staring at all those dancing people.

I want to introduce you to Erin, my mom says, coming up from behind with some woman she knows. Erin's my future daughter-in-law, she says, and Erin smiles and laughs and I'm just staring at all those dancing people. And Erin gets up and goes to the bar to get some virgin drink and she asks if I want any, and I say no, barely audible over all the music. And she goes up to the bar and gets a drink for me anyway, me at the table just staring at all those dancing people, all together; they've all got their own rhythm, all smiling and they're all pretending that this is their wedding day, too, and for a moment all that young love is alive like it was twenty years ago inside them, and I'm watching them. I wish I had that old camera now, that ancient thing on my shoulder. I wish I could film this, could film everyone's faces and feet, stepping in and out, each couple synchronized. And Erin comes back with a drink she got for me, and she raises her glass and says, Let's make a toast, just us. To not losing touch when I go to college. And to never change or keep secrets. And to get married and adopt a bunch of babies. And I'll be an actress and you'll write all the movies I'm in, she says, and we'll be happy. And our glasses clink, and she smiles so I smile and we drink, and we take in big sips of whatever it is we're drinking and she puts her drink down and wipes her mouth and I just keep staring at all those people dancing.

Leighton Braunstein, 13
The Dalton School
New York, NY
Teacher: Ariel Levenson

Leighton Braunstein will be a ninth grader at the Dalton School in New York City. She thinks that growing up in New York City influenced her to think independently, and she tries not to emulate other authors in her writing. She is very interested in neuroscience and would like to pursue a career in that field.

ARTIFICIAL LIGHT
Personal Essay/Memoir

Even before I was born, a major part of my existence had already been decided. I was Jewish from the second the harsh hospital lights shone through my wet, delicate eyelids, causing me to crinkle up my little face so that it was impossible to tell the difference between my face and the folds of the soft pink blanket in which I was cocooned. It was not as if upon the moment of my arrival into the world, a glowing Star of David clung possessively to my thin curls. It was just simply the knowledge my parents had that I would grow following the eternal faith of my father's family, an idea that became reality during my baby naming a few short weeks later.

For the first several years of my life, religion held no sacred or spiritual meaning for me. My mental representation of Judaism conjured up images of a mouthwatering ball of dough doused in salt, floating temptingly in its thick yellow pool; the memories of feeling nearly suffocated in the awe-inspiring tide of affection and sugar when Chanukah was at Grandma's house; of the pride I felt when I got to bring ice cream to school for my birthday because I was convinced it fell during Passover. Being Jewish when I was little meant a constant wave of excuses to eat as much frosted, powdered, buttered, sprinkled, and sweetened items as I could possibly cram down my throat.

At that time, I did not question anything. God was real because that was what my parents told me. The pretty stories of long-tongued camels and a rainbow sewn into a coat were my version of history, because they were the stories told in my temple. It was the naiveness of childhood that made me accept wholly the idea that God was everywhere, as the rabbis informed the congregation. I would think I saw Him sitting on the cotton-candy columns rising majestically at the front of temple, and I would smile trustingly, my eyes crinkling at the corners over my innocent toothy grin. Then, in third grade, I started Hebrew school.

Hebrew school hit me with a barrage of scrawling characters that were equally illegible as the scratch of chickens in the dirt, a profusion of miniature mezuzahs that were instantly discarded in the trash can, and hourlong sessions where a student cantor tried to get 100-odd kids to sing "Tree of Life." It was the last part that got to me. I didn't understand how a religion that had been around for over a millennium could have bled down to a foppish man with Saran-wrap eyes nervously unrolling the parched yellow scroll of the Torah as no one responded to his enthusiasm-fused flourishes and guitar playing. Those classes, a constant during my weekly Hebrew school trips, gave me a feeling of coldness to my religion. I went so far as to openly insult Judaism during class on a frequent basis. I would drop some sort of snide comment during Purim about how the Jews had "heartlessly" killed Haman's family, then droop against the back of my chair with a smirk dancing mischievously on my face as the rabbis squirmed like someone had dropped a spider down their crow-wing robes. It was cruel. I know that. Somehow, though, the feeling that I had thwarted their attempts to draw me into what I now thought of as a web of lies seemed to negate the callousness of my actions.

However, that languid distaste I felt for that particular part of Hebrew school was minor compared to the burning anger that stormed in my head every time I was told about how my Jewish ancestors had suffered through genocide, slavery, and homelessness, and how they should be admired for their bravery. While I agreed that this was true, I could not stand how Hebrew school attempted to confine my sympathies to the Jews alone. Every Wednesday, I got shoved into a cramped, airtight box for an endless two hours, a box that blocked everything from me except for what the Hebrew teachers wanted me to see, causing that piercing and noiseless rage to creep up behind my eyes and fill my ears with a white-hot whining that nearly drowned out the teacher's monotonous, slavish words of praise. That is why, throughout the two years I had been going to Hebrew school, I slowly alienated myself from the religion. In order to prove to myself that I could see through those box walls, I made the decision to not call myself a Jew anymore. Instead, I just wanted to be a person.

I thought it would be easy to extricate myself from the religion, but I was completely wrong. So I made one more, final cut. I decided to stop believing in God. At first, invoking His name happened so naturally that I almost gave up. Gradually, I started dropping God from my thoughts, and my vocabulary. I might have been able to manage it if it were not for one thing: Ma Tovu. The Ma Tovu is a prayer sung at the beginning of every service. As I still attended temple on the High Holy Days, there was no way to avoid it.

When I heard that prayer during Passover in 2009, I could not help but close my eyes. Each word made me flinch as it coursed through my veins, each syllable was candle wax dripping on my skin. I do not quite know why this simple prayer has such a dramatic effect on me, but the opening stanza never fails to squeeze at my heart. Listening to it that one Passover, I felt closer to my God than I had in years. As my voice joined in the prayer, twining with the hundreds of other voices lifting toward the sky, I gave up. I did not realize it then, but at that moment I stopped fighting what was obviously a losing battle. It felt like a huge weight had been lifted from my shoulders.

I still did not think of myself as a Jew. That was easy enough to do—the word "Jew" was only a label for something I never really understood. I wanted to be an atheist, because it is a religious choice that people can understand. For some reason, though, the title of "atheist" felt equally as foreign. Yet the word "God" is branded in my skin, the name resonates in the air around me. I was fine with leaving the Jewish community, but I could not bring myself to let go of my belief in God. I've said His name too many times to banish it forever.

Sometimes I sit in my room at night, the absolute dark

shrouding my body like a cloak. I gaze sightlessly at the walls and rage against the unfairness, the broiling confusion, and doubt that sweep through my mind like a thundercloud. Through the uncertainty and disappointment clawing at my throat, I scream soundlessly. I rant and rave until my electrified nerves finally, haltingly settle. Unbidden, my tirade ends itself with a "Please, God," the pronouncement of these words reliable as clockwork. Those two words force their way out of my clenched teeth, but they are laden with sincerity and truth. So even though my only listener is the empty air, I still instinctively utter those two words, with the enduring hope that someday He will answer.

Evan Goldstein, 16
Choate Rosemary Hall School
Wallingford, CT
Teacher: Monique Neal

Evan Goldstein is a high school student from Wallingford, Connecticut. His first creative writing class in seventh grade inspired him to write. When he's not writing, he can be found playing the violin, participating in Model United Nations, and preparing arguments with his school's debate team.

AN OPEN LETTER TO THE SUICIDAL
Personal Essay/Memoir

Dear Person,

I don't know you, but you are the subject of most of my fears, strange as it seems.

I fear for those around you, for those who pass you by every day, taking note of your bright smile without realizing your dark secrets, and yes, I realize that that's cliché, but the point is they don't get it. See, people are supposed to be happy, no matter what, and they hate it when things don't go according to plan, so when they see you hurting, they just ignore it. Because that's not the way it's supposed to go. But I still fear for them, because I dread the day that will come when you're gone and in place of what they thought was a hopeful young person, they find a vast hole, a chasm of memories that they wish they could unremember, sounds they wish they could unhear, moments they wish they could unlive. But they can't, and they never will. And I fear for them, because for the rest of their lives, all they'll remember of you is what they wished they had done, even though they never could have seen it coming.

(I say this because I knew a girl who killed herself, knew in the sense that I spoke to her once freshman year at the squash courts. She was short, with black hair and a mind that filled pages with the products of an angsty teenage life. I could have gone to the Columbia University summer writing program last summer, which she attended, but I didn't. Maybe if I had, I wouldn't have felt so weird about crying the night after she died. Her poetry was so succinct, so beautiful, the literary embodiment of her life. Sometimes when I close my eyes, I feel her tears.)

I fear for your best friend, the person who knows your thoughts better than most people know your words. Surely they will have some idea, some vague notion that you're pondering the worst, surely they must know, but they'll never say anything. Nobody wants to take that trip, nobody wants to verbalize that thought, because they're afraid of the answer, choosing to deny the painful truth rather than admit your agony to themselves. They would rather turn their backs on your torture than risk even imagining you gone. But surely they knew. And surely the moment they find out, they'll be inundated with shame, plagued by questions of whom to blame, which will, inevitably, be themselves. They'll beg, crying out to whatever god they believe in to please help, please bring you back, please wake them from this dream. But it won't be a dream. I fear that they'll be crushed by guilt, guilt that nobody should incur. They'll hear your voice in every song, see your face in every picture, feel your warm embrace whenever they shiver. Alone, cold, bombarded by the winds of life, they'll call out your name and wish, just wish, that you were there. But all that wishing will amount to nothing.

(I had a friend who almost killed herself. She was naive and beautiful, conditioned to laugh like every other freshman did. She was secretly dark and broken, tortured by monsters that she didn't deserve, the products of a splintered family and a taxing schedule. She couldn't take the criticism at home or the lack of understanding at school, so she cut herself until the blood running down her arms assuaged her deepest demons. One night she called me to say goodbye, and the next day she wasn't in school. Nor was she the next. She was OK that time, but I always wondered. Always worried that the next day she'd be gone, and there'd be nobody to blame but me. I used to lie in bed, unable to sleep in case she would call. See, I thought that if I answered the phone, I could save her life, bring her back from the edge of the cliff. Sometimes, lying there in the dark, I would reach up and try to hug her soul.)

I fear for the world that you will leave, for the people who will cry at your funeral, the ground that will be dug up to allow for your misery, the classes at school that will be tragically left with one more empty chair. I fear for the swings that will remember your juvenile laughter, hearing the joy you harbored in the years before life became a burden. I fear for the music you'll never listen to (at midnight, when the utter silence of your house starts to become overwhelming), and more importantly, the songs you'll never sing, the repressed notes that will never come out of your mouth as vocal representations of the self you never showed. I fear for the poems you'll never write, the verses that won't flow like blood through the veins of your pen onto the tear-stained page. I fear that the only short story you'll ever write will be the note you leave behind before it's all over.

(I believe in the power of music to save lives. It's a cliché, but I remember long nights talking to my girlfriend, YouTube-ing songs because that's how I could save her life. Some of them we listened to for hours on end, just hitting replay and being infused time and again with hope that the struggle wasn't in vain. Maybe it sounds silly but it really felt like every word was life or death, the latter approaching with each passing second and the former only possible through placing our trust in the power of song. I used to send her MP3s when she wanted to cut herself, like the lyrics were little pairs of lips that could kiss her scars and set her at peace, spurning misery with love and healing her wounds. I think sometimes they were.)

This will sound selfish, but I'm also afraid for myself. For the last four years, there's always been one point or another where someone was dangling off the edge, tempting fate in threatening to let go. Suicide has been a presence in my life, like the awkward friend who follows you around and whom you just don't have the heart to tell to go away, or like the teacher who constantly berates you on the idiosyncrasies of your work, keeping you up at night with worry. Suicide was my Minotaur; I often felt like Theseus, roaming a cryptic labyrinth in order to fight a terrible monster. Theseus knew that the Minotaur was stronger than him, and that given a fair fight, the Minotaur would win. He knew that he may never find the Minotaur, and wander forever in the labyrinth like a 1960s Beat poet on a bad trip. But he knew he had to at least try, because the only thing worse than getting killed by the Minotaur would be not fighting the Minotaur at all, and leaving Athens subject to the cruel caprice of its fearsome evil. As pompous as it is to compare myself to a Greek hero, that's what I often felt like. I felt as though I was locked in a battle, David versus Goliath, for the sanity and safety of my friends (and also myself), one that I could not afford to lose. Every day I hugged them, striking a blow, but every night the phone calls piled up and I was inundated with the guilt and shame of failure. I think that's why it hurt so much when the girl I didn't know killed herself. Because up until that point, I was winning, subjugating suicide with the meager weapons I have (words, love, music). But suicide got me back, and that hurt. So I hope you won't be insulted that I'm afraid for myself. Perhaps you think it's silly or even disrespectful that I, one who doesn't know you (maybe), would claim to have such a personal stake in your struggle. It's just that I'm not sure I can look at myself in the mirror and claim victory over suicide. And victory over suicide has been all I've really wanted for the last four years. So please forgive me, but I fear for myself as well.

My fears aside, I have some questions. I hope you won't find it disparaging to be questioned on such an intensely personal matter by a high school writer whom you've never met (probably), but I've had four years to think about suicide, and the questions in my mind regarding it are numerous. Questions like, What will happen when you die? Not in the sense of the afterlife (or lack thereof), but in the sense of what will actually happen. What will it feel like? Will it be like a Band-Aid, ripped off quickly without full awareness of what's happening? Like falling asleep, your mind slowly taken away into the realm of nothingness to which we all return someday? Or will it be like a dentist's appointment, the feeling of dread setting in as the dentists rake your teeth with instruments that vibrate in a torturous rhythm, the intrusive discomfort that invades your entire being just before the tools are removed and a cool calm washes over you, a smile returning to your face. Is that facetious of me, to compare suicide to a dentist's appointment? Perhaps, but the question remains: Does death come quickly, before you even realize what's happened, or does it come only after the enormity of the decisions you've made has occurred to you?

The question that always occurs to me is, Who do you think will find you? My biggest fear in eighth grade, bigger than the fear that my friends would stay home and never come back, was that I would find one of them, sprawled out in some room in the basement, eyes closed in peace, feigning sleep. I wouldn't have been able to handle that, because what could I do then? Look on in disbelief, as if standing very still would change the scene in front of me? Cry? Tears for me always tasted like salty defeat, their presence streaming down my face like the most fragile effusions of my soul flowing out and enveloping me in weakness. The sight of a friend in front of me, killed by their own hand, would have driven me to insanity.

(It almost happened once. That girl, the pretty one I mentioned before, she handed me a note, crumpled and folded like the cruel partition of her life. It was about 7:45 in the morning, and she walked out of the room just after giving me the note, like she was going to class. I unfolded the note, and read what seemed to be an irrevocable ultimatum: "I'm sorry. Bye." I ran, carried by legs of desperation to the room in the basement where I knew she'd be. I knocked once. Silence. Twice. Silence. A third time. The door slowly swung open, the motion dripping with reluctance. There she stood, eyes flooded with tears and a knife in her right hand. Pushed to the brink, but alive. For the first time in what seemed like hours or years, I exhaled.)

But the biggest questions in my mind are the ones that I can never answer. Questions like, What led you to this? Every high school life is tenuous, like a bird holding on to an electric wire during a storm, but what led you to let go and allow the storm to take you under? It might seem strange that I ask that question, but it's a wonder to me, how quickly stress turns to coping turns to depression turns to thoughts of suicide. Perhaps it's the psychologist in me, or perhaps it's just some twisted side of my conscience that longs to understand what drives us to the edge, but that question, the question of why, is omnipresent in my thoughts.

Maybe it's because I want you to understand. Let's face it, even if I understand why you want to kill yourself (sounds scary when you put it that way, right?), there's not much I can do. Ultimately, the decision is yours. So maybe I'm just hoping that you're questioning whether this is really what you want, whether the accumulation of miseries that you've encountered sums up to this. Does it scare you to think about it? My friends always told me it did, that the notion crept into their thoughts like a silent bandit, tortured them with demeaning slurs, and absconded with their peace of mind, leaving them more scared and alone than before. It's a scary word: suicide. It reeks with the putrid prospect of impending catastrophe, singing eerie tunes into the ears of those who hear it. Just that thought, "I want to kill myself," is not one to be thought lightly. In some ways I feel for you, you being those who have had that thought before, had it recurring like the jingle of a bad commercial in your head. I feel for you because I cannot possibly imagine how terrifying it must be to have that thought on a daily basis.

I think that happens to the rest of us, too; we all realize when somebody is struggling, but nobody wants to take that step, nobody wants to say the S-word, because that makes it real. That makes it possible, and nobody wants to think that suicide is possible. Realizing that someone wants to kill themselves is the worst feeling in the world. All the questions I've asked here pop into their heads like flashbulbs, stalking them with the unremitting fervor of a virus. Stress is inherent in the high school experience, so it's easy to brush off someone who's been crying. It's easy to pretend like suicide is only for the crazies, not us (because we're all perfectly normal, right?). Even like it's something to be invoked in jest (how many times have you heard somebody say "I have so much work tonight, I'm gonna kill myself"?). I think in the back of our heads, we all realize that it's possible, that it's really just an additional symptom of the stress syndrome we've all inherited by becoming a part of the "higher-education system." It's easy to see high school as a four-year battle with tests and papers, fought in order to win the privilege of fighting a harder battle with harder tests and harder papers, and in that context, it's difficult to see the end. I think we all realize that some people would choose to forfeit the battle, and in doing so reinforce the magnitude of it. But nobody wants to acknowledge it. Nobody wants to make it real, even when we all know that we have to. Sometimes, given the choice between saving a person's life and upsetting the delicate equilibrium of our own, we choose ourselves, simply out of a desire to remain ignorant of the harsh realities that the battle entails. When the girl killed herself earlier this year, I think everyone at my school took a step back, and realized what was actually at stake. We all wished that we had stepped off the battlefield for a second in order to help one of our own. We all regretted our incessant obsessions with our own lives. We all took a second to reflect on the fragility of the balance upon which we walk. But mostly, we all took a second to wish things were different.

At this point, you're probably wondering why I'm writing this. Sure, I've told you a lot about my past and my general musings on suicide, but I wouldn't be writing this if that were all I wanted to do, right? There must be a point. And really the point is that I want you to understand a few things.

First, you're not alone. I know, it's cliché, but often our most trying endeavors can feel in vain, simply because it seems like nobody understands. Everyone feels that way sometimes, no matter how they choose to cope. The world moves at light-speed, and sometimes we all feel left in the dark. And when things get to the point where we decide to opt out, it can feel even lonelier. But hopefully you've seen in this that you're not alone; I am constantly thinking about you, praying for you, worrying for you. It may seem to be all in vain. Perhaps. But I don't believe so, because I believe truly that love will save the world. You feel the way you do because of a deficiency of love, whether that's from your parents, from your peers, or from yourself (most likely the latter). But if someone can be there to embrace you with all your flaws, scars, and fears, it is love that will save your life.

Second, killing yourself is not the answer. Cliché again, but it's true (funny how often clichés are true, and how often they are so false). Killing yourself doesn't solve any problems; it simply transfers the onus from you to those who survive you. As I said before, losing you will affect many more people than you would expect. They'll miss you, long for you, cry for you, but most of all they'll regret. Regret is a demon that allows no respite, no repose from its malicious claws. They'll fall into the hole that you've dug for yourself, assuming your burdens and wondering what they could have done. It's ironic. You'll be the one causing all of this, but they'll be the ones who would never forgive themselves.

The last thing that I hope you take from this is this is just one moment in your life. And sure, it's dark, but the beautiful thing about war is that those who survive one day fight the next stronger than they've ever been in their entire lives. And it's the same in this case. I know you're struggling, everybody knows it. But push through this, and you'll soon be Theseus after he slayed the Minotaur: conqueror of the most tenacious demon, fearlessly sailing into the future. In short, keep fighting, know that you are loved, and stay strong.

Sincerely, with love,
EBG

Eliza Kenney, 17
Exeter High School
Exeter, NH
Teacher: Dan Provost

Eliza Kenney grew up in Exeter, New Hampshire. She wrote her piece to explore the way in which she dealt with tragedy at an early stage in her life. One day, she would like to travel the world, speak a variety of languages, and make a living off of documenting her journeys.

REMINDERS
Personal Essay/Memoir

She says my name and I ignore her because she is my mother and I am her child. And because it is Sunday. I continue dragging the chair to the refrigerator. I can almost see over the chair back now and soon I'll be able to reach the cereal boxes by myself. I know she's watching me because I can feel my head start to tingle where she's looking. I still ignore her. It's Sunday. I'm allowed.

The tingling in my head starts to itch as I clamber down, one-handedly clutching the box. The itching spreads and then I give up at ignoring.

"Mom, it's Sunday. I'm allowed."

She still looks at me. "I know."

"Oh." I pull the chair to the cupboard, the bowls sliding against each other as I pull one out. The biggest one, the grown-up bowl. I find it easier to ignore her eyes when I pour the once-a-week chocolaty heaven into the grown-up bowl.

"Emily, I need you to sit." I ignore her because I am not done. I run to the refrigerator but I am still too small to pick up the gallon of milk. I turn to her and wait for her to come to the rescue. She just looks at me.

My hand tightens on the door handle; my eyes can't decide where they want to look. *Don't make me say it!* The cold air swirls in front of me, raising my skin into little mountains. Defeat.

"Mom, I...need." I stop. Take a breath. "I need—" *It's just a word,*

Emily! Only a word. I bite my tongue and say it. *Only a word.* "Help."

Her face doesn't look right, like it's too tight for her bones. I wait for congratulations, a "Good job using your words instead of whining! That Sally works miracles." I've been practicing. I want to be a miracle.

But she doesn't say anything. Instead, she closes the refrigerator door.

"Mom! It's Cocoa Puffs day, you said, it always is!"

"Emily, just sit for a minute."

I put my hands on my hips, like her. Inside of me, my volcano heats up, purple to orange. I know this is dangerous; Sally says so. Sally tells me that purple is good, purple is calm, purple is *no temper*. In Sally's office, she lets me make stories in the sand, play with clay, talk. She likes to hear me talk and I like to play. We spend whole hours just talking and playing. We don't get much done. For Sally's sake, I fight for purple. *Breathe, Emily.* Breathe, breathe, breathe.

Mom is still looking. I sit, breathing. Purple, purple, calm, peace.

"Emily," she says.

"Mom."

Watch it, Emily, Sally whispers to me. *Purple, remember?* I breathe a few times.

Mom doesn't notice. She takes a deep breath as if she's going to be telling me something she doesn't want to, something like... like Daddy died! I stop breathing. *That's what it is, I know it.* I knew *it, I told her he should never go back to work! Daddy died, his plane went down, I'm half-orphan.*

"OK, Emily," she starts.

Daddy died, I think and push away my cereal. A plane spirals down, goes up in flames with a *whoosh!* with Daddy still in front. I can't even think. I feel like I've just been dumped into the ocean and kept under by a giant pair of hands.

"Alex is sick," she says.

The cold from the ocean starts to thaw. "You mean—"

"Alex is sick," she repeats.

I bounce up like I'm a helium balloon. *Daddy's alive!* I dig into my cereal without the milk. It has a different taste without milk, one that I think I like.

"He probably has an older-boy disease," I say. "But tell Auntie Pam and 'specially Uncle John to be careful because Alex could pass it on, you know. I think Helen's safe because she's my age, you know, and she's a girl."

"Emily, Alex is really sick."

I keep eating. I don't need to tell her that I once had a fever of 104 degrees. She was there.

"He's in the hospital."

Uh-oh. The hospital. The hospital is for grandparents and old people who need to get shots every day and who take the swallowy kind of vitamins. Not for 16-year-old cousins.

"The hospital?"

She nods and runs a finger under her eyelashes like she's checking for tears.

"The hospital. But...but it's only morning time."

"He was admitted last night and—"

"Last night?" I say. "He's been there for that long?"

She disappears into the craft closet and emerges with paper, markers, and stickers. I brighten at the sight of the stickers.

"I'm going up to visit today. Make him a card, just to remind him."

"Remind him of me?" I grab a coyote sticker. It's howling, the *ooooo*s trailing off the sheet. I know Alex hasn't forgotten me. We had pizza just a while ago. He tickled me and drank my pink lemonade.

"Remind him of...of how much we all...love him." Mom is breathing funny, like me when I'm trying to cool down my volcano. I look up at her but she already left. I can hear her in the bathroom blowing her nose. She must be sick too.

I'm so happy when Daddy comes home later that I hug his legs and tell him that he's alive, but he doesn't pay much attention to me this time. He just wants to talk to Mom. So I go and sit in my chair with the princesses on it.

"I won't have any fun today if you don't play with me," I tell them.

They don't listen.

I sigh really big. Then again. They still don't notice. So I get down and start lining up my dolls because right now, they are the only people who love me.

But there is only so much love I can take from people who can't even talk because I've been playing with my dolls *all day* and now I'm bored. Bored, bored, bored. Daddy's not even cooking, even though it's almost dinnertime. I'm bored *and* I'm hungry. And then I hear something weird. I sit up and suddenly my mouth is very dry. Somebody's choking! It's Daddy, he's dying again! I run to the kitchen and he's sitting at the table. He is trying to breathe; I can see his shoulders going up and down. My head can't decide what to do. I don't know the Heimlich! And then I look around because if I can only find a phone. 911. "If you ever need help, call the police," Mom always says.

"Daddy, don't worry!"

He turns and looks at me with his eyebrows hidden in his hair. His face is red. And it's wet. And he's holding the phone.

"...Daddy?" The bad kind of butterflies are swarming inside of me. I've been dunked in cold water again.

He hands me the phone. It is hot, like it has a fever. I press it to my face. "H—hello?"

"Emily, it's Mom."

"Mom..." I want to tell her about Daddy and how he's sick too.

"Emily, remember how Alex was sick? Well, he...accidentally... he took too much medicine last night. There was too much medicine inside of him, Emily, too much for the doctors to..." There's a voice in the background that sounds like a siren.

"Too much medicine?" I ask, but only Daddy hears me. He starts choking again.

"Emily, listen." Mom is back in my ear. "He...Alex, he—he passed away."

A little ringing starts in my head. "Passed away...like Nanny and Grandpa?"

The phone starts making a weird sound, like my dog snuffling at me for a biscuit.

"Did he get my card?"

"What? Emily, what—"

"My card, the one with the coyote sticker. Did you give it to him? Did he see it?"

"Honey, no, he was...unconscious when I..."

He didn't see it. He didn't see the howling coyote. He didn't see that I wrote "I love you" at the bottom and drew a pizza on the front.

I can't breathe in enough to say it loud. "Then he didn't know. He wasn't reminded."

The phone snuffles some more. I realize it's Mom, she's snuffling. "Reminded...," she says.

"Remember?"

She doesn't say anything, just snuffles. I guess she forgot. I guess I have to tell her again.

"Reminded of how much we love him."

Andrew Kahn, 17
Bergen County Academy
Hackensack, NJ
Teacher: Richard Weems

Andrew Kahn will be a freshman at Yale University. He believes that writing is the most effective means of human expression and would like to major in something related to the humanities. His hobbies include bird watching and listening to classical music; Franz Schubert is his favorite composer.

THE WAY YOU'RE LISTENING TO IT
Personal Essay/Memoir

A few years ago my grandparents took me to the opera. I don't remember what we saw, but I know that by that point my grandfather's mind had already begun to slip. He didn't understand how the electronic titles worked. Every so often, his attention would drift and he would start pressing the red button on the seat in front of him, watching the titles cycle through German, French, Spanish, and back to English. I felt it my duty to still his hand, gently, and reset the language each time he decided to play this little game.

I was probably the most annoying child in the darkened theater as I fidgeted toward his seat, whispered in his ear, and fiddled with the device for a few seconds—all this every 15 minutes or so. He would have been happier left alone, giggling at the Germanisms flashing across the screen.

This was the first memory that came back to me when, less than a year after he died, my grandmother asked that each member of my family speak at the unveiling of his tombstone. "I hope this won't be how you'll remember him," she had said, crying in the kitchen after the opera, "as a doddering old man who can't follow the titles." But this is how I have remembered him, and this is how most of my other memories go: Grandpa confused, Grandpa gentle and forgetful, Grandpa silent and soon dead.

That is not the complete truth. I also remember Grandpa terrified. The summer before he died, I was working in the city and sleeping at their apartment. I had planned to spend my evenings reading, but it didn't turn out that way. A few images come to mind: coaxing Grandpa to eat a bowl of lentil soup, convincing him that it was his meal and not mine; coaxing Grandpa to eat a cup of blueberry ice cream near Central Park; coaxing Grandpa to stay calm, Grandma would be home soon. Time passed not quickly, or slowly, but respectfully, and sitting in the air-conditioned apartment as July's light drained from the walls, the floor, the carpets, I felt more than ever that the time was pressing hard against my skin and eyes. I was totally present as I guided his mind like water to a lower place.

But this is not what I mean by Grandpa terrified. One day I walked into the apartment—even the walls and light seemed all ears—to hear him screaming down the hall. He was generally an introverted, serious man. That day it sounded as though his most sensitive appendages were being pushed through a wood chipper. He was constipated and receiving an enema from his caretaker. The impression was so far from any I had had of him—there he was, howling "Stop!" into the bottomless chaos of his world; there was the vagitus and the panic—that I sat at the kitchen table, my countenance one of stone, my thoughts still, perceiving the currents of cold air.

That is not the complete truth. I do not remember if I sat at the kitchen table.

There is one more Grandpa. All the other Grandpas are husks, and only once did I ever see him shed these husks, did I ever saw anyone shed all of their husks, besides the body. He did not shed the husk of the body, but the husks of his mind fell to the ground all at once.

He was listening to Mahler's First in our living room. He had listened to Mahler's First three or four times that day, on car rides, but that was of no importance. A chair had been set up where chairs are rarely set up in my house, next to the coffee table. A blue hat lay on the table in front of him.

The first movement of Mahler's First begins as night, as a shapeless void—like Beethoven's Ninth or Haydn's *Creation* oratorio. Offstage trumpets soon enter with a martial fanfare, soldiers. They blend: soldiers in the night. The rest of the brass enters: a long, tender dawn. A descending fourth—the cuckoo in the forest. The day blooms and we get about our business; we overflow and then we face music and music alone. Throughout there is a mother rocking her child, and throughout we are rocked.

As he listened, this man, whose brain had shrunk, whose body had shriveled, whom language had long ago left for dead, came into being. "I feel like I'm running!" he said. He waved his right hand through the air: "It's like this, right? Right?" He twirled his hat, flapped his arms, conducted fancifully, whacked large books against the table, winnowed and sung, presented his innards as frankly as possible. My solipsistic conventions broke down, and suddenly experience itself was emanating from him, we were a part of his world, orbiting around him, and there he was—where *he* was *his thoughts*, Grandpa was the core, everything was on the outside. "It's—the way you're listening to it," he said (that was his way of explaining). "It is what it is!"

That is truth. I cannot remember whether my grandfather passed down any wisdom to me. In all of my memories, he is either very loud or very quiet; there is nothing in between. As he died, on a gurney in the small living room, he would hold fast—as fast as he could—to our hands. The night before he slipped away, I clumsily played the accompaniment parts to some Schubert lieder on the piano, in the dim light.

"I am weak enough to drop, fatally wounded," sings the protagonist of *Die Winterreise* as he passes by a graveyard. "O unmerciful innkeeper"—the graveyard is an "inn"—"do you turn me away? Then further on, further on, my faithful walking stick!"

What was I thinking?

Death is the greatest aggrandizement. We may die wrung dry and drawn inward, but when we stand over the mound, the man underneath reverts to his greatest self. The man underneath is as stately as the letters of his epitaph; when he occupies our mind, time has allowed him to lower his sail and set up camp on the shore.

In dying, though, my grandfather was the greatest self. There may not have been much of him left, but all of it was pressed to the surface, aflame with feeling and candor. What more could anyone aspire to be? Freed from all but the senses, freed from what Aristotle called the *nous*. In death itself—I saw his body—he was not anything or nothing; my first reaction was that the body couldn't be his, not because I couldn't accept the reality of his death—I could—but because he wasn't in it.

But I know where he is. For me, he is in Mahler's First; together there we are rocked, rocked by the same, rocked not in tandem but together and close, in night, in what it is, in the way you're listening to it.

Uchechi Kalu, 17
South Carolina Governor's School for the Arts and Humanities
Greenville, SC
Teacher: Scott Gould

Uchechi Kalu will be a freshman at Princeton University, where she plans to study psychology and creative writing. She credits her teachers at the Governor's School for the Arts and Humanities for teaching her how to write in an honest, open way. Her family and her Nigerian-American identity are her sources of inspiration.

LAUGHING AT BULLETS
Personal Essay/Memoir

It's morning, I'm in Nigeria, and our bodyguard, Wednesday, is shooting in the air again. I know that's a strange name for a man, but think of Wednesday as our John Doe and you'll see how some Nigerians name their children after days of the week. The best I could do that Christmas was go to my parents' homeland. They bought flights and bolted every lock on our house when we left. So I'm on a porch in Nigeria that morning, dreaming of my American home, though I wouldn't even have a key inside.

Flashing between laughs, Wednesday's teeth seem painted, whitewashed each morning with some toothbrush. He lowers his machine gun. My father had always told me not to be scared, that the bullets would never reach me, and this look-alike soldier was just having fun. Wednesday dressed in army fatigues each day, as if a uniform made him some sort of trained soldier. This was my fourth trip back to Nigeria, where the air is always thick with diesel smoke. Even that morning the stench tickled my nose, though there weren't many cars out. Wednesday didn't seem to notice, inhaling like this was clean air and he wouldn't want it any other way.

If we're talking about desires then, I'll admit I never wanted Wednesday's security. But after a while, I stopped telling my family that. They always handed me the same mantra: *You've never lived here. You couldn't understand.* And maybe that's true. But ten years earlier, the first time I came to Nigeria, there was a gun battle outside our Greyhound bus. *Cut the headlights*, a man yelled from behind me. The driver turned off the engine entirely, and night enveloped us. The gunshots sounded cheap, like they'd come from some Western my father can never tear himself from. This is what we heard for minutes: the pop and bang of ammunition. A mother cradling her frightened child, whispering some joke so he laughed just a little. Another pop. Another bang. A little laughter. A scream from outside, then silence. I don't even know how we ended up on that road. Men and motorcycles sped away, passing without acknowledgment.

So yes, I understand danger. But I see machine guns and think Vietnam, not street battles, not men like Wednesday, who are paid to protect the people who can afford him.

I should have expected the next round of shots. Wednesday had counted down from ten. But I was halfway listening, and forgot to cover my ears and muffle the sound. I regret that. Because the blast of a machine gun is ruthless, it's a punch in the gut that leaves you dazed, and then laughs at you.

When the shots rang, I dropped down on the porch where we stood, the way I assume soldiers on some battlefield do as soon as bullets fly. This may as well have been a war zone. Shell casings rolled down the concrete, stopping only to bump into me or lodge in cracks of the pavement. Wednesday pulled me up, laughing.

"You could kill someone with that," I said. The porch bordered a market. Below us an old man in only gym shorts pushed a cart along. Its wheels creaked like hinges needing oil.

Wednesday said, "I'm keeping all the bad men away. Do you want to shoot?" I examined the gun's body, the barrel that seemed longer than my arm, the Nigerian flag painted on the shell magazine. I said no, and Wednesday laughed again. The sort of hysterical cackling that I've only seen in movies, where the character actually ends up in a deep sob. Wednesday stepped a foot back to keep his balance and pointed the machine gun up. It was heavy. He wavered. Again the countdown. I plugged my ears and backed away. Shells sprinkled the ground like gold coins.

That afternoon, I found a fruit vendor by a diesel fuel shop,

PERSONAL ESSAY/MEMOIR

and expected some tropical blend of bananas and mangos and guava to fill me up. But something else did, one I couldn't sniff out just yet, one I can't help but remember. Behind the shop, a black cloud rose higher and higher, painting the afternoon with that kind of smoke you only get from burning gas. I would've asked about it myself, but knew the woman keeping shop wouldn't know English anymore than I knew her language. I asked Wednesday instead and he translated, the machine gun held so tightly his chest seemed to embrace it. You'd think at least the young shopkeeper would notice fire behind her, but she didn't or maybe didn't want to. Maybe since there's so much heat in Nigeria, she couldn't even tell the difference. This marketplace seemed thirsty. Palm trees straddled the dusty roads, a much-needed shade, but no one escapes the dust, dust that climbs up your legs and grits your fingernails.

The young woman spoke, then turned to a box of mangos, feeling each for firmness.

"The Bakassi boys burned a man who stole today," Wednesday said. I'd heard of the Bakassi, whom some called vigilantes and others a saving grace. They went through cities and fought crime with machetes and assault weapons.

"So they burned him?" I asked.

So many faces around me, and I wondered how no one else questioned. A woman balanced water on her head as a toddler trailed behind. Two little boys danced in only underwear. A vendor yelled "Rosaries for sale" while draping picture frames from his arms like wooden bangles. And I heard laughter everywhere, cackling, saw men and women and children throw their heads back in uproar. So many teeth. So many smiles. As if everyone knew some joke I hadn't been let in on. Smoke rose in the close distance, black and unrelenting.

There was no track or sidewalk safe enough. So I ran along my uncle's cobblestone driveway, on a night so quiet I wouldn't have noticed the push of a passing wind had it been there. In Nigeria, heat blazes even when the sun has abandoned its sky.

Up, then down again, my legs pumped past the gatekeeper who looked drowsy as usual. I've never known a kinder man, but he wasn't good at his job, always forgetting to lock the gate. A man and a teenage girl ran into the driveway. She had a nose like him—broad and bent upward. I couldn't say whether their eyes shared any resemblance. His left one was punched bloody and swollen, his right bloodshot from crying. "Lock the gate," the man screamed and dropped to the ground in front of me, trying to catch his breath and keep his composure. The girl pulled at his tattered V-neck, "Daddy, get up." He said robbers came to his house, then he put his fingers against his temple and said they put the gun right here.

"Who are you? Get out of here." Wednesday ran up, yelling. This was the first time all day he hadn't carried his gun. His arms bare, I finally saw them, and their thick veins running down the sides like swollen rivers.

"I'm his friend," the man said, pointing to my uncle's balcony. The front lights were on, though no one was home. Wednesday grabbed the man's torn collar. "Robbers. They came to my house and put a gun right here." He demonstrated again. The girl sobbed harder.

I stood quietly and tried to empathize, understand maybe, but there was no way I could even look at the man's bloody face without getting sick. You know I could've used some laughter right then. I mean some gut-wrenching comedy. The kind Wednesday couldn't help but dish out that morning on the porch. The kind that erupted from the bellies of those marketplace people and filled the streets. Laughter growing by the moment, pregnant, leaving its offspring in the throats of those people. I'm convinced of one thing now: They laugh to muffle the pang of bullets, to be carried above Nigeria's violence. And what else could do that better than a mere chuckle, the sweetest sound I've ever heard.

Jodi Balfe, 16
Madison High School
Madison, NJ
Teacher: Julie Harding

Jodi Balfe hails from Madison, New Jersey. Like her favorite authors, Fitzgerald and Dostoyevsky, she seeks to convey the many facets of society in a single story. She would like to study physics and mathematics and integrate these pursuits with her interest in creative writing.

ABSOLUTE ZERO
Personal Essay/Memoir

Absolute zero is defined as the temperature at which molecules cease to move and motion terminates. This phenomenon has always been regarded as purely theoretical; absolute zero has never been reached experimentally. The extremely frozen circumstances would require almost complete detachment from the familiar universe.

Throwing open the door and dumping my obese high school backpack on the ground, I charged into the house after school. I exhaled and extended my arms toward the ceiling, a wave of relief washing over me as I stretched and walked upstairs to my room with headphones in my ears. I met my father in the stairwell—his eyes are sunk into and brimmed with red, and he clutches a bottle of wine in his left hand and his tie in his right. I reeled backward in surprise; my father is never home before 6 in the evening. My father, the epitome of the 9-to-5 business executive, was always composed, punctual, and calm; I stood shocked at the person before me.

I staggered to my bed and sat at the edge, tremulously clenching the sheets. Everything felt foreign to my hands, and as an overwhelming fear rushed into my head I fell back onto the mattress. I felt for the blanket with my hands, and pulled it up over my face so all I could see was darkness.

My father had been laid off in a mass firing spree at his company. There is a certain sense of invincibility one experiences when reading about the recession, as if it were a distant issue, far away from one's own immediacy. Within the span of a single day, an anonymous corporate hand had decided to take away our entire lives. I wanted to see the face of the person who would later send a curt, impersonal e-mail to hundreds of employees to professionally inform them that everything had been stripped away from them. I wanted to reach over and shake the shoulders of the faceless, faraway decision maker, and ask why, and how, over and over again, as if that would make a difference.

Cold is viewed relatively trivially nowadays, and at most is an inconvenience for many. In reality, something like temperature can have devastating effects: People freeze to death every year, or suffer in extremely low temperatures.

When we envision the global suffering at temperatures around freezing, and multiply that hundreds of times to reach absolute zero, the pain is too much to put into words.

Absolute zero has the power to strip matter of all essence of warmth, movement, and life.

My father changed completely. His hair started to grow gray and even white, he always seemed tired and rarely smiled, and he would disappear during the day to come back at night. He started to drink more, and lines started to etch into his skin, which crinkled not from laughter anymore but worry.

My mother looked for work, and struggled to learn English. Painstakingly combing through literacy textbooks and grammar handbooks, she studied her *who*s and *whom*s and her *there* and *their*, but she was never even offered an interview. Sometimes she would spend all day in her room in the dark, sleeping and crying.

When I left my house a few weeks later, the air was frigid and the town was still dark, except for the occasional blinking streetlight. I could hear the sound of my shoes pressing against the pavement since everything was so softly quiet. In a couple of hours, the tranquility would be shattered; the streets would be filled with cars blasting their horns down Main Street in the rush-hour traffic, businessmen and women intently fixated on their Bluetooth-equipped BlackBerrys as they briskly strode into Quick Chek to demand their coffee and bagel, and the wheezing garbage truck as it trudged down the street, stubbornly ignoring the impatiently tailgating drivers behind it. I breathed in the silence. The wind was cool but never harsh, and I inhaled the clean air, filling up my entire entity, and exhaled. Soon after I left, purple and orange clouds slowly smeared the sky and the sun gently rose, warming my shoulders, which had started to ache under the weight of my backpack, and the sidewalk beneath my feet as the distant horizon was silhouetted against the painted sky. As light tenderly fell over the town, the tree boughs and the outlines of houses were delineated by an ethereal glow, as if the town, and I myself, was in a half-asleep, half-awake reverie. I walked to school, not just because gas was now too expensive but because I was too afraid to ask my father for fear of encountering his sorrowful face. From the mansions up on top of the hill to the affordable housing a little closer to where I lived, I walked across my town.

One day, the sidewalks iced-over, the snowbanks haloed with the rising sun, I stopped at the iron gates of one of the biggest houses. I stood outside, my hands chapped red from the wind and clasping the curved pieces of metal in the gate, feeling the indentations in my palm, shifting my backpack from shoulder to shoulder. One, two, three, four: I counted a four-car garage silently in my head. Even from the end of the expansive driveway, I could see the crystal chandelier hanging in the entrance, framed by icicles.

Unwanted tears leaked from my eyes, and I hit my fist against the gate in desperate frustration.

When I arrived at school that same day, I was numb with cold and filled with a melancholy, panging ache. Walking down the driveway, I saw a blue BMW with a red ribbon proudly adorned over it—someone must have received it for their birthday. There was a crowd of students in awe surrounding it, and the owner occasionally interjecting with a smirk and warning not to touch. I saw some friends by the car, but instead I entered the school directly and went to the bathroom. Grabbing paper towels, I closed the stall door and started to wipe the mud and slush off my shoes. It is not that I really cared about my sneakers. I just did not want my classmates to realize I walked to school.

A couple of years ago, researchers came within a billionth of a degree of absolute zero, but the actual condition of zero energy was declared unreachable. If absolute-zero temperature were to manifest in reality, the results would be indescribable. Our universe would be forever altered—with the cessation of the motion of molecules, which is a corollary effect of absolute zero, matter would completely collapse. Our universe would almost instantaneously fold in on itself; all physical entities would cease to exist and be replaced by a vacuous state of complete nothingness.

In January, I was walking home from school when I received a call from my little sister asking me to stop by the elementary school and pick her up. I was surprised, since she normally walked home by herself; nonetheless, I detoured toward my old grammar school. I smiled at how I could take four steps to the door at a time, while as a second grader I struggled to take two. My little sister was standing forlornly outside the office, all alone since all the others had left right after school ended. She looked so small next to the secretary that I resolved internally that we would stop and I would use my allowance to buy her a cookie on the way home. The secretary indicated that I had to sign my sister out of the discipline list. I was shocked—my sister was quiet, shy, and it never would have occurred to me that she received a detention. As we walked outside, I took her tiny gloved hand and wrapped a scarf around her and buttoned her coat. When I got to the third button, I realized it had fallen off, and the coat itself was worn on the edges. I asked her if she was cold, and she fervently shook her head no, but I could see that her lips were purple and numb. Hand in hand down the sidewalk, I asked her how she had gotten in trouble. She said that in class, the teacher was talking about different jobs, and the teacher went around the room and each student had to stand up and announce to the class what their parents did for a living. When it was my sister's turn, she refused to stand up and kept shaking her head in silence as the teacher grew impatient. Finally, the teacher threatened to call my mother, and my sister stood up, trembling, and whispered that her parents did not work. A boy next to her then asked loudly if my father had gotten in trouble and then fired, and my sister lunged at him and knocked him out of his chair, yelling and crying, "My daddy didn't do anything wrong, nothing wrong, nothing wrong!" The teacher had sent my little sister to detention, and she had called me because she did not want one of my parents to come pick her up and find out what happened.

That Christmas, I had to keep explaining to my little sister that she was not going to be getting any Santa gifts—not because she was bad that year, but because Santa and the elves were sick so they were going to bring her the gifts next Christmas. She was still so worried and anxious, thinking she had misbehaved and Santa's wrath had been incurred. On Christmas morning, I could not look into her eyes.

We arrived at the supermarket, where my little sister carefully picked out a snickerdoodle cookie about the size of her face, and I paid 85 cents at the cash register, then we sat together on the bench in the desolate gray parking lot.

She never let go of my hand.

Absolute zero is approximately –459.67 degrees Fahrenheit; the range at which this phenomenon transpires is so beyond the familiar at we created an entirely new temperature system, the Kelvin system, to adapt. Absolute zero occurs at exactly zero degrees Kelvin. Sometimes, when an event is so far beyond the ordinary or expected, we rush to explain or ameliorate, to cover up and to feign normalcy.

For every morning that I can remember, my father sat at the kitchen table with a cup of coffee in the mug I painted him in kindergarten and read through *The New York Times*. One cold winter morning, I pulled on a sweatshirt and went downstairs, expecting to see my father placidly reviewing the events of the world; however, he was gone. I assumed he went out for a walk, so I sat down and started reading the newspaper. On the fourth page I saw an article titled "Laid-off Struggle to Find Jobs; Rising Bankruptcies Signal Unemployment Crisis." The article discussed a Wall Street executive now earning minimum wage as a janitor, a former banker now in bankruptcy himself, and the rising unemployment rate all over the country. I rushed to the desk for a scissor, thinking to myself that

I would explain to my father that I needed the article for a school current-events assignment. As I started cutting the edges of the article carefully around the black borders, I stopped when I saw a small coffee stain in the corner.

My father had already read the article. He did not come back home until late that night.

Unemployment insurance came as a little check every month, and it is dissected and carefully allocated by my mother into food, clothes, rent, gas money... My mother always saved a little money to put in the church collection Sunday mornings. Every Saturday night, she would take a small white envelope out of the drawer and put a couple of bills in it and carefully seal it, and while the four of us sat in the pew, she would give the envelope to my little sister to place in the golden plate.

One Saturday night, I saw my mother deliberating over how much money she could possibly squeeze for the next morning, and I grew angry with frustration. I argued and yelled, saying that our family needed the money, that we could not afford to be giving any away, and that she should think of her own daughters first. My mother remained silent, but her face was sorrowful, as she quietly told me that I should remember others who were in much more dire circumstances than we were.

I immediately felt the surging burn of guilt, followed by desperation. The next week, I took the money I received giving piano lessons and placed it in my mother's wallet. If I had offered it to her directly, she would have never accepted it.

I hope at least some of it ended up in the church collection plate.

The architecture of the universe is such that absolute zero is nothing but a technicality; as long as there exists heat, such a level of total arctic desolation can never be reached. Even if the source is comparatively minute or physically insignificant, such as the flame of a small candle, the radiation is enough that molecules will continue to move. We may get infinitesimally close, but as long as there is that single ray of warmth, we will be okay.

I would often end up going to Quick Chek late at night, the perpetually open convenience store with Extreme Caffeine Coffee (30 percent more caffeine than regular coffee) always ready to appease the high school student faced with looming finals and paper deadlines. Next to the cash register, there is a screen that shows the results of lottery tickets when they are scanned underneath. So as we wait in line, we watch the screen flash "SORRY, NOT A WINNER" whenever a hopeful customer carefully slides the ticket into the machine.

My father would always warn us against buying lottery tickets, arguing and demonstrating mathematically the minuscule probability of victory and presenting his careful calculations until we laughed at his steadfast logic and rationality. However, after he had lost his job, he would buy lottery tickets occasionally. Sometimes I saw him with a nickel in his hand, scraping away at the ticket nervously to see the numbers underneath the ink.

My heart broke at the idea of him standing by the machine with the words "SORRY, NOT A WINNER" flashing before him.

As I paid for my coffee one night in late February, I turned my head away from the pixelated screen because I did not need to be told I was not a winner.

I opened the door as slowly as I could when I got home that night, to try and stop the door from creaking too much and waking up someone, then sat down in front of the television, shivering while removing my coat. We kept the heat on very low this past winter and normally walked around in multiple sweaters and gloves. My little sister liked to wear this soft red sweater that was so big it made her look like a little marshmallow, and the sight of her waddling around even brought a despondent smile to my father's face. I sank into the sofa and flicked on the news channel, while I started to proofread my term paper.

President Obama appeared, and announced that the economy was improving, while I thought, "Well, Mr. President, that's wonderful, but what about us?"

The two news anchors returned on screen to discuss the recession, and my correcting pen burst, spreading red ink all over my hands and paper.

"Hope for the unemployed is dwindling," said the female anchor.

I cursed to myself and started to search for paper towels to clean up the pool of red accumulating on the floor.

"That's right," said the male anchor. I sighed and watched the red ink set into the carpet. "For the children of the recession," he continued, "they've reached absolute zero."

Jesse Shulman, 16
Upper Canada College
Toronto, Ontario
Teacher: Terence Dick

Jesse Shulman grew up in Toronto, Canada. He cites the fearless style and bold imagery of Toni Morrison, Alan Moore, and Jonathan Safran Foer as sources of admiration and inspiration. He hopes his piece will raise awareness about the dangers of factory farming. Outside of writing, his favorite hobby is reading philosophy.

THE CONDONED AND CONDEMNED
Science Fiction/Fantasy

Takes me ten minutes to catch its scent, then twist my neck toward its shrieks. First glance I see nothin' but rocks, stalks, twigs, and limbs, but then through the dead branches, I glimpse the thing dancing into the distance. It's still in earshot and eyesight, but won't be for long. It stops screaming and hides, but that doesn't fool me none. It's there somewhere. I can smell it. Probably a quarter-mile off but it shouldn't be tough to track if I keep my nose up. See, they have a stench that stays, lingering behind like a comet tail and leaving an easy-to-follow trail. Off the stench, I can follow, then flank it, catch it, then kill. Show it the trusty ol' one-two punch and it'll be all Batman from there on in: *bam, kapow, kaput*. Maybe Holden'll even let me take it home for Mary Ann to cook for the kids and me at dinner. But first I need to catch it.

Thank God for Mama Nature, right? My footsteps be soundin' off like a gosh darn jackhammer while they crumple the fallen foliage—which ain't the dandiest when you're going for the stealthy kill. Lucky for me, nature's always been the hunter's top patron; every cricket, bird, and beast—everything in this forest that moves—hides my noises from the enemy. It's an odd night, I'll tell ya. The moon's staring through the canopy of conifer carcasses, looking down on the world like it done something wrong. Everything's tinged blue and looks livid. The breeze is tickling me silly on the naked bits of my skin, and whispers sweet nothings in my ear, as if Zephyrus was tryin' to get in my pants or something. Anyway, hush up—I hear something. Yup, it's near...I can feel its fear, it's somewhere here...

You hear that? Breathing. Panting. Yeah? Behind that tree, in the ditch. I sneak beside without scaring it, then dive, grab, latch my arms, and try to squeeze, which would've been enough if it hadn't been wriggling its darn body like the feistiest son of a fish I ever saw. Anyway, one knock of a rock against the back of its head and it goes silent. Dead silent. It had already ripped off its clothes so they wouldn't slow it and now nothing's on its skin but dried sweat and a leatherbound book that I wrench from its lifeless, vise-grip arms. I'd caught this inglorious little basterd. Say who's the boss? Yeah, I'm the boss. Tony Danza's the boss? Nah, this guy's the boss. Hoo-ha, baby—job well-done.

See, this all kicked into gear an hour ago, when the sun was only starting to set. Holden the foreman saw it fleeing the factory and sprinting for the woods, through the fields, flailing and flapping its arms as if it were flying from a cuckoo's nest, like that Indian feller in the Jack Nicholson movie. Well, Holden tapped my shoulder to watch, and ten seconds later it had disappeared into the forest, free to roam in its natural habitat like the animal it is, yelling in some delirium: "Apollo breathes!" Holden put on his thinking cap and judged the matter. A slow smile curved the line between his lips.

"Heh. I got the last one. Don't play like you don't know whose turn it is this time, big guy."

See, hunting escaped livestock is what us factory men call a bitch job, if you don't mind the profanity. It's a bitch job because who wants to scour the deadwood lookin' for some animal that's only worth about fifty bucks anyway. But, y'know what...who gives? Looks good on the weekly report. Shows I follow protocol. And it's an excuse to take a breather from the factory. I'm not complaining—I got a decent job with decent pay—but the air in there's stuffy as a morgue, and after working nine to five overseeing factory operations, a cold blast from outside is an inhale of ecstasy. So maybe, I thought, I'll take my time catching this escapee...

But now the sun's fallen from the sky and I realize just how much time I did take, so I run back to the factory with the book dangling in my left hand and the livestock (I suppose just "stock" now) swung over my shoulder. Once I've said my goodbye to Holden and headed home, Mary Ann sees the car pull past the white picket and into the driveway. She opens the door for me. A kiss on the cheek and a "How was work?" followed by fluff talk and ended with a "Dinner'll be in thirty minutes, honey." A half hour to kill and a book in my hands—why not? Stuck in the factory every day with these things, I can read the language jotted on its pages. Upstairs in the study, the entries read:

HARKER RENFIELD'S JOURNAL
Day 8 since I was brought into the farm

Neither survival nor death here will suffice—the only salvation that would satisfy me now would be never having survived childbirth. That is my wish, my only other being that Jonah and Celine are in a better place, wherever they are, though part of me's realized there isn't any invisible kingdom in the clouds for them to take shelter in. God won't save me and won't save them; the windowless walls of these factories mean no one can see us, no one can hear us—no prayers reach ears. But thinking of Jonah and Celine won't lead anywhere but insanity, till I'm some crazy, running around yelling gibberish and begging for a straitjacket. No more thinking of them; the past is dead—inconsequential now. All that exists here is the stench, the starvation, and the overseers.

Overseers. There's a trillion names for 'em, depending on which factory you're from, but that's what we call them. Cruel, callous, and cold-blooded as gas chamber attendants. Never any tears. They're the reason we're here, so we can be fattened before being dismembered. To be processed into packaged meats, delivered to display fridges at supermarkets, and brought home for a dinner of family fun. I don't know why I'm writing about this as if it's small talk. A coping mechanism, I guess. To veil our tortures as something that we can think about and laugh. Children born in this giant room who have never known anywhere else; men fattened up not with sugars and sweets like a Hansel and Gretel tale but instead antibiotic and growth-hormone-swamped gruel; pregnant women separated from their families and starving themselves so that they won't bear the guilt of bringing new life into this world. Then they're all tossed in here, to wait for death. Yeah, real funny, Harker. Real funny.

...I don't know who I'm writing this for. Not me. I'll be dead too soon to reminisce on these scribblings. Not for anyone. The past will be as dead to them, too. Maybe this is as meaningless as everything else. So who are you, reader? Will you repress me, like a bad memory, so you can continue the life you've been living? Probably. But maybe you'll understand. It's a slim chance, but it's worth it.

Well. I guess now I know why I'm writing this.

<u>Day 13 or 14</u>

Knowing what horrors I've been spared torments me further while I wake and sleep in this hell. Each week, shipments of men and women are transferred to our ghetto. They each have terror-soaked tales to tell. In comparison to the places they were transferred from, they make this factory seem like Elysium. Here, unlike the factory to the north, the room's not so crowded that I must squirm away my final hours in a mound of men, each person's exhale another's inhale, children stomped to the mound's bottom, asphyxiating unto writhing, breathless ends. Here, unlike the factories in the South, I'm not stripped of my clothes and books. Here I'm not forced into a cage so small that without room to lie down, I must sleep standing. If you're out there, God, just don't let Jonah and Celine be anywhere like there.

One man I met told of a factory where food rations thrown into the crowds were so small, men honed any blunt object they could scavenge and slaughtered each other over crusts of bread. Hormone-stuffed bread. The brutality of circumstance had stolen from them any last civilization stored in their DNA, and self-interest had seduced them away from morality, from humanity. Men made into animals. The overseers watched and thought about profit loss—livestock killing each other? That's bad business. How's that gonna look on the weekly report? So they organized the livestock into an assembly line and marched them into a room. They stripped the people's clothes so there wouldn't be any concealment of weapons, then personally lopped off their arms so they couldn't kill each other again. Over a thousand of them, naked, armless, and hopeless, in a slate gray,

windowless factory—waiting for God, Godot, and the release of
death. All because the overseers didn't want to spend money to
increase the food rations.

Fourth week in the farm

There are rumors of a new machine. It has a retractable bolt that
punches into the skull. It immobilizes the victim, so the overseers can
drag it to Room 101 without resistance, before slitting its throat and
hanging it on a hook to let the blood drain.

At set intervals, the hook carries the hanging dead into a
mechanized butchery, a colossus of a machine that deskins and
debones, leaving high-quality "Just Meat," as its slogan sings. But
what if they're not dead? What if this new system malfunctions and
a man whose throat hasn't been properly slit has the fate of being
deskinned and deboned while still alive to feel the pain?

These are rumors, I tell myself. Just rumors.

Sometime in Month 2

I found John this morning. Skin parched till papyrus-dry and
bones brittled until broke, but it still looked enough like him for me
to know. His gray-blue eyes were lifeless and his breathing was
haggard. Not the same boy I'd played hide-and-seek with when we
were young. Not the same man I made Jonah's godfather after Celine
and I walked the aisle. I held him, and he stopped breathing in my
arms, staring up at me with dead pupils.

Month 3

I've accepted their truth, and part of me's gone.

*"Consider if this is a man...who knows no peace, who fights for a crust of
bread, who dies by a yes or a no."*

I am livestock.

Entry 6

It is night. For us, it's forever night. This place has no windows.
It has no sun. If I could see the sun before I died, I might know it
still existed.

Before he died, he saw the sun, but not Entry 7. The reader of his journal flipped through the rest of the empty pages searching for more but knowing that after Entry 6 there would be no author to fill them. He closed the book with both hands, placed it on the desk, and sat with his face in his fingers, allowing silence to swallow the room until "Dinner, honey!" pierced the floor from downstairs and the smell of steak wandered into the study. Dinner. It took a moment to remember—remember what he'd asked Holden if he could take, brought home in the backseat, and told Mary Ann to cook—but then his eyelids opened wide, frozen till the clock ticktocked another ten seconds and he yelled downstairs.

"I have to finish writing my weekly report—for work. Start without me."

He grabbed a pen and raised it above the page, but a tremor in his hand made him clench too tight, and it burst. The ink oozed like oil and looked like black blood. It painted the white page black. In the washroom he turned the tap and the water flowed but the ink stayed. Dried into the wrinkles of his palm, the stain was already created and couldn't be cleansed, not even by the tears streaking his face.

The clatter of cutlery downstairs cut through the silence, and he saw visions of the dining room table: the glint of fine china the meat was being served on, the kids beaming smiles while they impaled their forks into flesh. His eyes shifted to the window in the washroom wall, gazing into the black as the black gazed into him. There was no sun. No light.

Night.

Amanda Miles, 18
Cedar Cliff High School
Camp Hill, PA
Teacher: Angela Maxton

Amanda Miles lives in Cumberland County, Pennsylvania. She defines herself as an outgoing lover of new things who defies trends and expectations. Her favorite novel is Get Shorty *by Elmore Leonard. She constantly cycles through new activities, but has stuck to volleyball as a main hobby for some time.*

ALLISTER REESE
Science Fiction/Fantasy

Pasta's a lonely meal. I make it when I'm tired or alone, and certainly not expecting company. It's quick, easy, the best option when a meal for myself isn't worth slaving over. It was a nice dining room. It reeked of an aged renaissance, smothered in thick, rich tones of red and accents of creamy white—a well-blended atmosphere in no urgent need of interruption.

I had never believed in ghosts or demons, any paranormal phenomenons like that. I'd been completely psyched about this Tuesday: moving day. The little, bleak blue house down on the corner of Maple and Haver seemed perfect, well-suited for me. Until I realized it was that little blue house located on the sputtering, questionable ends of Maple and Haver, which seemed to have their reputations dampened by this traumatically tainted house. They never told me who had lived here, or informed me who had stabbed himself in the parlor, however many years back. They never told me his name or what he'd been like, or why he'd done it. Never shared with me anything of his infamous afterlife, never showed me the list of victims, or told me how many souls he'd eaten.

"Sssskkkkeeooooohhh."
Sand in the time sift drooled like droplets of molasses as I stood up. My wineglass in perpetual motion, falling to the parlor

floor, never seemed to shatter or splatter. I couldn't hear it. Couldn't see it. All I heard was the voice. All I saw was the man.

He was calm and cool. Stood firm and fresh in front of me. The glass slowly lulled around the floor as I watched him. A moment of trance unable to be broken by a human persona of an awkward silence. Jeans, pale shirt, unbuttoned at the top. The chiseling began at the V and pulsed down his torso in ravishing ripples. He looked new and clean, too pure for something damned to an eternity in this lonely house. He didn't strike me as a suicide—didn't look like he'd want to take away anything of the *everything* he'd been given. He looked confident, but curious, something rather odd for someone who had a countless amount of time to inquire. I wondered when the first question would come; I could feel them, there were plenty, dancing like little caged insects inside his empty soul, fireflies matching in luminosity inside his fluorescent figure.

He didn't move to advance on me, yet I felt a pull to him. Like the supernatural force that claimed him reached for a hold on me, too.

"Hello, my name is Allister. Allister Reese," he bowed. His choice of formal greeting seemed out of place for the situation. I eyed him suspiciously.

"Hello…I'm—"

"Venya, I know. Pleasure to meet you," he nodded.

"Just Ven." What a mysterious little creeper. He already knew my name.

He spread his arms wide, "Welcome to *my home*."

Perfect; a territorial numen—just what I needed my first night in. When I didn't answer, he proceeded, "Please, continue your meal."

I never broke eye contact as I cautiously slid back into my chair and tackled another meatball, forgetting about the spilled wine.

"You just gonna sit there and stare at me?"

"I felt it more proper than rudely concealing myself, promoting my presence as something more of a friendly household companion than a spy."

I absentmindedly twirled up a few bites of spaghetti on my fork as I continued to inspect him.

"How long have you been here?"

SCIENCE FICTION/FANTASY

"A long time."

"I mean today."

"I'm always here."

I was quiet again. Not too sure how to proceed with our introductions, not sure what to ask a ghost. He sensed my confusion and a smart little smile emerged.

"I'm sorry, you shouldn't feel this uncomfortable in my home. Would you like me to leave?"

"Are you going to leave or just disappear?" I asked.

"Disappear."

"You're right. This is less creepy."

He laughed, leaned back in his chair, and settled in.

There were a few specific things that sparked my inquisitions about Allister's being as I came to know him over the next few weeks: Allister never left the house. I didn't completely understand why. And when I asked, he said he simply never felt like it. Allister never talked about his death and wasn't confined to after-hours; he was out at all times of the day and would occasionally meet me for breakfast in the kitchen. Slowly our conversations became more fluid. He'd greet me when I came home from work, unless he was unusually bothered by something. If I didn't bring work home from the office, we'd stay up all night at the kitchen bar. He'd ask all the questions, about my family, my childhood, my old house, and which house I liked more. Sometimes I wished he'd let me join in on the cross-examination, but then again I didn't know what I'd ask.

The bigger the space grew between his knowledge of me and mine of him, the more I was attracted to him. He was a mystery, a puzzle that I wanted to take all the time in the world to solve, and the small sense of vulnerability intrigued me.

Allister also developed a strange fascination with my cooking. When I couldn't see him in the kitchen, I'd feel his presence lurking over my shoulder. The next time I made pasta, he sat and watched. He didn't talk, just sat in silence observing my work. It confused me. I figured this would be a typical action of someone who had a desire to re-create the dish later himself, but Allister was stuck here in quite a peculiar state, a twilight—able to move, unable to do, able to talk, yet unable to interact. It bothered me. I wondered how much it bothered him—if it did at all. I couldn't find a trace of irritation, couldn't read a thing from his transfixing transparent face.

"Yes?"

He caught me staring at him. I'd absentmindedly slowed to a stop in my stirs around the boiling fettucini.

"Nothing, nothing." I refocused on the stove. He continued to watch.

"I forget what it's like."

"What's like?" I asked.

"To eat."

"Oh." I couldn't think of anything better to say. "It takes up a lot of time."

He threw me a funny look.

"I waste so much time preparing food, eating food, digesting food..."

"I wouldn't mind making another meal."

Allister had too much time. He'd forgotten to be human. He didn't remember what it was like to be irritated, or how annoying the chores of everyday life were. It made me wonder how old he really was—how much time had lapsed since his last painfully normal day.

"What's it like?" I asked.

He already knew what I was talking about. He thought for a moment.

"Different. Very different."

"Does it look different?"

"It feels different...everything feels so hollow."

I waited for more.

"It's hard to remember life, it used to be hard to compare, but with you around I get a taste of it—a refreshment. You're different, apart from all the inert objects that occupy my existence. I sense something else with your presence that I can't in others."

He sounded so alone. Suddenly I was where he was, trapped in this box, and just the moment sucked all my happiness away.

On nurturing instinct, I took the steaming teakettle from the back burner and went to grab him a mug, but then caught myself. The situation nipped at me. I felt helpless. I poured myself instead.

"Does it tease you?" I asked.

"It's better to feel something than nothing at all."

Allister got dangerously close. He plotted further than the physical boundaries that disconnected us. It was hard to keep him out, especially when I was mad or frustrated—or found myself set off by a past lover. They were nothing alike, but the poltergeist seemed to always weave webs of relation back to himself in my head, no matter how hard I fought against it, or how black and white the differences were between him and anyone I'd ever met.

He heard it before it happened and was already there waiting.

I slammed the door shut, threw my bag down on the kitchen floor, and hurled the keys against the wall.

I screamed hysterically.

He waited.

I flew around the kitchen in a bull-run tirade, thrashing open the cabinets, roughly shoving things around in search of a clean glass. Soon, without success, I slammed that shut, too.

"Godforgetit. Just forget it." I sat down on the barstool. Took a breath.

He gave me some time. Then came over to sit beside me. Fumes slowly smoldering to death in his presence. He didn't have to say anything. Just look.

"Bad day," I said. I didn't really want to talk. Sometimes I felt silly, like I was sitting in front of an overly patient psychiatrist. Allister kept looking, waiting for further explanation. I loved that about him. His euphonic aura infected me, like an incurable mutated strand of disease so advanced there was nothing I could do to stop the contamination.

"You know, I wish more people were like you."

"Explain."

"Just relaxed...understanding. I dunno."

"You come to understand a lot when you've been here this long."

"I know. I just...wish people could sit here like you can."

"This is my house. I've been sitting here a long time."

"I wish everyone else had the time."

"Ven, all I have is time."

"I know, forget it."

"No. I understand." His frozen eyes dug further into me. He moved like he wanted to rest an arm around me. I hated our wall. "I wish I had more for you than just my time."

"It's more than what I could ask from anyone else." I considered offering an eternity in this transaction of smile, but I turned to get up.

"Biscotti tonight?" Sparks of excitement flickered across his face.

"I guess I promised, didn't I?"

"Doesn't have to be tonight."

"We have enough flour?"

"There's another bag in the back cabinet."

"All right. But first, hot bath."

"Take your time. I'll be here."

I stopped in the bathroom to turn the old handles of the clawfoot tub. I left the water on, steaming up the room, dense and thick like a sauna. It thawed my mood and dampened my anxiety. I let the water sit and went into my bedroom. I stood in front of the mirror on my old mahogany dresser; the glow of the warm sitting lamp gave me a new hue of color, and I admired the romantic light. Alone in my room...and the man came flooding back into my head. Allister confused me; for some reason he still wanted a part of this place in me, but I cut him off, snipped the web.

I slid my blouse off, felt the sticky air hug my body. I looked down at my chest, traced the bones with my soft, slender fingers. I stopped at the places that had last been touched. I hung for a moment on the reminiscent fingerprints of that man who seemed so far away. I dragged my hand to the edge of my bra, right where his kisses had caressed last. I could still barely feel his lips there, but the sensation soon slipped away, growing further and further from me as I couldn't see his face anymore, or hear that once-so-powerful voice ring in my ears and hurl my heartbeat.

...But the demon still tugged at the strings to come back.

I caught Allister in the corner of the mirror, his apparition hung by the door in the shadows. Something in me wanted to feel uncomfortable, like he shouldn't be here, but I couldn't. This was his house, and I was too accustomed to the strange vibrancy between us. I took him in again—as I had the first time I saw him. Body carved from white marble, eyes shimmering like the ice coating on sheets of snow. He looked even prettier this time—more innocent—even more curious. And no longer a demonic figure, but godly—that angelic, heavenly white. I held with his eyes, an unbreakable bond—signing in blood as I gave a flick of my lashes to him, telling him I was OK.

He waited a few moments, bookmarking our moment in time. Then approached as I slipped out of my slacks. He came to stand behind me as I readjusted the lace at my waist. I felt his phantom presence, a shift in the air circulating my vulnerable body. I watched his eyes follow down the line of my spine.

"You can see me." He whispered on my neck.

"Of course I can."

"No, in the mirror. You're not supposed to be able to do that."

I fell silent again. Drowning in the edge and tension of the moment.

I unhooked my bra, slid the straps off my shoulders, let the silk fall to the floor.

His aura came closer; cool fresh energy hummed between us as he reached out—the perfectly sculpted porcelain hands. He didn't touch. But lingered…stared. I felt the pull again. The black whole of his being was dying to eat me up.

"Isn't this how you got here in the first place?" I breathed back, "from breaking all the rules?"

I went down to the coffee shop and thought about him. Meditated the evening away over the warming mist of my spiced apple cider. Flamboyant vibrant beings bounced in and out from the streets in their autumn festivities, each time blowing gushes of the chilled September air onto me. It crystallized and clung to my skin, attacking me like a foreign body. I held onto my mug as the people whirled around in dizzying colors and conversations.

I felt apart from them. And that's when I realized how hollow I was.

My time with him suffocated me, denying me the simple pleasures of everyday life, which he had so foolishly deprived himself. And now he was out to spread his curse. He sucked the life out of me, a heartless death dealer. I grabbed my coat and ran out, left the piping cider untouched on the table.

I had to know.

"What did you do? Why are you here? I need to know."

At first he refused to answer, just like before, but then it bubbled. "Allister, why did you kill yourself? Who are you?"

I set it off.

Every ghost was damned here for a reason. Every one residing here on this earth with a piece of Hades hibernating within—I had resurrected it.

And then for the first time I was scared.

I felt the icy claws of his evil energy grasping for me. His being surrounded me, coming in on me from every direction, smothering me.

"I think you know why I'm here."

I gasped. "Stop it, Allister—"

"You've heard the stories. You know the truth. What makes you think you're different?"

I couldn't breathe. "Allister, *stop*."

"I'll take you with me, take your heart, drag you along with me to hell."

I fell to my knees, covering my ears, pleading for air.

"You can rest with all the others, all the other hopeless souls— another in my Hades book."

I looked up at him. "Who *are* you?" I whimpered.

"I'm a demon, Ven. You know very well what I am and what I do," he leaned in and hissed in my ear. "I'm the 'who' when they call 'Who's there?'"

"STOP!" I screamed, pulling at my hair in distress. The air pressure strained to push me six feet through the floor.

He came to my face, red embers gleaming in his sockets. "I'll take you with me. Aren't you scared?"

"Yes, but this isn't what you want," I panted.

"What?"

"Can't you see that? This isn't your purpose. You're not here to control or manipulate, scare or condemn."

He retracted. "Then what am I here for?"

I staggered to my feet with him. "You're here for me. Here for me to teach you something. Teach you something about the life you never had, and the life you won't take from me."

He began to shrink, the fury slowly died away.

"I'm not here to be terrorized, I'm here to teach you something. You're so messed up, I think deep down you know the answers, you just won't accept them. How long do you want to stay here? Growing older and older, becoming more and more confused and further apart from life, it's only getting harder for you to pass on. I won't be here forever. And I won't be taken with you."

"...I don't want you to leave." He struggled.

"Do you want me to suffer with you, share the same fate?"

"No, I just...want you."

"I don't need to be taken. You have me, just not forever. Nothing is meant to be forever, neither are you."

I sensed his want, felt his need. He was desperate—so curious, extending a hand to my face...

Curious again.

He touched me.

As soon as the moment was born, it was destroyed. The hourglass would not wait this time, the grains raced faster and faster slipping away, frenzied in hyper motion. The hours that I could have spent in this one pause went forgotten, rejected by the gods of time. His hand burned my cheek; the coldness that I'd always thought to represent him was nonexistent. He felt like a human. He was human, for that one wisp of time vibrated in full-color—solid-color—life. He was no longer paranormal.

But as soon as I felt the human, he was gone.

Starting first at his warm, fleshy fingertips, he dissolved; fiberglass fragments withered into rainbows, evaporating into the air.

"I want you to move on," I gently cried.

A shiver, and he whispered.

"I'm already gone."

Benjamin Sprung-Keyser, 17
Harvard-Westlake School
North Hollywood, CA
Teacher: Christopher Moore

Benjamin Sprung-Keyser sees his piece as the start of a conversation in which readers disagree about and discuss the issues it raises. He was inspired to write the piece after he took part in a one-act play festival at his high school. He is actively involved with the debate team and also participates in science research.

WHAT ALL SCHOOL CHILDREN LEARN
Dramatic Script

CHARLIE JENKINS – 11 years old, a small seventh grader, son of Martin and Katherine Jenkins
STEVEN – 15 years old, a ninth grader and bully
COOPER – 15 years old, a ninth grader and co-conspirator with Steven
LUKE – 14 years old, a ninth grader and co-conspirator with Steven
MARTIN JENKINS – early 40s, a UPS worker, father of Charlie Jenkins
KATHERINE JENKINS – late 30s, a housekeeper, mother of Charlie Jenkins
MR. BARKLEY – early 50s, school principal
LINDA – mid 40s, a parent
PATRICIA – mid 30s, a parent
MELISSA – mid 40s, mother of Steven
SUSANNE – mid 40s, a parent
JEFF – late 40s, a parent
TERRORIST – early 20s

*"I and the public know
what all school children learn,
those to whom evil is done
do evil in return."*
—W.H. Auden

SCHOOL YARD – DAY

A middle school lunch area. A large metal trash can sits stage right. In the middle of the stage is a lunch table.

A school bell rings.

CHARLIE, a small prepubescent boy of 11, walks on stage, happily carrying a tin lunchbox. He looks around for his friends. When he sees none, he sits dead center at the table, facing us. He opens up his lunchbox and sets out on the table a sandwich, a banana, a package of cupcakes, and a carton of milk. He starts to eat. Three older boys, each halfway between boyhood and manhood, appear in the lunch area. COOPER, the first of the boys, sits down next to Charlie so as to be uncomfortably close. LUKE, the second bully, sits on the other side so that Charlie is sandwiched. STEVEN, who is clearly their leader, comes up behind and takes Charlie's sandwich out of his hand. He takes a bite and then puts it back in the lunchbox. He picks up the carton of milk and pours it out into the box. The two other boys just sit and laugh. CHARLIE, on the verge of tears, collects his things and runs off stage. The three older boys run off stage after him.

They cross with eight adults, who enter as the boys leave. We are now in a

SCHOOL CONFERENCE ROOM – EVENING

Two of the adults—a man in a UPS uniform and a woman—carry two chairs with them, place them in the corner, and sit. The other six turn the table on an angle. One of them—MR. BARKLEY, dressed in a jacket and a tie—stands behind it. The remaining five gather in front, animated and upset. Their conversation begins at the moment they appear.

PATRICIA

Let me get this straight. A teacher goes to get lunch, she doesn't tell anyone, and she leaves 100 kids unsupervised.

JEFF

The school let this happen, Mr. Barkley?

MR. BARKLEY

A mistake. It was a mistake. I promise you—

LINDA
—How many teachers were supposed to be watching? I mean, how many kids were left without someone to watch them?

MR. BARKLEY
Normally we have one teacher for each play area. And we never have a teacher look after more than 100 children at a time. This was a simple miscommunication.

PATRICIA
None of us want to hear excuses. Do I have to worry about my son being bullied?

MR. BARKLEY
Your child is safe. All of your children are. I—this is an isolated incident.

LINDA
How do you know? I mean it, how do you know? How can you be so sure? Things like this don't happen out of blue. There are reasons, there are warning signs. You need to keep an eye out—

MR. BARKLEY
(Trying to be more forceful) —And we are. I've scheduled a meeting with all of our teachers. If everyone stays calm, Ms. Constantino, we—

SUSANNE
—We have every right to be concerned. Pushing, shoving, a fistfight or two—that you'd expect. Kids are kids. But this is different. I hate to say it, but a normal child doesn't do something like that.

LINDA
If my son where the victim of this, I wouldn't be sitting there so quietly. Melissa, are you sure there's nothing you have to say?

There is a moment of silence as everyone waits for her to respond.

MELISSA
What do you want me to say? Mr. Barkley and I have talked privately, and the school knows exactly how I feel.

MR. BARKLEY
Ms. Lewis' son is being looked after. You have my word.

SUSANNE
Well, that's great, you're fixing the problem now that it's already happened. Guess what? That's not good enough. I need to know how this could happen here, in our school? Something this disturbing and, I hate to say it, this evil. How does a little boy do something like that to a kid four years older and twice his size?

The five parents exit. MR. BARKLEY comes down stage and speaks directly to the audience.

MR. BARKLEY
Three weeks earlier.

He exits the stage and we are in a

SCHOOL ADMINISTRATION OFFICE – MORNING
KATHERINE and MARTIN JENKINS, the two parents who were sitting on the side of the stage, pick up their chairs and place them opposite the table, which is now the desk in Mr. Barkley's office. They place a sign on the desk that says "Principal." MARTIN paces, and KATHERINE checks herself in her compact mirror.

KATHERINE
How do I look?

MARTIN
You look fine. *(Checks his watch.)* I'm gonna get sacked.

KATHERINE
Don't say that, you—

MARTIN

—I'm telling you, I'm gonna miss my shift. *(Gets up to pace.)* Next shift starts at 9, and Peterson gives no leeway. *(Checks his watch again.)* Jesus Christ, do you know how long we have been—

MR. BARKLEY walks in. He clenches his back.

MR. BARKLEY

—I'm sorry I'm late. Back problems. They're the worst, and the Advil's not helping. I'm so glad you came in, Mr. and Mrs.... *(Glances at the sheet in his hand.)* ...Jenkins. I...umm— *(He sits down for one second before popping back up, and paces periodically around the room.)* —Do you mind if I stand? Doctor says I've got a fused disk. I'm not sure what that means. I suggest you avoid one. *(He massages his back.)* Anyway... your son, Charlie, right? There's been an incident in the lunch area.

MARTIN

"An incident"? Yeah, you could call it that. Our son is being bullied by a kid three times his size, and there doesn't seem to be anyone trying to stop it.

KATHERINE

Charlie's very quiet. He's not really physical, if you know what I mean. He doesn't like to defend himself. That doesn't make my husband happy but— *(Martin shoots her a look.)* Every day he comes home crying.

MR. BARKLEY

I'm sorry to hear that, Mrs. Jenkins. That must be very upsetting. With so many in such a small space, incidents are bound to happen. I always find these things have two sides to them. They're all pretty good kids, you know. *(Clenches his back.)* Jeez, I—

KATHERINE

(Trying to be polite) —But there aren't two sides this. Our 11-year-old is being tormented.

MR. BARKLEY
I understand. Let me ask you a question: Was there a history between Charlie and Steven?

MARTIN
A history?

MR. BARKLEY
Of antagonism?

MARTIN
I don't think you understand. My son is in seventh grade. He is four years younger. He doesn't know this kid from Adam. The kid's a bully who messes with Charlie for kicks.

KATHERINE
Martin!

MARTIN
What? There aren't two sides to this. This isn't like the Palestinians and the Jews or some such thing. You got a bad kid who needs to be punished.

MR. BARKLEY
You may be right. *(Grabs his back, grimaces, and stretches.)* I hate getting old.

MARTIN
(Laughs.) You're not gonna do anything, are you?

MR. BARKLEY
What?

MARTIN
You just want this to go away.

MR. BARKLEY
That's not— This may be just kids being kids, Mr. Jenkins. I know Charlie is a sensitive boy, but there is a big difference between roughhousing on the playground and—

MARTIN
You're so fair—

MR. BARKLEY
Thank you.

MARTIN
You didn't let me finish. I was gonna say you're so fair, you're useless. You know that? *(Checks his watch.)* I gotta go. I'm late for work. I just wanna know someone's looking after my kid.

He leaves. And there is a moment of silence.

KATHERINE
I apologize for my husband. He's under a lot of pressure at work. *(Beat)* Martin wishes Charlie were the kind of kid who stood up for himself. I just want to know he'll be safe.

MR. BARKLEY
Of course you do.

KATHERINE
Isn't there a way you could put a few more teachers on the playground during lunch?

MR. BARKLEY
Mrs. Jenkins, I've got 1,500 kids to look out for, and I don't have the money or the manpower to run the school the way I'd like. I'll do the best I can. *(He smiles.)* Don't worry too much. I find that stuff like this blows over quick.

MR. BARKLEY *takes his name plaque, and he and* MRS. JENKINS *exit the stage. They cross with* CHARLIE.

The school bell rings. We are now in the

SCHOOL YARD – DAY
CHARLIE *carries a few binders in his hand as he enters, looking around nervously.* STEVEN, *by himself this time, enters the yard and approaches Charlie.*

CHARLIE
Leave me alone. I'm not bothering you.

STEVEN
Don't tell me what to do.

CHARLIE
I didn't mean to, I—

STEVEN
—What's for lunch today?

CHARLIE
Sorry, I already ate.

STEVEN *comes toward him, menacingly.*

CHARLIE
You better not. I'll tell on you. I'll get you in huge trouble—

STEVEN
Yeah, I don't think you wanna do that. Cuz you know what I'll do to you.

STEVEN *approaches* CHARLIE. *With one swat, he knocks the books from Charlie's hands.* CHARLIE *hesitates, and in a moment of newfound courage he stands up tall.*

CHARLIE
Pick them up.

STEVEN
You're kidding, right? You're trying to be brave? Think you can scare
me?

*Without warning, STEVEN grabs Charlie by his ankles and dangles him
above the books. He begins to "walk" Charlie across the yard. Charlie kicks to
loosen Steven's grip.*

STEVEN
I think you're gonna pick 'em up.

*CHARLIE gives up his thrashing and goes to collecting the books, while still
hanging.*

CHARLIE
Why do you always have to pick on me?

STEVEN
I dunno. Cuz it's fun, cuz you're tiny, cuz I can. What does it matter?

CHARLIE
You could choose someone else once in a while. Why does it always
have to be me?

STEVEN
No reason. But I picked you, so live with it.

STEVEN drops Charlie.

STEVEN
Its like you're my prey or something. I'm strong, you're weak, I make
the rules.

STEVEN walks off. He leaves Charlie to collect his stuff and run off on the verge of tears. CHARLIE crosses with Mr. and Mrs. Jenkins. KATHERINE and MARTIN bring in plates and mugs to set what is now the table. We are in the

JENKINS HOME – MORNING
MARTIN takes a seat, rubs his eyes, and starts reading a paper. KATHERINE pours coffee. CHARLIE walks in. He's wearing a bathrobe, but it is obvious that his school clothes are underneath.

MARTIN
Morning.

CHARLIE
Really bad news. I can't go to school today.

KATHERINE
Why not?

CHARLIE
Cuz I'm sick.

MARTIN
You're sick? You don't look sick. Don't play games with me. Is something actually wrong?

CHARLIE
'Fraid so. Don't be scared but...I've got rabbit fever.

KATHERINE
Rabbit fever?

CHARLIE
Yeah, it's very dangerous. I looked it up online. It's definitely rabbit fever. I bet I got it from playing with mice in science.

KATHERINE
If you got it from mice, why is it called rabbit fever?

CHARLIE
You can get it from lots of animals. They had to pick one. They picked rabbits. It causes fever, duh, and swelling, and pneumonia. And I've got all those symptoms. *(He coughs.)* I would go to school, but I'm trying to keep my friends safe.

KATHERINE
Come here, let me feel your head. *(She feels his forehead.)* You're not warm. *(She looks at him with disappointment.)*

CHARLIE
Really? Then I definitely have it. Cuz part of the disease is when the symptoms come and go really quickly. Don't ask me why, but that's the way it happens.

MARTIN
You're not sick. Your just lazy and you're gonna go to school.

CHARLIE
Mom!

MARTIN
Charlie, I'm tired, I just got in from the night shift, and I'm gonna go to bed. I don't want to hear anymore about it.

CHARLIE
(Serious) I can't go to school. It's too dangerous.

MARTIN
Dangerous, Jesus! It's just some stupid kid. Stay away from him and you'll be fine. Listen, you're going to school, that's final.

CHARLIE
Mom, don't make me go.

MARTIN
Alright. You know what? This is ridiculous. Come here.

CHARLIE
What?

MARTIN
Come here. I'm gonna teach you how to fight. Put up your fists.

CHARLIE
Dad.

KATHERINE
Martin!

MARTIN
Put up your fists... Higher. *(Charlie does it.)* OK. Now punch my hand. Punch my hand, Charlie! *(He puts out his hand for Charlie to punch. Charlie complies weakly.)* Well, you might be able to hurt the mouse that got you sick.

KATHERINE
Martin!

MARTIN
Fine, you're never gonna punch him, anyway. How about kicking? Give me a good strong roundhouse.

CHARLIE
I don't know what that is.

MARTIN
It's where you swing your foot wide out to the side...I'll show you. *(He does a kick and taps Charlie lightly at the end.)*

CHARLIE
Owww!

MARTIN
That didn't hurt.

CHARLIE
You kicked me!

MARTIN
There is no way that a little kick—

CHARLIE
—Mom, Dad kicked me!

MARTIN
You're telling on me!

CHARLIE
Well, you did. You kicked me!

KATHERINE
We're done here, boys! Marty, get to bed. Bed!

MARTIN
Alright, alright. We'll finish this lesson tonight. You're gonna learn to kick that kid's sorry ass. Have a good day at school. You'll be fine, just stick up for yourself.

He gets up and goes.

KATHERINE
Come here, Charlie. *(She kneels to talk to him.)* I can't afford not to go to work today. And I don't have anyone to look after you. Sweetheart, you're gonna be OK. *(He diverts his gaze.)* Look at me. I promise. Just keep an eye out for yourself. *(She takes off his bathrobe.)* Now give your mom a hug, get your lunch, and hurry to the bus. *(He listens, and she watches him run out the door.)* Love you.

CHARLIE
Yeah, yeah, yeah.
The school bell rings, and we are in the

SCHOOL YARD – MORNING
CHARLIE walks onto the playground, carrying his lunch. Voices begin in the distance.

STEVEN (O.S.)
Charlie? Charlie? Where are you?

CHARLIE moves farther downstage, huddling behind the trash can. STEVEN appears. He's searching for Charlie, facing upstage and away from us.

STEVEN
Come on, Charlie. I'm hungry! Don't you have lunch for me?

CHARLIE slinks further behind the trash can and pulls his legs in to not be seen.

STEVEN
You can't hide the rest of the year, Charlie. If you run from me today, tomorrow's gonna be worse… Just you wait. I'm coming for you.

STEVEN walks off stage and CHARLIE relaxes. He takes another bite of his sandwich. KATHERINE walks in carrying a mixing bowl. She hums as she whisks away at the brownie mix. We are now in the

JENKINS KITCHEN – EVENING
CHARLIE takes out a PSP and starts to play.

KATHERINE
Charlie, what are you doing over there?

CHARLIE
Nothing.

KATHERINE
You know, if someone got themselves up and back to the table to do their homework, there might be some extra brownie mix.
CHARLIE puts away his PSP and runs to the table.

CHARLIE
This math homework is fascinating.

KATHERINE
No kidding? What kind of problems are you doing?

CHARLIE
What am I doing? Uhhh... *(Glancing down to figure out what's on the page.)* Double negatizing. Ms. Green said it was tough, but she was trying to scare us.

KATHERINE
OK. What's negative 12 times negative 12?

CHARLIE
One forty-four. I'm not stupid. Hey, where's the brownie mix you promised me?

She hands over the bowl and he sticks his finger in and takes out a big glob.

CHARLIE
Mom?

KATHERINE
Yeah, Charlie.

CHARLIE
This is good... Listen, about school tomorrow, I—

KATHERINE
—Charlie, we're not going through this again. You are going to school.

CHARLIE

No, I know. That's not what I was going to say. Jeez. I was just gonna to ask for a special lunch.

KATHERINE

A special lunch?

CHARLIE

Yeah, you know. Something to look forward to during the day.

KATHERINE

(Smiling) I think I can do that. What do you want?

CHARLIE

Um, well…uhhh… How about…fried chicken?

KATHERINE

Your favorite.

CHARLIE

And ummm…Sprite… And something for dessert—

KATHERINE

Brownies?

CHARLIE

No, peanuts. A bag of peanuts.

KATHERINE

OK, you got it. Now run upstairs and wake up your dad for the night shift. *(He complies, but he is still on stage as she finishes.)* Charlie, I'm proud of you for doing the right thing. I mean, finding something good to get you through the day.

He runs off. She sticks her finger in the brownie mix as she exits. The school bell rings, and we are back in the

SCHOOL YARD – DAY

CHARLIE walks back on stage and sits at the lunch table. He lays out his food in front of him. STEVEN and the other two boys sneak up from behind. CHARLIE is about to take a bite of his chicken when STEVEN interrupts.

STEVEN
Not so fast.

STEVEN grabs the chicken and takes a bite before CHARLIE gets one. He holds on to the chicken as he picks up the can of soda and drinks.

CHARLIE
How was it?

STEVEN
Delicious. I'm gonna have some more. *(Takes another bite.)*

CHARLIE
You can have the whole thing if you want.

STEVEN
Very funny.

CHARLIE
How 'bout some peanuts with that?

STEVEN
What? *(A little flustered)* Nah. I'll pass.

CHARLIE gets up with the bag of peanuts, and STEVEN backs off.

CHARLIE
What do you mean you'll pass? Come on, have some peanuts.

CHARLIE walks closer.

STEVEN
Get away from me!

CHARLIE
What's wrong? Why not peanuts? You want my food. Take my food.
(He offers the peanuts again.)

STEVEN
Get away, you freak.

CHARLIE
What's the matter? Can't you eat peanuts? Oh, wait, maybe you can't.
Maybe you can't eat peanuts. Maybe you're allergic. *(He walks closer
with the bag of peanuts outstretched.)*

STEVEN
I'm telling you to get away.

CHARLIE is emboldened by Steven's fear.

CHARLIE
Oops. Maybe it's too late. I mean, maybe you already ate some. Right,
cuz maybe they were on my chicken. Maybe I rubbed them in the
crispy stuff. Same color. You couldn't really tell the difference, could
you?

Suddenly, STEVEN drops the chicken.

STEVEN
Did you? Did you put peanuts in the chicken? Tell me now. I'll kill
you. You asshole. I'll kill you.

*He walks toward CHARLIE, who grabs a bunch of peanuts and grinds them
in his hand.*

CHARLIE
(With unnerving calm) I wouldn't get any closer if I were you.

STEVEN

What the fuck is wrong with you? I need to know if you gave me peanuts!

CHARLIE

I don't feel like telling yet. *(Thinks for a second.)* How 'bout you tell Cooper that you love him first.

STEVEN

What? Are you serious? Just tell me if I—

CHARLIE

(Louder) —How 'bout you tell Cooper that you love him?

STEVEN

(Quickly, to get it over with) Cooper, I love you. Now did you put peanuts—?

CHARLIE

—Oh, c'mon, no one believed that. Tell him like ya mean it...NOW.

STEVEN

(Scared, but more sweetly) Cooper...I love you.

CHARLIE

What?

STEVEN

I love you!

CHARLIE

That's better.

STEVEN

Now tell me if I ate any peanuts, Jesus Christ! I don't think you get it. I could fucking die—

CHARLIE
—Yeah, I know.

It is all changed now. CHARLIE has the power, not Steven. Charlie likes it, and he hates it. It excites him and it scares him.

STEVEN
Why are you doing this? Please, I need to know if you gave me any peanuts!

STEVEN is on of the verge of tears. He shakes. A wet spot appears on his pants.

CHARLIE
You wet your pants.

STEVEN tries to cover up.

STEVEN
What the fuck is wrong with you? Tell me if I ate peanuts.

CHARLIE's had enough. Time to end this.

CHARLIE
Let's get some things straight. You will NEVER come near me again.

STEVEN
OK—

CHARLIE
—Cuz you'll never know where I put some peanuts. In my food, on my lunchbox, on my books, on me. I'm gonna have peanuts everywhere. Are we clear?... Are we clear?

STEVEN
Yes, yes, we're clear. God-fucking-dammit. Just tell me if I ate any peanuts.

CHARLIE
These... *(He holds them out.)* Not today. *(He pauses.)* Now get away from me.
STEVEN runs off. CHARLIE stands there for a moment, then calmly packs up his lunchbox and walks out.
He crosses with the eight adults just as he did before. They take their places, just as before, and we are in the

SCHOOL CONFERENCE ROOM – DAY

MELISSA
What do you want me to say? Mr. Barkley and I have talked privately, and the school knows exactly how I feel.

MR. BARKLEY
Ms. Lewis' son is being looked after. You have my word.

SUSANNE
Well, that's great, you're fixing the problem now that it's already happened. Guess what? That's not good enough. I need to know how this could happen here, in our school? Something this disturbing and, I hate to say it, this evil. How does a little boy do something like that to a kid four years older and twice his size?

KATHERINE
He was provoked. My son was tortured.

MELISSA stands and responds more angrily. She has been offended by this last remark.

MELISSA
No. He may have been teased, had his lunch taken one or twice, but he was not tortured. My son was tortured. Whatever Steven did, he didn't deserve what he got back.

MARTIN
And what was that?

MELISSA
Your boy tried to kill him.

KATHERINE
He did not.

MELISSA
Yes, Mrs. Jenkins, he did. Peanuts are no different from a gun or a knife—

MARTIN
—Charlie scared him, that's all. He gave him a fright, which your kid damn well deserved... A fright, by the way, that's gonna keep your kids safe. 'Cause next time, bullies will think twice about messing with little kids. If anything, my boy did you all a service, but you're gonna turn on him.

SUSANNE
I find the whole thing very disturbing, but he's got a point. This started with bullying.

MELISSA
My son is not a bully. He's not a bad kid. He goofs around sometimes. He roughhouses. Maybe sometimes he goes too far. Just 'cause he's big for his age—with all that testosterone—just 'cause he's physical doesn't mean he's a bully. Why can't we let boys be boys anymore? If they're not sitting quietly somewhere, acting like girls, there's something wrong with them. Well, there's nothing wrong with my son. For God's sake, if a few boys decide to have some fun and toilet-paper a house, that doesn't give you the right to take out a shotgun, like some nutjob, and gun them down.

KATHERINE
That's not what happened. Charlie just did what he had to do.

LINDA
What he had to do? Even you can't believe that.

KATHERINE
It's the truth. He took care of himself. No one else would.

JEFF
That's ridiculous. He could have gone to a teacher, to the principal—

MARTIN
—He tried!

KATHERINE
Everyone who was strong enough to protect him walked away. My husband and I—we were too busy, too tired. We didn't want to hear about it every day. So we just sent him to school and told him to keep to himself, to do the best he could. And the school? The school did nothing.

MR. BARKLEY
Mrs. Jenkins, we sat down together—

MARTIN
—You did nothing!

MR. BARKLEY
We can't have eyes everywhere, Mrs. Jenkins. We can't protect every child every time. Things happen. Things slip through the cracks. We make it as safe as possible, but we can't make it a perfect world.

MARTIN
Then don't blame my kid for figuring out how to survive in your screwed-up world. He's 11 years old. Tiny. He hasn't even gone through puberty yet. What's he supposed to do? Day after day he's humiliated by a kid who might as well be a man. Like some sadistic boss who's got it in for you—

KATHERINE
—Martin!

MARTIN

(To Katherine) No! *(To the other parents)* You tell me you don't know what that's like! To be at the mercy of some asshole who treats you like crap just because he can.

KATHERINE

Martin!

MR. BARKLEY

Mr. Jenkins—

MARTIN

—All we did was send my boy back to be tortured, again and again. And we said, Oh, yeah, you can fight back. Just do to that kid what he did to you. He punches you, punch him. He stole your lunchbox, steal his. But here's the problem: That's not gonna work. Charlie could do it, but he's gonna get killed. My boy knows that. Maybe someday, but not now. If he can only throw a punch once one's been thrown at him, he's gonna lose. So what did he do? He found a new way to fight. A new weapon. One that made things even again. And that's what really gets you. Cuz it turns the world upside down. A few kids get beaten up on the playground, who gives a crap, right? Because you still think you understand the rules. The game still makes sense to you. But not anymore. This changes everything.

The next lines come right on top of each other as the room turns into a frenzy.

LINDA

You're right, it changes everything. I don't care what the circumstances are. There is something wrong with a kid who would do what your son did.

KATHERINE

There's nothing wrong with him, he just—

PATRICIA

—What? Snapped under pressure?

KATHERINE
It's called defending yourself—

LINDA
—Threatening to kill a 15-year-old is not self-defense.

MR. BARKLEY
OK, this is not helping—

LINDA
—How is this so different from the kids you hear about on the news? You know, like the ones at Columbine. They were bullied, they were teased. And they went home and got their guns, and came to school and—

KATHERINE
—How dare you?! How dare you! My son didn't hurt anyone.

JEFF
But he got close. He threatened to. What if he gets teased again? What happens next time?

MARTIN
OK. That's it! I'm done with this crap. You take any action against my son, you're gonna hear from a lawyer. *(To Katherine)* C'mon, we're going.

KATHERINE
I don't—

MARTIN
Circus is over. Come on.

MARTIN storms out and KATHERINE follows. Silence.

LINDA
(Quietly) I don't feel safe having my child at school with that boy. I

hate to say it, but his father was right. A kid getting his lunch stolen I can deal with. A brawl on the playground I can deal with. I don't like it if a kid gets hurt, but I can live with it. Because I understand it. I get how it happens. But this—this is different. It's scary. This changes the whole world.

BLACKOUT.

LIGHTS UP ON TWO BEDROOMS.
On one side of the stage, CHARLIE sits cross-legged on the ground facing us. On the other side, behind the table—now a desk—sits a young man, a TERRORIST. Next to him lies an assault rifle. He speaks aloud as he writes a letter.

TERRORIST
Mom, this is my last letter to you. Don't listen to what they tell you about us. This is the only way. What's right and wrong, anyway? Everyone swears by God that they're right. Right and wrong are nothing. All that matters is the power you have to make your own right and wrong. *(Stands up and brandishes his gun.)* They have armies, and planes, and tanks. We have nothing. They occupy our home, they make us prisoners, and then they kill us when we fight back. And all of it, the whole thing, within rules of war. Made for countries, by countries. We have no country. When we fight, they say we're doing it in the name of terror. But what is terror? Terror is what makes those who make the rules afraid. *(He loads ammunition.)*

The lights dim on the TERRORIST and rise on CHARLIE with a video game controller in his hand. Sounds from a war game fill the room, and CHARLIE accompanies them with his own explosions.

KATHERINE (O.S.)
Charlie! Charlie! Come downstairs, Charlie. We need to talk.

BLACKOUT.

Tammy Chan, 17
Girls Write Now!
New York, NY
Teacher: Meghan McNamara

Tammy Chan attends high school in New York City, where she grew up. She sees journalism as a way to bring the issues that affect her life and the lives of those around her to a wider audience, where awareness can be raised and solutions can be found. In ten years, she'd like to be working for The New York Times.

To Combat the Recession, H.S. Students Turn to Military as a Way Out

Journalism

War may be hell, but so are unemployment, rising college costs, and small prospects for the future. So what's a teen to do? Join the service, of course.

Increasing college tuition. Rising unemployment. For students on the verge of finishing high school and for their concerned parents, it has an all-too-familiar ring. The economic instability in the world is rapidly affecting everyone, with no obvious end in sight.

Because of economic factors, more teens are considering joining the military as they make decisions about their post–high school direction.

Military recruiters hold school assemblies. This makes some students feel pressure to enlist.

"It's uncomfortable," Travis Clemington, 17, said. "They sort of hunt you down and suck you in a warp and ask you lots of question till you break down and begin to think about the military more and more. It was that or they asked more questions about our plans— which mine at the time weren't looking too good.

"After getting monthly mail and regular calls from the recruiter checking up on me, I'm beginning to see his way. I'm still unsure about enlisting, but it seems that it could actually be a good experience, maybe see new things. I don't even know what I'm going to do tomorrow, but I know I don't want to sign away my life...yet," Clemington said.

With the country's economy worsening, the number of young people considering a military career has significantly increased for the first time in about five years, buoyed by more positive news out of Iraq, according to Staff Sgt. Curtis Lancaster of the Air Force recruiting center in Jamaica, Queens. All branches of the military are experiencing an increase in recruitment. Military officials are predicting that interest will rise even further if the economy continues to suffer.

People join the military for a variety of reasons: Some want to nobly defend their country against attack; some seek training and education otherwise unavailable to them; some are following a family tradition; some crave being a hero; some wish to take big risks to experience life to its limits; some are ambitious for high rank and power; some want a ticket out of ghetto life—to get a job they hope will provide credentials and employable skills for the future; and some just need money during this time of economic struggle.

Andrew Walters, 17, of Kew Gardens plans to be among those joining up. "It's something I've waited for since I was 9. After seeing the commercials on TV, I knew it was my calling. The money would be great [too]."

Mandatory registration for military service ended in 1973; since then, the United States has relied on a volunteer military. However, the term "volunteer" doesn't accurately describe why teens consider the option of the military. By the early 1980s, the term "poverty draft" had gained currency to indicate that the enlisted ranks of the military were made up of young people with limited economic opportunities. Patriotism and "duty to one's country" motivate some enlistees, but many young people wind up in the military for different reasons, ranging from the promise of citizenship to economic pressure to the desire to escape a dead-end situation at home. People join "more because of the money," said Lancaster, the Air Force staff sergeant.

According to a 2007 Associated Press analysis, "nearly three-fourths of [the U.S. troops] killed in Iraq came from towns where the per capita income was below the national average. More than half came from towns where the percentage of people living in poverty topped the national average."

In 1970, the Gates Commission addressed the notion of a volunteer military becoming "too black." In the years preceding the inception of an all-volunteer military, the armed forces were predominately male and white. Nowadays, a military paycheck could be particularly appealing to blacks who have poor economic prospects. The Gates Commission also stated that the military could be seen as "creaming" qualified black youths for service in the military—taking them away from jobs in the civilian community where their talents could very well come in handy.

The question remains: Just how many youths are enlisting in the present day?

The percentage of young people who said they would probably join the military increased from 9 percent to 11 percent in the first half of this year, according to a Pentagon-sponsored survey. The poll questioned 3,304 people ages 16 to 21.

"I have no job," said Andrew Walters. "I wanted to do something I was interested in. That's why I wanted to be an airman. That and the money."

As a senior at Thomas Edison High School, Walters views this as his best opportunity, even though he has an 87 grade average. "I have no other options beside this," he said. "I want something to do after I graduate. Going to college isn't for me; it just won't feel right.

"I know this is what I want," said Walters. "I can feel it."

Patrick Gilles, 17, of Cambria Heights, dreams of attending New York University's Leonard N. Stern School of Business, but because of his family's financial problems, he struggles to keep his dream alive. "I've always dreamt of going to NYU, but I have no money, especially for a school like this in the city. Damn the recession."

Gilles is now relying on the military as a solution to the financial problems, and he plans to use income or benefits from the military to pay for a college education in the future. "Through a friend was when I first took into consideration joining the Army," said Gilles. "I'm athletic, so I guess it was an alternative. $40K? That's a lot, enough to put me through a year or two maybe. And after the contract is fulfilled, the recruiter said it's guaranteed to be enough to put me through four years of college. I might finally get there [to college]."

Financial hardships drive many like Gilles to view the military's promise of money for college as their only hope for studying beyond high school.

"At least those like Gilles and Walters have some sort of plan; the others, they're not going anywhere there. This place is a dead end. I can offer them more," Lancaster said, referring to the folks who will stay at home after high school.

Whatever reason young people have for joining up, now is the time when they are making important decisions about the future, when summer is almost over and school is about to start again.

"If the Army's the only place that will give me a decent pay, then so be it," Gilles said. "It'll test my limits, anyways. Maybe I'll get lucky and finally make a change for this country that it so desperately needs."

Danielle Leavitt, 17
Karl G. Maeser Preparatory Academy
Provo, UT
Teacher: Matt Kennington

Danielle Leavitt writes to tell people's stories that would otherwise be forgotten. She grew as a writer when she visited Ukraine, and her submission to The Awards reflects the impact that journey had on her. She will study English at Brigham Young University, and would like to thank her parents for their support.

WOMEN ON GREEN STOOLS
Journalism

In the wintertime, the market at the end of Kreshatik Street smells of burning individual space heaters and warm fish. In the summertime, the bricks sweat and tiny droplets of humidity get caught in the creases of your skin. The rusty letters on the outside of the building spell "RYNOK," or bazaar, which the tourists pronounce with their differentiating versions of Ukrainian accents. The Ukrainian summer sun beats down like a soft-boiled egg. Inside the *rynok* it is hot, and the stench of exhausted body odor and 10 stands of caviar, kilka, and salmon beat out the fresh air. But inside it is cooler by a few degrees, and the pungent odor of the rynok is preferable to the choking second-hand smoke on the sidewalk.

The rynok is like a small circus. Five dozen different fruit, vegetable, meat, fish, flower, and hat stands; each run by a babushka or frail old man, but usually a babushka. There is very little talking, which makes it hard to explain the intense sound inside: 200 shuffling feet, a thousand tiny flapping plastic bags, 100 whispered Ukrainian conversations, and the occasional noisy tourist.

There is a tourist group at a meat stand. You can tell they are tourists because they hold their noses or scoff at the primitive nature of the rynok, one girl in pink flip-flops squeals at the slabs of flesh open on the table, and they make their way through the circus with digital cameras and a book on the Top 20 Things to Do in Kiev.

They speak loudly and flash pictures of the meat stand and the babushka who sits on a green stool behind the booth. The girl in pink flip-flops laughs loudly and doesn't see the woman—the woman who sells meat that hangs from a bloody string, slabs of beef and pork legs and red muscles that grow less and less shiny as the day goes on. She is slow, moving her feet in rhythm with her blinks, sitting alone on the green stool, her hands pressed against the seat, bracing her side like the end of a church pew. She shoos away the flies that parasite her only income. She does not embroider tablecloths like the other women, but she sits in silence while the tourists come in laughing or whining with loud expressions on their faces. She is old and her loud expressions are long past spent, so she only watches.

To the tourists, she does not have a face, only wrinkled brown paper-bag skin surrounding tasteless almond eyes that whirl into a thousand tears and 83 years of trying to understand God. The pictures they take will likely end up on Facebook, where someone's 897 "friends" can all clickety-click through the 43 pictures of the meat lady, her meat, and her eyes that she would have never allowed on camera. She looks down, hoping that no one's Canon PowerShot G10 catches what her eyes are whispering.

She looks down to hide that she has two ingrown toenails and a pain in her lungs. That she rides the metro 12 stops into the city every day, carrying 20 pounds of meat to sell. That she stops at every block corner to lean against a building and catch her breath. That 65 years ago she had a baby girl in the summertime in a village called Oplitsko. That after two months the baby died of diphtheria. That she used to be in love, that she never got her cavities filled, that she started her period later than all the other girls. She looks down to hide that her father hit her only once when she was 11, and that she cried.

Perhaps if I slowed down. Perhaps if I, the girl in pink flip-flops, stopped for just one moment I would see that I had missed her. That what marinated inside her old fleshy eyes was something much more intriguing than a trip to the rynok. I did not see her face. And likely I will never know that she saw my eyes when I didn't see hers, that she would have told me if I would have asked, that I left the market a sliver more incomplete because she holds a piece of me that I will never think to discover.

Too much goes unsaid.

I cannot stop thinking of the woman. She falls over and over again in my mind where she is 10,000 people whom I wish I had seen. A sea of faceless, nameless people who each hold a breath of wisdom I will never understand, people I never talked to, people I pass on the street or at school whose faces float in my memory for less time than it takes to see them at all. These are them that I will never know, the women on green stools, the ones that, if I ever see them again, I want to understand that I am sorry for not seeing their faces.

Scott Yu, 18
Montgomery Blair High School
Silver Spring, MD
Teacher: Judith Smith

Scott Yu is inspired by authors such as James Joyce, John Updike, and Jane Austen. One day, he would like to be an internationally recognized singer-songwriter. He will attend Harvard University and intends to major in government, economics, or applied mathematics.

FINISHING THE JOURNEY
Persuasive Writing

The year is 1620. Under a pallid November sky, dark cerulean waves gently lap against cold sand. Atop dunes, shrubby pines overlook the bare, weathered shore. The day moves slowly, reluctant to expose the sweet wood further inland to the bitter winds of the coming winter. At first glance, it is a typical autumn day: Small fish swim about in the chilly waters while the vegetation onshore, swaying with the breeze, seems to cheer on the courageous creatures as they brave the cool water. But today is far from typical. Beyond a low shoal appear square-rigged sails, and a ship of moderate size interrupts the horizon. As the ship approaches, a face appears, disappears, and then returns with many others. The travelers aboard the ship look like they have been at sea for too long. They are travel-worn, fatigued, and undernourished, yet even from afar, a strange excitement can be seen, a peculiar enthusiasm radiating from faces that have become accustomed to seeing nothing but ocean. But theirs is something greater, for their eyes behold not only the shoreline of a new home but a harbor for religious freedom. They are the Pilgrims who sailed from Southampton, England, pioneers of religious freedom, and the founders of our country.

Nearly four centuries later, the journey of the Pilgrims has long ended, but their torch of religious freedom still lights the path of a longer journey ahead. In today's postmodern era, scientific innovation is commonplace, democratization and globalization have spread to some of the remotest corners of the world, and freedoms and individual rights hold a solid place on the international agenda. But work still remains to be done. As a fundamental expression of autonomy and free will, international religious freedom should be a matter of consequence to every young American. Ensuring this freedom ought to be a central focus of United States policy because the U.S. government may claim legitimacy at home and abroad only if it enforces existing law, because intolerance in America's own past demands that we provide for a freer future, and because religious freedom is a central component of our country's origins and of the philosophy underlying the whole of our government.

In order for the United States government to claim rightful legitimacy for its own people as well as other countries on the global stage, it must demonstrate a respect and adherence to existing law. With the passing of the International Religious Freedom Act (IRFA) of 1998, the U.S. officially declared religious freedom as one of its overarching policy objectives. Furthermore, the U.S. has acknowledged, "The right to freedom of religion is under renewed and, in some cases, increasing assault in many countries around the world. More than one half of the world's population lives under regimes that severely restrict or prohibit the freedom of their citizens" (22 USC 6401, 1998). In addition, a recent annual report by the U.S. Commission on International Religious Freedom (USCIRF) named 13 countries, including world powers such as China, as "egregious" violators of religious freedom and recommended that these be named "countries of particular concern" (CPC) for their systematic violations of religious liberty (USCIRF *Annual Report 2009*). These alarm bells call for action by the U.S. secretary of state as well as by the president himself. In particular, CPC status requires the secretary of state to pursue "a range of specific policy options to address serious violations of religious freedom" (USCIRF *Annual Report 2009*), and the 105th Congress has declared, "The entry into force of a binding agreement for the cessation of the violations shall be a primary objective for the President in responding to a foreign government that has engaged in or tolerated particularly severe violations of religious freedom" (*Congressional Record*). For the U.S. government to disregard its own exhortations and reports would surely weaken its legitimacy; hence, international religious freedom must be maintained as a policy objective.

Not only do the United States' own legal actions mandate a policy focus on international religious freedom but international law also commands a U.S. initiative in religious freedom endeavors. Presented and coauthored by former First Lady Eleanor Roosevelt, the Universal Declaration of Human Rights (UDHR)—adopted by the United Nations in 1948—expresses adamantly and unambiguously in Article 18, "Everyone has the right to freedom of thought, conscience and religion." As one of the few countries with a permanent seat on the U.N. Security Council, the U.S. has an obligation as a global leader to guide the promotion of this declaration, so that one day its promises can truly be "universal." With partner countries on the Security Council—People's Republic of China and Russian Federation—having been labeled as countries showing marked disregard for religious freedom (USCIRF *Annual Report* 2009), that the U.S. should set a positive, proactive example is even more imperative. Indeed, the fulfillment of this duty is essential for the United States' image as a crusader for freedom and as a government determined to fulfill its own lofty promises; in a way, the U.S. is even committed to act by its status as a ratifying member of the multilateral treaty known as the International Covenant on Civil and Political Rights, or ICCPR.

Though the alphabet soup of international laws such as the UDHR, ICCPR, and IRFA is a modern phenomenon, throughout our history we have fought our own battles against intolerance. Considerable progress has been made: America has evolved from a loose association of towns populated by Christian whites to a vast land of religious diversity. Discrimination against religious minorities has decreased dramatically, and the last century has witnessed the rise of leaders of myriad faiths, including the first Roman Catholic president in 1961. Nonetheless, vestiges of intolerance still stain the progressive face of our country. A California political ad aired as recently as 2008 viciously targeted Mormons and roused public assault against Mormon establishments (Goldberg), and former president George H.W. Bush has stated in a public press conference, "No, I don't know that atheists should be considered as citizens, nor should they be considered patriots. This is one nation under God" (Dawkins 43). These incidents, among countless others, show that the U.S. has not yet erased its past of intolerance and that increased efforts are needed to secure that future of freedom so passionately envisioned by our Founding Fathers.

When the Founders established our government centuries ago, they borrowed heavily from a philosophy of natural rights by the Englishman John Locke. Locke argued for the existence of certain unalienable rights—life, liberty, and property—which all men "hath by nature a power…to preserve…against the injuries and attempts of other men." The importance of these principles to our government is evident in the Declaration of Independence, a document centered on Locke's ideas. When the Pilgrims arrived at Plymouth Colony in 1620, they brought with them that same spirit of self-determination, which surfaces today in laws such in the IRFA and the UDHR.

It is crucial that as young Americans we be familiar with the continuity of America's passion for individual liberties, since the task of finishing the journey toward international religious freedom—through community advocacy, smart voting, and individual open-mindedness—is in our hands.

Works Cited

Congressional Record. 27 Jan. 1998: 1-30. *U.S.* Department of State. Web. 27 Nov. 2009. <http://www.state.gov/documents/organization/2297.pdf>.

Dawkins, Richard. *The God Delusion..* New York: Houghton Mifflin, 2006. Google Book Search. Web. 27 Nov. 2009.

Goldberg, Jonah. "An Ugly Attack on Mormons." Editorial. T. *The Los Angeles Times,.* Web. 27 Nov. 2009.

Locke, John. *Two Treatises on Government.* London: C. Baldwin, 1824.*Center for History and News Media.* Web. 27 Nov. 2009.

Smith, John. *A Description of New England.* 1616 Ed. Paul Royster.. Lincoln: University of Nebraska–Lincoln, 2006. *Digital Commons at the University of Nebraska–Lincoln.* Web. 27 Nov. 2009. For descriptive material in introduction.

United States. Commission on International Religious Freedom. *Annual Report 2009.* Washington: n.p., 2009. Web. 27 Nov. 2009.

United States. *International Religious Freedom Act of 1998.* 22 USC Sec. 6401. n.p., n.d. Web. 27 Nov. 2009.

Lillian Selonick, 16
Evanston Township High School
Evanston, IL
Teacher: Alison Loeppert

Lillian Selonick is a native of Evanston, a suburb of Chicago. She believes that growing up near a large city fueled her appreciation for authors of the Beatnik generation. When she is not writing, she spends her time watching and studying film and knitting. She will spend next year teaching English in Korea.

No Straight Lines in Curved Space
Short Short Story

This is how it goes:

I work the graveyard shift at a 24-hour Walgreens. For eight hours every night, my universe shrinks into that 6,000-square-foot fluorescent temple. Ten minutes into the shift, the grumbling of automobiles is my only line to the world outside. Thirty minutes later, the cash register becomes the center of my existence. I don't hear the cars anymore. Time slows to a tortured crawl, and the clock becomes the bane of my existence. My life implodes into a rush of sickly faces and bloodshot eyes and "thank you, come again."

All of the customers past 2 a.m. are zombies. Once, a woman held two cartons of ice cream—one chocolate, one vanilla—in her hands until her forearms swam in cool syrup. Her green eyes, dulled by the steady monochrome fluorescents in Aisle 4, had the glassy look of the consideration of the dead. She left without buying anything. I mopped up the mess with neither resentment nor pity.

This is how it goes:

Three hours into the shift, time loses all meaning, and I lose all traces of humanity. I am C-3PO, human-cyborg relations. I am the dead, going through the motions of life. Sorry, sir, we only have plastic, and fuck you, R2-D2.

Mostly frat boys and unhappy working-class husbands come on midnight runs for cigarettes and milk and Red Bull. I don't care. I don't know. Sometimes it's something different. But all I do is ring it up, and the crash of the cash register ricochets in my skull until finally I don't think anymore. Kids in their parents' cars buy Marlboros with fake IDs—they always pay with change. Limp dollar bills and a thousand pounds of silver clatter gracelessly into the appropriate plastic tubs. There's a little dish for loose pennies. A single piece of copper has been rusting there contentedly for the past few eternities.

This is how it goes:

On the graveyard shift, autobiography becomes fluid. Some nights, my name is Sarah; some nights, my name is Carrie. My nametag reads "Lisa" and my ID says I was born in 1982, but none of that matters. My identity disappears along with time. This is the Bermuda Triangle.

A small man sits at the electronics booth. His name is Pablo, and he gets paid $5 an hour. Pablo is a thin, nervous man who constantly checks his fly. He jumps when the door chimes.

Sally is older. The late nights eat away her time between middle age and menopause. She mops the floor with harsh black hands. Pablo is fucking her. They go through the "Employees Only Please" door 30 seconds apart. They don't talk to me because I'm white.

Sometimes I wake myself from the daze and look at the clock. The numbers leave bitter déjà vu behind. The fans cycle stale air endlessly. I slip back into the blur. This nothing place is holy. Curiosity is replaced by comfort. Undertones of malaise permeate my dream state in waves, but it's better than being alive.

This is how it goes:

It was a dark and stormy night. I use cliché because my memory holds no emotion. Thunder crashed and the windows wept. The noise was enough to drown out the cash register, and the monotone ventilation was completely lost. It was a dark and stormy night, but we were lit up like some fluorescent lollipop purgatory. Sally and Pablo had disappeared into the stockroom again. Maybe it was 4:30. Slow night. I was unable to deafen myself to the storm. I heard the windows shudder in their frames. I heard my heart beat in my chest, as if it were still pumping blood to my brain. All night, I tried to get caught in my temporal slipstream. I felt like a person again, and how strange the sensation! Perhaps it was the collective unconscious preparing me for the bizarre intersection of fate. I don't believe in stuff like that.

I heard the gentle bump of tires against concrete from the parking lot. A haggard transvestite wobbled through on five-inch heels.

"Two packs of Chesterfields, darling."

Blush like scarlet fever jumped from his cheekbones. His eyes fluttered glitter onto the counter, and his lips were painted coral. He removed one of his pumps to dote on a blister, then slipped his foot back into the satin-lined puddle.

"God, it's really coming down, isn't it?" I said, stooping down for the cigarettes.

"Oh, yes, my wig aches when it rains like this."

He winked at me, and I let out a surprised bray of laughter. The graveyard shift does not invoke laughter.

"Have a nice night, ma'am," I said as the door chimed again. I still had a smile on my face when the other unusual stranger came in.

This time, I heard tires screech and a smack of the car's nose against the wall. A man in a shirt and tie ran in, cradling his hands against his chest. He sang a strangled mantra: "Oh Christ oh Christ oh Christ." When he passed by the front cash register, I saw that there was blood on his hands and splashed across his shirt and pinstripe pants. I let out a kind of choked gasp and sat heavily back onto the stool behind the counter. I kept wide eyes on this rain-battered man as he cleared out of the liquor aisle with an armful of clinking bottles. As he came closer, I saw smeared coral lipstick on his palms and glitter swiped across his sweaty forehead. He was crying.

"All of this, all of this, all of this," he muttered. His breath already spoke of alcohol.

"Um." My mouth gaped open and shut stupidly. I noticed it had stopped raining.

The man reached for his wallet, balancing the liquor precariously with his one arm and his chin. Somewhere, blocks away, a police siren started up, then another. He screamed and the bottles crashed into a flood of broken glass and alcohol. I jumped. The terror in his eyes grew. He lives a nightmare, I thought. He lives in life. With each anguished breath he took, he shattered my listless paradigm. I shrank from him and everything he represented.

The sirens raced toward us.

"Oh Christ!" he moaned.

Pablo and Sally ventured out of the stockroom, holding hands. They looked like children.

I started to cry.

The drunken man ran out of the door, skating on broken glass. The door chimed. Pablo checked his fly.

Presently, I became deaf again. I shrank into a fluorescent spotlight, feeling the tears I had not shed drying on my cheeks.

There were no more customers that night. By dawn, everything had receded into that foggy, hallucinatory existence. At 7:30 I walked, with a clean line, into the world. The door chimed on my out.

This is how it goes.

Haley Mosher, 14
Timpanogos Academy
Lindon, UT
Teacher: Shannon Cannon

Haley Mosher was inspired to write her piece by her interest in World War II, and would like to thank her seventh-grade teacher who introduced her to the subject. Besides writing, she is interested in gymnastics. She will attend Karl G. Maeser Preparatory Academy as a ninth grader.

STANDING IN LINE
Short Short Story

It was nearing my turn.

Not just mine, but many others were about to come with me. It was against our will, but it was less painful than what would happen if we turned around and tried to run. I almost *wanted* to go into the small chamber, to be rid of all the pain and hatred against me and my people. I looked ahead of me, past the skinny, shivering bodies and to the shower. The chamber never gave us what we wanted—a nice, hot, cleansing shower—but instead gave us a thick, smelling steam. Only a few who went into the enclosed space ever came out again. And if they did, they were being hauled by soldiers to the incinerator. And they were pale. Oh, so very pale.

As I thought about what my friends were doing, back home, in Poland, I felt a sharp jab in my lower back. *Oh, no* was the first thing that came to mind, *a gun*. I slowly turned around and faced emptiness. Then I looked down. Standing there was a young boy, probably not over 8, with dirty brown hair that was crudely cut just past his ears and deep brown eyes. As I stood there, looking at the scrawny thing, he noticed me, and said quietly, innocently almost.

"I'm sorry, sir. Was I bothering you?"

This boy has a good mother, I thought.

"No, my boy, you weren't. Just watch where you put those elbows of yours, all right?" I said, smiling.

"I'm sorry, sir." He replied, "I will. Thank you."

I turned back around to face the deadly room. They were getting rid of the bodies inside, I was sure of it.

"Sir?" came the small voice from behind me. I half-twisted my body so I could see him.

"Yes?" I replied.

"Sir...I was wondering." He seemed to need to think before he spoke. "Sir, where are we going?"

"Don't you know? Didn't your mother tell you?"

"No, sir. We were standing here, in line, when a soldier came with a gun and pulled her out of line. I wanted to follow, but she pushed me back, saying to be strong, and that she loved me. I don't know what happened to her after that."

"How long ago was this?" I asked.

"I'm not sure, sir. Maybe about 15 minutes or so."

Tears sprung to my eyes. That was about the time the firing squad had left with a dozen or so people. I had no idea that one was so close to me in line, and this boy's mother. And she didn't have the heart, bless her soul, to tell him what would become of her.

"And what of your father? Was he pulled out too?"

"I've never known my father, sir," he replied. "My mother said that he left us when I was born, and I haven't seen him since."

I wiped tears out of my eyes. I wondered what had happened to him as I looked at this boy.

"Sir," he repeated, going back to his original question that I had nearly forgotten about. "Where are we going?"

"Well, where do you want to go?" I asked after a minute.

"Oh." His eyes lit up. "I want to go to the malt shop on 47th Avenue. I went there once, and I got a double fudge chocolate malt, and it was the most delicious thing I've ever tasted."

"Well," I replied, wiping my wet eyes. "That's where this leads to. You see, it sort of acts as a...a teleporter to anyplace you want to go. You can go to your malt shop and have as many ice creams as you want."

"Really?" he asked, his eyes getting bigger at every word I said. But then he suddenly thought of something, and the sparkle in his eyes dimmed.

"Sir," he said, "my family—we don't have much money..."

"Oh, don't worry about that," I replied. "It's all free. It'll just be you, your mother, and your malts."

At this, the smile returned to his lips, cracking them almost to the point of bleeding. It was obvious he hadn't smiled in a while.

"Oh," he said, relaxing a little. "I can't wait then. When do we go?"

"When they finish clea—getting it ready for us," I replied. I turned back around. Just as I got comfortable, I felt a soft tug on my rags. That's really all they were. I turned around to face another set of questions from the boy. But he had only one.

"Sir, where are you going?"

The question itself was enough to tear me apart. Tears sprung to my eyes again, but this time I almost sobbed. Trying to hide it as best as I could, I replied, "I am going back to my house in Lublin. It's always warm there, and there's my favorite foods always in the pantry. My sister will be there—she has already gone through something like this. I will go there and eat and sleep and have a merry time. That, my boy, is where I'm going."

I heard the scratching of iron against concrete. The doors to the chamber were being opened.

"That seems like a long way from here," the boy from behind me said.

"Yes," I sighed from relief. "Yes, it is."

The line inched forward, but quickly gained speed as the soldiers pushed the people in front of us in.

"It sounds like far away from my malt shop, too."

I pulled him up next to my side so I could look at him. His eyes were solemn, sad, as if in the few moments we had been together, he had adopted me as a second father, one he hoped he would always know.

"Yes," I replied, surprised at his question, and then saddened by it. "I guess it is."

"Will you visit me?"

The line was going fast now. I quickly pulled him next to me, although we could barely talk and hear each other because the chamber was nearing fullness and everyone was crying out. He seized my hand when I put mine out for his, and when he did, it was as if he were falling into a river and I was the only branch that he could hold on to. I couldn't believe how close he had come to me, both physically and in my silent heart. He had seemed to be snuggled next to me, even though he wasn't cold. Tears streamed down my face, and I let them fall to the hard, cold floor.

"Yes," I said, as we marched in. "I will."

Ryan Kirk, 17
Cab Calloway School of the Arts
Wilmington, DE
Teacher: Lisa Coburn

Ryan Kirk was inspired to write his piece by a quote about conformity by George Kennan that he heard in English class. He will attend Oberlin University, where he plans to major in microbiology. One day, he'd like to go to medical school and write about science-related topics.

CONFORMITY
Humor

I wrote this piece in AP English Language in response to an essay that asked me to argue for or against a quote from George Kennan about the likeliness of Americans to conform. I argued for this statement, but did so through a humor/satire paper.

In a purely social setting, the First Amendment is severely neglected in exchange for conformity. The freedoms granted to us by this amendment protect us as individuals, but George F. Kennan observed the tendency of Americans to conform in "Training for Statesmanship." He writes: "…we Americans place upon ourselves quite extraordinary obligations of conformity to the group in utterance and behavior…" This striking observation isn't only true among peers socially, but in political and economic settings as well.

At the LACI (Los Angeles Conformity Institute), Dr. Richard Seuss has been testing the extent to which Americans conform in a social setting. His tests involved local "cool kids" Roger Rogers and Nancy McLady starting outrageous fads in their high school to spark the conformity of their fellow students. Said Dr. Seuss, "Our researchers had Roger represent the 'orange turban and platform shoes fad' while Nancy sported the 'severed hand fad.'" Sure enough, in weeks students in schools surrounding the LACI were parading around in turbans and disco shoes with bloody stumps where their hands once were. A local wannabe, Jeff Smith, was interviewed as saying, "When I saw Nancy's handless look, I knew the fad would catch on, so I cut off both my hands!" Jeff had no regrets. Parents too have been following the ridiculous clinical fads to appear "hip and funky-fresh" to their kids. These attempts were ultimately failures.

Political conformity can determine elections, the passing of bills, and even impeachments. When Obama was elected last November, over 80 percent of Americans who voted for him said it was either "because Oprah's voting for him" or "because he seems like the cool person I always wanted to be." Only 16 percent of the population actually supported Obama for political reasons. Conformity's sinister grasp has also affected the Senate, where the passing of the economic stimulus package was many freshman senators' effort at popularity. Sen. Christopher Christopherson (D-NJ) said, "[Vice President] Biden and [President] Obama get invited to all the cool parties with pretty women, so I figured voting for the stimulus package might snag me an invite." Several other senators agree that their votes were based on Obama's popularity.

Our failing economy has only been hurt by the tendency of Americans to conform. Commercials for products like the George Foreman Pocket Grill that are endorsed by celebrities have made many Americans give in to frivolous spending. The GF Pocket Grill is a revolutionary grill that you can operate from inside your own pants pocket. Though it may seem a bad idea at first glance, Conan O'Brien said, "When I'm cooking small meat or poultry on the go, the George Foreman Pocket Grill is there for me!" His opinion, along with those of Mandy Moore and Rosie O'Donnell, has people flocking to Kitchen & Co. to buy the dangerous and unnecessary grills. The grills have a tendency to cause second-degree burns when left on, and have set pants on fire on many occasions, yet their popularity is immense. At a price of $999.99, the grill can take a chunk out of your savings, and the purchase has bankrupted many, but they continue to fly off the shelves as Americans try to be like celebrities.

Kennan's ancient (1953) observation that Americans are extremely likely to conform is upheld by clinical and statistical evidence. He predicted that the likeliness of Americans to conform was increasing, and sure enough, today conformity levels are at a dangerous high. In the Land of the Free, we tend to look and act like our neighbors without anyone forcing us to. Though individuality isn't illegal, it is made nearly impossible by the masses. People continue to conform to conformity because "other conformists told me to!"

Ian Campa, 18
Coral Reef Senior High School
Miami, FL
Teacher: Eleanor Dorta

Ian Campa is excited to attend Columbia University. He would like to major in chemistry and eventually pursue a career in biomedical engineering. He believes that his writing is shaped by his Hispanic heritage and his interest in technology, spiced with a sense of humor that is inspired by The Simpsons.

OUR iFUTURE
Humor

2012: the year that mankind will be obliterated. At least that's what we're being told. History's most prominent, intelligent, and influential authorities all seem to have reached the consensus that about three years from now everything we know and love will cease to exist. The Book of Revelation, Greek oracles, astronomers, Nostradamus, the Mayans, even John Cusack are all advertising their own special brand of apocalyptic mayhem.

The scientific community will find its answer in the prediction that a planetary alignment will cause Earth's poles to shift, thereby forcing up to become down, north to become south, and every day to become opposite day. The solution: Every cartographer in the world—yes, all four of them—must start designing maps of our new upside-down world so that the tourism industry does not suffer. Christians, however, can look forward to a much warmer and brimstone-filled prophecy; their only hope for salvation is to align themselves with one of the two sides: a soldier of Christ or a devil's advocate. Adherents to the Glenn Beck school of thought believe that President Barack Obama has some sort of secret magical power that will eventually bring about the end of the world but can only be activated by passing socialist programs and universal health care; their arsenal against the apocalypse seems to be drawn-out Fox News segments and demands that their country be returned to them from some nonexistent band of nation-burglars. Hypochondriacs maintain that either bird flu or swine flu or al-Gadhafi's fish flu or some other flu in which the animal itself is unaffected, but that is the bane of human existence, will decimate the world's population and reduce the survivors to wandering, cannibalistic nomads; they can be seen stocking up on hand sanitizer, canned food, and hazmat suits for their Cold War-era underground shelters. Of course, among all the confusion and terrifying theories, Hollywood is there to guide us like a crooked lighthouse shining its light in the wrong direction during a torrential night at sea. Hollywood's extensive budget and special-effects technology make its doomsday hypotheses especially convincing; its method of survival somehow involves convoluted plots and hundreds of millions of dollars from disgruntled moviegoers.

Regardless of which theory is correct, it is apparent that 12/21/12, which looks more like an arbitrary date selected by a lottery machine than a seriously concerning portent of disaster, will be devastating for anyone still alive during that time. But what if there was another theory, one in which doomsday is avoidable and the future is perhaps even hopeful? Fortunately for the human race, my doomsday auguring is just that. It involves a company that started out small and laughable but has grown into an electronics industry giant and developed a cult-like following. I am, of course, referring to Apple Inc. Its iconic lowercase "i" prefix is found in all aspects of life from the iPod to the iPhone to the controversial iUrinal, so it is only a matter of time before Apple takes over the world. Skeptics will say, "That's impossible. Anyone that lets me listen to my hundreds of Britney Spears songs anywhere I go could not possibly be evil. Steve Jobs loves us." Be that as it may, Steve Jobs no longer has control over his own destiny. He is the Dr. Frankenstein of our era, and his monster has already been unleashed upon our unsuspecting planet—except this grotesque crime against nature is not a reanimated corpse or sentient robot army. No, it is something much worse. Steve Jobs' monster is the "app."

Granted, it is difficult to comprehend how such seemingly harmless, albeit occasionally useful, programs could lead to the complete downfall of the species that put a man on the moon, invented existentialism, and created the McGriddle. However, that is a naive and superficial observation. To truly know and analyze apps is to recognize their destructive and dangerous nature. Although spawned only a few years ago, apps have taken the world by storm. Everyone has come across an app at one point or another in their life. No matter the location, from the crowded streets of New York to the remote heights of the Tibetan countryside, it is guaranteed that someone will be using one of these little seeds of evil. About $200 million worth of apps are sold from the iTunes store each month. If the government released its own app instead of sending billions of dollars to failing corporations, the economy could have recovered by now. Apps, such as a government Magic 8-Ball in which the only answer is "another government bailout" or a quail-hunting game featuring Dick Cheney and his friend/victim, could have generated enough revenue to end the global recession. It is their ever-outstretching reach and continuous permeation into the lives of all inhabitants of Earth that give apps their truly destructive power.

Most iPod and iPhone apps appear to improve our quality of life, make tasks easier, or sometimes just entertain us when we are bored, but beneath this guise lies an inherent, perhaps even accidental, evil: Every app slowly gnaws away at our evolutionary adaptations. Speaking in strictly Darwinian terms, apps, one by one, replace the genetic traits that have enabled us to survive and thrive. Something as simple as the flashlight app—in essence a blank white screen, yet a favorite among users—reduces what little remnants of night vision humans have left to nothing, completely crippling mankind in the dark. The GPS app, a default feature on all iPhone models, eliminates any natural sense of direction people have to the point that some of them can't even navigate to their kitchen from their bedroom without the use of technology. Consider this: Every mating season, across vast expanses of ocean, green sea turtles can instinctively find the same beach where they themselves hatched— and they don't use iPhones. The correlation is undeniable. Apps even reach across age barriers with old favorites like Pac-Man, Tetris, and Sonic the Hedgehog. Sure, they appear to be nostalgic walks down memory lane, but with the reemergence of these video games comes the reemergence of such epidemics as Nintendinitis and Pac-Man Fever. In the '80s and '90s, these conditions afflicted thousands of gamers, and now they have become available as mobile applications for cell phones. Now that players no longer need to take breaks, the numbers of victims can only be expected to increase. Books available electronically will evolve into books that read themselves to us, and texting, as it continues to be more and more popular, will overtake speech as the main medium of communication. Apps will simultaneously bring about the end of the written and the spoken word. Thus, mankind—once rife with great achievements and even greater aspirations—will be reduced to a society of mindless Facebook-checking, perpetually Twittering automatons.

Luckily, as I mentioned before, there is hope. The salvation from imminent destruction I propose is best summarized as "keep your friends close and your enemies closer." Apps do serve as useful assistants in everyday life. In fact, I suggest that everyone become familiar with apps. Only through education about the hidden potential of apps can we hope to avoid collapsing as a society. We must become the sentinels watching the apps and the vanguards of our future. Steve Jobs, with his hypnotic hand gestures and mesmerizing black turtlenecks, must never be allowed to become too powerful. Thankfully, Bill Gates and Microsoft Corp. are keeping Apple at bay. Until that fateful day in 2012, no prophet can possibly know for sure what will happen. But as we wait, some in crippling fright, others in strange anticipation, we must remember that apps can never replace the indomitable human spirit.

Michael Connors, 16
Xavier High School
New York, NY
Teacher: Mary Grace Gannon

*Michael Connors lives in New York City. He looks to such authors as Umberto
Eco and Shakespeare for inspiration, and thanks his parents for encouraging
him to write. In addition to writing, he is involved in a military program at his
school, scouting, and his church.*

TERROR OF THE KARNATAKA
Short Story

Over the years of my charmed life, I have become very
well versed in the hunting of man-eaters, a label with which my
contemporary journalists and pseudoscientists like to brand any
predator of decent size. Personally, I consider it a misnomer; for
one, oftentimes they are not actually interested in eating a man, but
killing him for the sake of maintaining a firm control over their
territory. And secondly, on a more personal level, might I interject
that although I have come into contact with many of these dangerous
creatures, I haven't been eaten yet. Not that I haven't had my close
calls. From a vicious pack of hyenas I encountered on the Serengeti
plain to a massive grizzly bear with whom I acquainted myself
during a trip to the United States of America, there have been
numerous beasts that have come dreadfully near to forcefully
enacting my transformation from predator to prey. However, no experience I underwent was so terrifying—and no foe was so monstrous
as the creature involved—as in the tale of what I encountered while
investigating disappearances on the Karnataka river in India.

First, a bit of background so that you might have a picture of
the man I was during that season of my life. I was still young when
I came to India, and in peak physical condition. I was naive, and
searching vehemently for a new, worthy quarry. My first big-game
hunting experience had taken place not more than a few weeks
before, in which I had taken down a rampaging male lion while on

safari in South Africa. At that time I felt possessed by an intense bloodlust, a desire to satisfy the hunger still driving me to pit myself against the most fearsome adversaries nature could produce. I'm not sure whence exactly the drive originated; perhaps it was simply the natural reaction for a boy raised in a tediously bland middle-class London household...especially when he was being fed wild stories of conquest, adventure, and exploration in Her Majesty's colonies throughout his upbringing. But I digress; after all, the motivators of my psyche are not the subject of this account.

The purpose of my visit to India was by no means ambiguous. Whereas when I arrived in Africa I was entirely inexperienced and had no tangible goal but to (if I may utilize a cliché) put the first notch in my gun, this time I had a certain direction. On my return to England from the Dark Continent, I came across a brief article by one of our journalists operating out of Calcutta. Apparently, there were several dozen reported incidents of men disappearing along a certain river known as the Karnataka (alternately referred to by the name Kali, for the Hindu goddess of destruction). The story intrigued me; the clues reeked of the involvement of some monstrous creature. There was nothing that could possibly appeal to the appetite of an aggressive upstart as I was at the time more than the opportunity to solve this mystery and claim the culprit as my own trophy. In next to no time, I had arranged my passage. The game was on.

When I arrived in Bombay, I made it my business to ascertain the location of this river, the Karnataka. That was not difficult. Now, I needed to hire a team of men to handle my equipment and a translator to help me handle the team of men. I feared such complications would hold me up for at least a day or so, but to my delight, the ripe supply of unemployed labor presented me with a full entourage less than an hour and a half after I had made my inquiries. As a matter of fact, due to my determination (or one might call it impatience), we had left for the Karnataka on the backs of elephants less than three hours after I had set foot on Indian ground. My only real difficulty involved pronouncing my translator's name. After roughly eighteen tries at it, I decided to simply refer to him as Thomas for communication purposes. This was partially because of the saint's relation to the evangelization of India, and partly because of the fact that my doubtful guide had no faith in my monster theory, dismissing any accounts that might provide evidence in my support as either primitive rural superstitions or the hyperbole of foreigners. I had faith that his assumptions were ungrounded, and soon, little did we know but that faith was going to be vindicated.

The trek to the region surrounding the Karnataka was less tedious than I would have imagined. Yes, it was a lengthy venture, but I found the natural and cultural distractions en route to be more than enough to pass the time. I spent my days watching the landscape and people of India with a reverent awe, taking in the many colors and customs that make the land so very different from England, or anywhere else I'd been for that matter. My nights were spent in a similarly entertaining fashion, quietly and hopefully waiting for some predator to emerge from the forest, that I might bag the beast before it got to me and claim a supplementary kill while on my journey. To my dismay, however, nothing of the sort took place. I blamed the damned elephants; I know that if I were a predator I wouldn't go anywhere near a convoy of the great lummoxes.

And such was the way we arrived at Karnataka. I was taken in quickly by the gorgeous landscape. It was truly incredible, and in a different way from much of the rest of this particular colony. Whereas much of India was wet and fairly swampy, the higher altitude here provided a somewhat drier climate. The river was rocky and clean, alternating between tumultuous stretches of whitewater rapids and placid, serene sections of smooth flow. The surrounding forest was quite able to match the Karnataka for its calm beauty, and the people and their homes were quiet and agrarian. It would have been the idyllic place to live, were it not in India, and not the site of frequent animal-attributed deaths.

I must admit, I rather enjoyed the pomp and circumstance to which we were treated by the villagers, who regarded me as a celebrity despite my general lack of any kind of true recognition at that point in my career. Immediately I set out, gathering clues about what was going on in this remote sector of the subcontinent. The stories were puzzling; according to witnesses, they usually involved the victim being pulled underwater abruptly, snatched down to the depths without even a chance to scream, as onlookers watched in horror.

No descriptions of what was responsible could be found.

As if the mystery wasn't curious enough, several of my primary suspects from prior reflection were ruled out from the start. The aquatic nature of the incidents made the thought of it being a Siberian tiger impossible (not that I ever seriously considered the prospect of a member of their species being called a river monster). Crocodiles were proven innocent of the deeds as well, due to the fact that they were not indigenous to the region. This deeply disturbed me, as they had been my favored scapegoats. Nonetheless, I would not allow presumptions to prevent me from conducting an accurate investigation, and checked them off on my lists (I must admit, however, that the thought of a rogue croc in this higher terrain, feeding off humans, still loomed in the back of my mind).

My inquiries began to grow painfully fruitless as time went on. By the time one week had elapsed, I'd learned virtually nothing. I had finally had enough when one of the elders, claiming to know the identity of the perpetrator of these killings, led me on for hours before finally telling me it was a water pig (this of course earned me a triumphant "I told you so" grin from Doubting Thomas). I made the decision to shift focus, and rather than try to learn what the beast was, I was now going to very simply lure it out and kill it.

What intense joy it brought me to finally be on the hunt again. Reinvigorated by the prospect of drawing out and trapping this abominable killer, I swiftly made plans for it to be baited. In a decision that many humanitarians have in retrospect deemed unsavory (to hell with them, anyway—I am not one to be put down and patronized by a bunch of frauds who cast moral judgments on others while leading lives more licentious than my own), I ordered my aides to string themselves out along the section of the river in which the most incidents had been reported, a series of calm pools located between two sets of rapids. The idea was that the scent of human flesh in the water would tempt our elusive opponent to move in, and sure enough, it did.

As Thomas and I waited in an observation post overlooking most of the area being patrolled, we heard a brief cry from one of our sentries. Delighted, I knew this meant our trap had been sprung. Charging out as fast as I could with my elephant gun slung on my shoulder and a massive harpoon gun following behind me in Thomas' diligent arms, the elation of the chase was in my blood once more. I came to the spot and ran into the water, scouring desperately for either the man who had been attacked or the creature that had done it. Neither was visible, and I began to panic—the prospect of losing a man and yet not identifying the quarry was quite distasteful. Then, in an extraordinary stroke of luck, just as Thomas arrived with my harpoon gun, the man's head and chest burst forth from the water, his arms flailing wildly as he tried to escape the vice grip of whatever lurked beneath. I seized the harpoon gun from the shocked Thomas and, aiming directly below what I could see of the man, fired.

There was no visible reaction at first. But soon, the man and his still invisible captor began moving toward me at alarming speed. It was now a last-ditch effort on the part of the creature to charge me. I tried to move back, but it was far faster than I and had advanced half the distance between us before I had gotten into a shallow-enough shelf that my torso was above the surface. As I leapt back, the thing came almost flying out of the water. Fearing that I had met my end, I closed my eyes and said a lightning-fast prayer. But when I opened them again, I was unharmed.

The creature had landed not a foot away from me, now grounded and unable to return to its environment. In that moment it occurred to me that good fortune had blessed me with a perfect shot; it had pierced straight through the jaws of the beast and the waist of the man, which was locked between them. It had seemingly performed three feats in one. To start, it had put the man mercifully out of his misery (I am sure he preferred the point of the harpoon to a slow death in those gaping jaws). Secondly, it had locked the thing's jaws shut that it would not be able to open them for an attack on me, a blessing for which I was quite grateful. Finally, it had pierced right through the thing's brain, causing it to die only a few seconds after I had fired. I was quite pleased.

But the strangest sight before me had nothing to do with the blessings bestowed upon my aim by Providence. Rather, it was the demon which I had killed in itself. It was massive, measuring up to what I would estimate to be roughly eight meters in length, with a mouth large enough to swallow a tiger whole. And interestingly, it was a fish. An immense catfish, to be specific. I started laughing despite the strenuous ordeal. What insanity! All this over a fish. I ordered the carcass to be attached to my baggage, and began the journey home. Oh, how I would relish the moment this was reported to the Queen's scientists. I would go down in the annals of history as the discoverer—and vanquisher, might I add—of a monster.

But then we were befallen by tragedy. Scavengers descended upon the aquatic carnivore's carcass like the locusts upon Egypt. I moaned in agony night after night as I watched it eaten away by the merciless, cruel horde, myself and my employees powerless to stop them from destroying the only evidence of the fruit of our toils. What a monstrosity! To come all this way and lose my prize... And yet, that is what happened.

Of course, when I came back to Bombay, I was scoffed at as a fool, even despite the testimony of those who'd accompanied me. (Much of that testimony was negative, involving something about my having no respect for human life, et cetera, et cetera. Nonetheless, it correlated, and should have validated, my claim.) But no, no one believed me. Even in Britain, among family and friends, I found difficulty finding those who would give me the benefit of the doubt. And so, I allowed my tale to die away into memory, and I advanced to other hunts in other regions of the world. None of it was the same, though. But what can one do?

My story is both outlandish and heart-wrenching, I know. If no event before has proven solidly that the truth is stranger than fiction, then this is the irrefutable evidence for that adage. I am old now, and my glory days are over. I no longer care if I am laughed at, or called mad. What I have told you is pure fact, no elaboration, no fabrication; it is the real tale of the terror of the Karnataka.

Natasha Cox, 18
New Orleans Center for Creative Arts Riverfront
New Orleans, LA
Teacher: Andy Young

Natasha Cox works to be experimental in her writing and wrote her piece for this year's Awards to examine apathy and decay through an unusual lens. She dabbles in a wide variety of art forms, regardless of her skill level, and is currently trying to learn how to play the guitar. She will attend Florida State University and intends to major in creative writing.

RENOVATIO
Short Story

The boat rolled on the conveyor belt through the three-foot-deep channel of clear water. It came to a soft, slow stop. Those on board stood and stretched, gathered their belongings, and stepped off the boat onto the tile floor. One remained in his seat on the far left of the first bench—an old man, his bald head tilted back, lips parted. The operator pressed the button on the console to open the gates, and three people sat next to the man. The rows behind filled and the operator pressed a second button.

The boat surged through the water, left an elegant ripple in its wake, and disappeared behind the wall. The narration, *Aloe vera, medicinal plant of North Africa that...*, echoed into the waiting room, the monotonous mechanical drone that subsided like a fog in the operator's ear. The small collection of people stood in silence in that bleached, square room and passed before the operator through the maze of metal guardrails. A blur of faces, they stood mesmerized by the whitewashed walls and thin lines of black grout, little streets that ran between the white tiles. The operator leaned his chair onto its back legs, kicked his feet up onto the operation console, and inspected his nails.

Again and again the old man rode through the greenhouse, around the channel: *Aloe vera, medicinal plant of North Africa that...*, *Aloe vera, medicinal plant of North Africa that...* New people slid in and out of the bench and the man went with tilted head and pearled eyes, disturbed only by the stray elbow of another passenger knocked into his ribs. He shifted and his chin fell meagerly onto his white button-up shirt. Wispy gray hairs on the sides of his head stirred in the gentle push of the air vent.

The line of people disintegrated as the sky darkened, and by the end of the workday just the old man remained on the boat. The operator massaged his eyes with the backs of his hands and combed his fingers through his scraggly hair, long and burnt red, the same as the Braille on his cheeks and chin. His eyes dwelt momentarily on the still figure of the man. He pressed the button on the console and the boat moved off, its formless shadow stretched long across the wall as it turned into the channel once more for the evening. *Aloe vera, medicinal plant of North Africa that...*

The operator flipped the switch of the fluorescent lights, and they dimmed and died one after the other as if a plague gently fell upon the cylindrical bulbs. He hunched in the dark and closed the shades of the front windows and at the main power box, turned off the lights and sprinklers and automated narration in the greenhouse. He waited, rubbed the sole of his shoe on the tile, swatted at his face when he mistook a loose piece of hair for an insect.

The boat returned and the operator turned off the power to the conveyor belt. It halted and the old man jerked, his body tipped forward so his back was at a slant and his head hung over his knees, his stature straight and strained, like pulled tendons.

The operator sighed and stepped onto the vessel. He hesitated above the man for a moment, leaned down so his face was level with the man's face—that face, purple and waxy, eyes sunken into the fragile skull, and motionless, cheeks that sagged with the gravity and the stench of stale air and feces. The operator poked the hard, thin shoulder and shook his head, quickly pushed the old man's chest up so that he leaned back on the bench erect, and rushed out.

The operator dreamed about the old man. He dreamed that a solid, prickly pumpkin vine grew across the man's lap, its coarse hairs weaving themselves into his black, pressed pants. Leaves like elephant ears rested on his shoulder, shaded his eyes from the sun.

Young, sweet green tendrils spiraled out to lock the vine in place, tendrils that wrapped around his wrists and arms, bound his legs, and crawled like ravenous kudzu up his chest and over his face. They reached into his ears and nostrils, crept between his lips, and the purple-gray color of his uncovered skin took on a soft green blush as the vine hardened and the tendrils enveloped him like a mummy. The pumpkin grew in his lap, beneath the shade of the waving leaves. Gold and orange, the color of harvest, the pumpkin inflated, filled itself with its thick, meaty interior, and pulp, and seeds. It grew round and fat, grew bigger than the old man's lap and then bigger than the old man until his bones crunched and his flesh gushed beneath the weight. The pumpkin grew larger and larger, shattered the benches, and invaded the entire boat. It pushed against the plastic canopy overhead, and the four metal support beams bent out before the mast. With a crack the canopy too shattered, and what was left of the boat commenced its journey into the greenhouse.

In the morning the operator entered, walked into the air, and wrinkled his nose. Foul, the old man's piss and shit and slowly rotting meat, left to swelter in the heat of the night. The operator switched on the lights and turned on the air conditioner, adjusted the thermostat. He opened the blinds on the windows and let the rays of morning sun stretch across the sterile tile floor. The room was clinical, the white walls like lab coats, and the metal railing like needles. The pale flesh of the old man contributed a hint of color, but his white shirt and black pants faded again into the colorless uniformity of a grayscale image.

The operator cracked his knuckles. The sound of his steps evaporated into the vacuum of silence as he approached the boat, slow and calm. The man seemed serene, relieved with the final release of his bowels; he was content. The operator knew he was content, as he felt the same and both had enjoyed a decent night of sleep. By the boat, the weight of the stench filled his nostrils, the air heavy with the smell of dried urine. The urine and crinkled skin of that old face reminded the operator of a rhinoceros—a rhinoceros, with saggy, baggy, bluish-gray skin, and even the old man had taken on a bluish tinge.

The operator took a step back, and another, stepped back to the utility closet behind his console. He propped the door open with the back of his chair—a black hole in the expanse of white. He pulled the gray-green water hose from the blackness and dragged it across the floor, dropped its mouth into the boat. He turned the spigot, and water flowed over the man's black patent shoes.

The operator drenched the old man, hosed him down, and the sparse white hairs on the sides of his head clung to his ears. His white shirt grew heavy and clear, transparent, and the faded muscles and skin shone through the fabric. Folds of fragile skin on his chest and navel adhered to the thin shirt, and the white was replaced by the gray, bloodless torso. The water rolled down the old man's face and chest and arms and saturated his pants. It soaked his lap and seeped out again from the bottom of his thighs, now a brown river that poured off the bench and swirled on the floor by the leather shoes. A centimeter of water drifted on the surface of the boat floor, tainted, dirty.

The operator coiled the hose and stored it, closed the closet door. He dragged his chair into place, its wooden feet scratched along the floor. He sat, slouched, stretched his arms above his head, and yawned. He closed his eyes, rested his forehead on the edge of the console.

He heard his slow breath. He heard the faint rattle of the air conditioner. He heard the groan of cars as they drove by outside. He heard the drip of water fall from the tip of the old man's nose onto his lap. Behind the red tint of his eyelids, he saw the water, ovular, undulate, ripple against the push of the air. He saw it splatter on the black cloth.

He heard the door push open. Footsteps on the tile floor. He lifted his head, a trench imprinted in his skin by the metal edge. He pressed the button to open the gates. Heard the splashes, feet in the water that coated the boat's floor. He pressed the second button, sent them away, and replaced his head on the console.

At the end of the third day the operator turned off the fluorescents overhead, and again the bulbs were taken when he heard a soft tap on the door. A girl, silhouetted by the glow of the moon, her figure slim and curved at the hips, purple and glossy in the night, like an eggplant. Her breath painted a thin film over the glass; she tapped again and spread her fingers, flattened her hand on the pane. The operator unlocked the door, cracked it open, and the girl slipped in. She smiled, sweet, brief, unfamiliar, blond hair tucked behind her ears, eyes cast to the floor. She stepped around the operator, danced through the maze of rails, and seated herself on the last bench of the boat. Waited. He stared at her and she stared at his legs, his feet, the tile beneath his shoes. The operator relocked the door and turned to her. She patted the seat, motioned for him to join her.

He approached the boat and the girl looked up at him. He noticed her eyes were blue. His own eyes were in no way interesting, brown, and he found that her blue irises were alive and spirited. He pushed the button on the operation console and hopped onto the boat as it glided slowly forward, ducked his head under the canopy. He sat and the boat moved behind the darkness of the first turn. In the black he could feel the girl's warmth, the warmth of her thigh against his and the warmth of her shoulder against his. She laced her fingers between his fingers and he felt a white heat in his lower stomach. *Aloe vera, medicinal plant of North Africa that is most commonly used to treat and soothe burns and scratches. It is an ingredient in many pain-soothing lotions.*

The boat rounded the turn and emerged into a shower of electric light. The moon, full and round, glared down at the jungle through the high glass ceiling, sickly and faded, masked by the tropical heat lamps. A lush thicket of banana plants lined the channel, and green leaves brushed the boat's canopy as it coasted past, stalks tall and lanky, roots spread out in the dense soil; water sloshed between the side of the boat and the cement track. The mist of the sprinklers landed on the operator's face and he closed his eyes to the beads of moisture that gathered on all of the green. The girl moved her hand to his leg and he felt himself grow under her grasp.

She stopped and pointed to the hunched figure of the old man in the first row. He appeared frailer from behind, his neck too weak to support his head, his scalp echoed soft indentations like the skull of a newborn. But his body was swollen, round, and a blue-green pallor spread under his skin. The operator shook his head, took the girl's chin in his hand, and forced her face to his. He pulled her onto his lap and she fumbled with her buttons.

The old man's glassy eyes reflected the trees and leaves and flowers as they drifted before him and disappeared on either side. The deep, dull monotone of the narrator whispered from the speakers hidden in the bushes, called the genus and species of each crop that suffocated the little channel, pushed on all sides and hung over the water like leafy curtains. *Hylocereus undatus, fruit of the cactus species of the genus Hylocereus, a night-blooming cactus. Typically referred to as* pitaya *or* dragonfruit, *native to Central and South America.* The cactus hid, needles buried behind the palms and ferns, its fruits round and pink, sour and succulent. *Vanilla planifolia, flowering orchid of Mexico most commonly used to produce vanilla flavoring. The name vanilla arose from the Spanish word "vaina" (meaning sheath), derived from the Latin word "vagina."* The cream white orchids engulfed the boat in a familiar vanilla perfume that lingered on the old man's eyelashes. *Hevea brasiliensis, grown in the Amazon, widely known as the rubber tree, largely used in the harvest of its sap, known as latex. This sap extract is the primary resource in the production of rubber.* Trees whose assemblage of tiny leaves cast dappled shadows over the water and the black and brown earth. All around, flowers of deep, luxurious colors dangled from branches and overburdened stems—amber and sapphire and ruby all embedded in the sea of emerald. The old man was numb to the heavy, humid air.

The operator spilled his semen on the boat's floor and the girl collapsed on the bench, panting at his side. Sweat dripped down their foreheads and their cheeks were flushed. The operator zipped his pants and the girl slid to the far end of the bench, leaned her head back, and closed her eyes.

The girl left without a word, left the operator alone in the boat with the old man. She jumped to the tile as the boat drifted into place, hurdled over the rails, and threw herself into the glass door. The glass shattered, shards showered to the ground like rain on a tin roof, and the girl sprinted into the night. The fire sprinklers exploded and the alarm *whooped* in a steady rhythm, settled like a heart throb behind the operator's eyes as water trickled down his face. His blank gaze followed her figure until she disappeared from his sight. Water covered his arms, soaked his hair and clothes. He stood and blinked as droplets dripped from his bangs into his eyes. His shirt hung heavy, wet rags on his shoulders. His hair, stringy, whipped around his neck.

The operator moved to the front of the boat, his shoes sloshed through the water gathered on the floor, his toes wet and cold in his socks. He sat on the first bench and felt the stiff presence of the old man at his side. Their icy, drenched thighs pressed together. The operator shivered as a chill traveled up his spine. He leaned over, stretched his fingertips to reach the console, and pressed the button. The boat jerked forward. Water tapped on the canopy.

The operator turned his head to the man, his decayed skin hardly attached to the flesh and seemed to crumble away like sand. Blisters had risen on his neck and arms. Putrid. His abdomen was grotesquely bloated, a balloon filled to bursting with distilled blood and cooking grease. And the smell, like spoiled, molded beef and melted fat. The operator leaned over the edge and vomited into the water.

Aloe vera, medicinal plant of North Africa... The moon still glowed full through the glass ceiling, outshone by the electric plant lights that scorched the operator's pupils. He squinted and glanced over at the old man. The man had not yet moved. The muscles in his face had lost their elasticity and the old jaw hung agape. His eyes always stared ahead.

The smell ached inside of the operator's nostrils, and abhorrence swelled inside his chest. That old man who too sweetly sat there and too sweetly rode the boat over and over, calm and peaceful and content as if nothing ever happened. Nothing ever did happen, nothing except *Theobroma cacao* and, soon after, *Rubiaceae coffea*. The operator leapt to his feet and jarred his head against the canopy above. But then his hands were about the old man's neck and he shook. He shook. He shook. The old man did not look away from him, eyes arctic and vacant. The operator released the man and let out a stifled sob. He wiped his hands on his jeans and pressed his wrists to his forehead, shifted his weight. The old man did not look away.

The operator scowled, straightened his face, and pushed against the man's shoulder, shoved him to the side of the boat. The man tumbled over the edge and landed with a soft thud on the dirt, a burst of air expelled from his distended stomach. His arms stretched out over the ground and his hands fell between large orange pumpkins as the boat slipped away through the water. The operator did not look back.

The sprinkler splattered the old man's face. Water landed in his open eyes, in his open, toothy mouth. It fell into his nostrils. *Cucurbita moschata, the gourd-like squash originated in South America. Presently the United States produces over 1.5 billion pounds of pumpkins each year. A very sturdy plant; if damaged, its leaves and vines can quickly regrow and adapt to its environment.*

In time the sprinkler shut off and the alarm ceased its wail. But the operator had not had the time to turn off the lights in the greenhouse sooner than the sun managed to peek through the glass into the old man's lazy eyes. Before long the boat returned, stole past the old man, half-full of people. *Presently the United States produces over 1.5 billion pounds of pumpkins each year. A very sturdy plant; if damaged, its leaves and vines can quickly regrow and adapt to its environment.* A vein-thin vine crept over the old man's cheek. Its tiny hairs anchored themselves into his skin. And the boat moved on.

Benjamin Kline, 17
Pittsburgh CAPA 6 – 12
Pittsburgh, PA
Teacher: Mara Cregan

Benjamin Kline will be a freshman at Yale University. His classmates and teachers in high school helped him develop the tools he needed to begin writing seriously. His hobbies include languages, linguistics, and music, and he would like to work as a translator in the Middle East or Latin America.

LAST CHANCES
Short Story

Sometimes I believe that there are two men living inside of me.

There is the one that you see here, the balding, portly gentleman in front of you. He is colorblind and wears unstylish glasses, and when he smiles you can see teeth made out of gold and silver. His name is Stan Jordan and he lives on a farm in Ohio, alone ever since his wife died four years ago. A poor guy, you might say. If you are ever on the state road 26 miles outside Canton early in the morning, you might see him trudging across his fields from the small farmhouse to the barn, walking slowly with a limp or simply the feebleness of old age. He stares out across the neat lines of corn, and to anyone passing the Jordan farm he looks satisfied, dignified, and content with the life he has lived. You can imagine him sitting back by the fire on a cold winter evening and telling his grandchildren what's really important in this world. That is Stan Jordan.

There are some problems with this summary, however. One, I have no children, and thus no grandchildren. Dorothy waited until several months after we were married to tell me she could never have children. She was weeping, trembling.

"I'll leave right away," she said. "My bags are already packed."

But no, I held her and told her it was all right, and we stayed on for many decades more. I appeared to be sad about it, of course, but secretly I was very happy, so glad that I would have thanked God had I not lost my faith years before. I did not want children, you see.

I was not worthy of them.

With Dorothy gone, I have no family to speak of. At Christmas and other holidays I go to Akron to spend time with her family. I am surprised that no one has asked me about my own family, but I suppose that was Dorothy's doing. When she told them she had gotten engaged, she probably whispered to them something about her fiancé being an orphan, and they never mentioned it again. Well, it is true now: I am an orphan. My parents are probably dead; if not, they would be a hundred years old, which is too old, in my opinion. If everyone lived that long, nothing would ever be forgotten, and we would all lose the bliss of our ignorance.

I met Dorothy in Dayton, where I had gotten a job teaching in the foreign languages department at the university there and she was working as a secretary. I told her that I had grown up in an orphanage in Indiana and learned German from one of the teachers there. That was the first of my lies. It makes me feel so shameful calling these details lies. Every day, I would tell Dorothy some anecdote from my invented past. Part of me wanted to write down everything I told her so as not to contradict myself, but I knew that her love for me was so strong that she would blind herself rather than see my true face. Besides, over time I turned into Stan Jordan. I do not believe there is anything false about me.

Yesterday morning, after I had gone to milk the cows still left in the barn, a man was waiting for me, dressed in a brown uniform. He was holding a large envelope, something that must have been air-mailed overnight.

"Can I help you?" I asked as I approached, conscious of my dirty boots and milk-stained clothing.

"Are you…" the man looked down at the envelope, squinting at it. "…Stanislaw Jzerawski?"

I stared at him.

"Do I have the wrong address?" he asked after a minute. The autumn wind was blowing strongly through the fields.

"No," I said, gesturing for him to hand me the envelope. He did, and I signed the paper he gave me. "Have a good day."

I looked at the envelope once and knew that I would not have to open it. I knew what it meant. The return address was from the

Simon Wiesenthal Center in Los Angeles. I had heard the name before. Dorothy showed me a newspaper clipping once that said that Aribert Heim, a doctor who performed experiments on concentration camp prisoners during the war, had been captured in Spain by operatives from this center. He had been presumed dead for 13 years.

"I'm glad they're catching these monsters while they're still alive," Dorothy said. "Someone should make them pay before God does."

The name of the Simon Wiesenthal Center's Nazi-catching project was "Operation Last Chance."

And here is what I mean when I say that there are two people inside of me. I have concealed one half inside of myself for so many years, and this has served me well. Dorothy would not have married Stanislaw Jzerawski. The neighbors would not say they "never would have thought" that Stanislaw Jzerawski had been capable of such things, which is what they will likely say about Stan Jordan once I leave this place. But I feel that it is unhealthy to repress oneself, especially when there are those who know the truth anyway. I am still only half a person.

The picture to be released in the press is likely the one you will identify with Stanislaw Jzerawski. It was taken when he was a teenager at the Gymnasium in Krákow. He is smiling, which some will say is an eerie foreshadowing of his sadistic nature. I do not know why he is actually smiling; maybe it is a holiday.

My family was wealthy enough to send me to the Gymnasium in Krákow, even though we were originally from the countryside. My ancestors had been petty landowners, which is how I got my background in farming, but ever since Poland's independence, this lifestyle was largely seen as old-fashioned, and I was sent to the city to be educated.

I am not a stupid man, not ignorant like many of the people around here. In Krákow, I learned German, French, Latin, literature, physics, geometry, and botany. I even studied English with a young teacher, a Polish-American man who had gone back to his parents' country. This is how I perfected my accent enough to pass as a man from Indiana named Stan Jordan.

I cannot say what I wanted to be when I grew up, just as very few people of that age could answer such a question. And just like so many, I never got to decide. I want to make clear that my intention is not to play the victim; I know the gravity of what I have done, and nothing can make up for that.

When Germany invaded Poland in 1939, I was conscripted into the army and sent to the front. I had only had one training session, and I barely knew how to hold a rifle. I remember hiding in the woods as I watched the Polish army cavalry charge against German machine gun nests. I and many of the boys my age did what seemed logical at that point: We ran away.

But the country was under occupation, and we had nowhere to go. We could not go back home without running into either the German army, who would kill us because we were Poles, or what was left of the Polish army, who would kill us for deserting. We ended up in Warsaw, which was under siege.

I won't talk about what life was like during those first two years, because that does not matter.

The truth is that when the city was taken, I was found by the Germans and sent away. I will not tell you the name of this place, because you surely already know it. I was a prisoner, along with thousands of other Poles. Yes, there were Jews there, and gypsies, and communists, and homosexuals. It would be a lie to say I suffered as much as they did, but it would also be a lie to say that it was not hell. And I am through with lies.

One day, at roll call, I was pulled out of the line by one of the officers. I was sure I would be killed on the spot, and the man ordered me to come with him. I did, but as soon as we were out of sight of the rest of the prisoners, he embraced me.

"Stanislaw!" he cried. "Stanislaw Jzerawski!"

He was a man I had known at the Gymnasium in Krákow. I will not say his name, not to protect him but because he has most assuredly already met his fate. He was an intense, dark-eyed man, and I remember that I did not like him very much in my youth, but at the time he was no less than my savior.

"How did you end up here?" he asked me.

"Wrong place, wrong time," I said.

He told me he could help me. Not get me out, but get me a job. I would still be a prisoner, but I would have hierarchy over the others and get better treatment. I could take what possessions and women I wanted.

I accepted. What could I do? If I were to go back, I don't know if I would decide otherwise. But that is the strange beauty of time. It only goes forward, and over the years I have come to accept my decision as fact.

The following are facts: For three years, I served as a guard at this camp. I held no weapon heavier than a stick and I killed no prisoner. I saw many die, though, and I did nothing to stop it. It is a fact that I never enjoyed what I did; I never took the perverse pleasure that the other guards did in guiding the innocent to their deaths. Some might say that this shows that I salvaged my humanity. But I was too much of a coward to run away. And a coward I have remained.

In 1945, word spread that the Soviets were approaching from the east and that Poland would soon be liberated. All the camp buildings were to be blown up. I will go on record that I assisted in this. I will also affirm that I helped round up the remaining prisoners for the march to Germany. We walked past fields that were so gray it made me feel that all color had drained from the world. Even blood ceased to be red, just another tint of numbness.

Everything was chaos, but little by little the prisoners, too sick to keep moving, would drop by the side of the road.

"Don't waste your bullets!" the commanders shouted to their troops, who obeyed. And death was all around, slow and toying this time.

There was one woman who wanted to stay behind with her brother, who had probably died on his feet. She was ghostly pale, emaciated like all the rest, but there was a vibrant color in her eyes, a burning green. She was beautiful.

"Move along!" I said to her.

She just sat in that ditch, holding her brother in her arms.

"You!" I screamed. "Get up!"

"My name," she said, quietly at first, "is Rosa Edelman."

"If you want to live," I said, "get the hell up!"

"My name is Rosa Edelman."

My old classmate, by now a senior officer in the camp, came running up to me.

"Jzerawski!" he shouted. "Is there a problem?"

"She won't move."

He looked her up and down, slowly. He saw her strength. He knew that she would not waste away on this road, that given the chance she would tell all.

Rosa Edelman spit on his boots. The saliva dripped down onto the dirt road.

My classmate took out his pistol and aimed it at her forehead.

"This Jewess, Jzerawski," he said, smiling at me, "is an exception to our rule."

He pulled back the hammer and aimed.

"My name is Rosa Edelman."

"Wait," I said. "Can I?"

He grinned at me and paused, gun still cocked.

"Sure, Jzerawski," he said, passing it to me. "I never thought you'd have it in you."

"My name is Rosa Edelman."

"Quiet," I said, my voice shaking.

"My name is Rosa Edelman."

"Shut up!" I screamed. The gun fired.

I will not say whether my hand moved out of nervousness or of my own will, but the shot missed. I did not shoot Rosa Edelman. I am sure of it, but I will not take credit because I am an honest man and I do not know Stanislaw Jzerawski well enough to say what his conscience did or did not tell him to do.

Still, Rosa Edelman crumpled to the ground and lay still upon her brother's body.

As I handed the gun back to my classmate, a shadow passed over us.

"Get down!" somebody yelled, as the field started to rock with explosions.

As I ran into the forest, I remember looking back at the fireballs and the human beings lit aflame.

Even there I could see no colors.

After the war I ended up in a DP camp. I had been separated from my group and they mistook me for yet another liberated prisoner, just one more refugee. The American guards liked me because I could speak English, and they would use me to communicate with the others. One GI in particular took a special liking to me; his name was Stan Jordan.

I won't go into detail of what transpired between us. All that matters is that by 1946, this man was living with his French girlfriend in her village, and I was sitting in uniform on a plane to America, armed with a passport, an honorable discharge, and a new identity.

When I first came to America after the war, I was very nervous about being found out. I had read about what happened at Nuremberg and I did not want to hang for what I had done. What young man would want to suffer for things beyond his control? But I soon learned that I had little to worry about. In America, if your skin is light and your accent is good, no one is going to ask many questions.

What I feared more than the police or the noose was that I would meet Rosa Edelman. Every time I went to the supermarket or boarded a train, I was convinced that she would be in the corner, watching me. In my imagination, her translucent fingers, thin as kindling, would point at me, her eyes reminding me what the color green looked like.

"I am Rosa Edelman!" she would say. "And you are not Stan Jordan!"

There was no reason for me to think this. I was sure that she did not die after I fired that gun, but in the following bombardment or the months of wandering afterward she could very well have perished as so many did. And if she had survived, why should she come to the United States? And if she had immigrated, why would she have come to Ohio?

I hope that Rosa Edelman is still alive. If I hadn't lost my faith years ago, I would pray to God that she be still alive. She kept me from forgetting. And in that strange way that time works, she kept Dorothy from ever knowing who I was, which would have broken her heart into so many rubies.

So when I received this envelope, I still had the sensation that it was Rosa Edelman who accused me, who remembered my name and decided all these years later to finally make it history. And whether I am guilty or not, it does not matter to me. Because if I had died a week ago, this tumor of memory would have grown in my chest and out of my grave.

I have not yet opened this envelope and read the details of the accusation. It is likely that there are errors, that someone has mistaken me for my classmate. I do not blame them; memories fail us all, and he was a monster. He did kill, and he enjoyed it.

But I do not have the strength for the fight. I have no reason to deny whatever is said against my case, because if I did not do it, then another did.

And to whoever is unlucky enough to find what I have written here, I apologize. It is unfair of me to pass on this burden of truth to a stranger, but I know no one and I am not as strong as I should be. So though he may suffer, I know that for the rest of his life, he will see colors that I have not had the fortune of enjoying.

For now, all I can do is pray that when I hang for my sins or forgetfulness, I will be in a better place. That I will see Dorothy with her loving smile and Rosa Edelman with her green eyes. And that there will be forgiveness and contentment. I would pray for these things, had I not lost my faith years ago standing in a ditch.

Abigail Savitch-Lew, 17
Bard High School Early College
New York, NY
Teacher: Rebecca Wallace-Segall

Abigail Savitch-Lew will attend Brown University, where she plans to major in literary arts. A Brooklyn native, she is inspired by the multicultural milieu in which she grew up. In the future, she would like to live in an Asian country and work in environmental journalism or education.

THE EUNUCH
Short Story

It was the last Sunday of March and Edward Wang was alone. At the top of Riverstone Hill, a wide stone tablet faced the dawn. All the way down to the marsh, smaller, duller tablets stabbed the mound, and each hour, new visitors arrived to decorate these stones with chrysanthemums, dahlias, and red paper. Wives poured wine onto the earth and read the stones' engravings with citrus voices. Children visited the one slab at the top of the hill and pretended to read the vertical script, but like their parents, they left this stranger's tablet no offerings. By sundown the visitors were gone, and a long black shadow inclined over the grass. Edward Wang was alone.

On the first Sunday of April, there swelled another tide of life, an even louder one, and smoke rose between the tablets. Firecrackers rumbled in the mud, and the odor of roasted pork blew into each curled nostril. Around midday, rain began to fall, and the well-prepared visitors trudged about with their heads down, in ponchos and green boots. Had Edward been alive to view the scene from his grave on the hilltop, he would have seen dozens of black umbrellas spring up like shiitake mushrooms to shield the tombs on the slope.

On the second Sunday of April, Dave drove his family to Riverstone Cemetery in the van that was a virtual Chinatown kitchen. In the rearview mirror, he watched the tangles of hairless, plump hands squeezing between car seats and slithering along the windows. Pork buns, bean soup, shrimp dumplings, and turnip cake were passed over heads and under seatbelts, and above the sound of slurping, he heard hasty orders for seconds:

"Chicken wonton."

"Are there grease balls?"

"I want half a wu gok, and an egg custard tart, and two shrimp dumplings. And a char siu bao. One rice-noodle thing. And an almond cookie," said Richard.

"Where does my nephew get his appetite?" laughed Dave's sister, Debra. "Not from his father." She prodded Dave's scrawny triceps.

Dave feared that when he returned home, his wife would not be pleased to discover the paper napkins that his sister was now stuffing into every crevice of the passenger door, or the apple juice stain on Richard's seat. Still, the feast had to go on. From 45 years of experience, Dave knew that his first and foremost duty was filial piety, and that nothing would satisfy his mother more than stuffing her grandchildren's faces. He was nothing like his brother Edward; Dave would never ruin a meal, never upset a table.

His niece hugged the top of her grandmother's seat, cackling, "Put wasabi on Rich's egg tart!"

The old woman laughed. "Susan, no wasabi!" She rummaged through the paper bags for Richard's selection, her square jaw set rigidly against her neck and exhibiting that well-known upturning of the lips, a kind of bracket-shaped, involuntary smile.

"Stupid girl. Why would Po Po have wasabi? Japanese people eat wasabi, and we hate the Japanese," Richard snickered.

"I like wasabi," said Susan.

"Then you're Japanese." He lazily knocked his feet against the back of the seat in front of him.

"Rich, don't kick Karen," said Dave, glancing at his other niece through the side mirror. Karen wore a faint look of disgust on her face, a look more appropriate for an older woman's visage than for a 16-year-old adolescent's. Her hair, sleek as seal flesh, was parted evenly at the middle and again at her ears to make room for the pale cord of her Walkman headphones. Dave was transfixed as he recognized the Walkman and the expression on her face. She'd sat in just the same way two years earlier, when the Wangs had piled into the minivan on the day of their father's funeral.

The day of the funeral, the fourth of June 1991, was the first time any of the Wangs, excluding Dave, had seen Edward in nearly two decades. It was apparent that something had happened to Edward. In his silence, in the listlessness of his movement, in the festering sores on his cheekbone and throat, it was so apparent that something unutterable had happened that no one dared to ask what. It was impossible not to contrast the existing Edward with the memory of his massive 20-year-old self, to look for the rash-colored, muscle-hard skin that had once wound itself about his skeleton and wonder when and where Edward had, with snakelike mysteriousness, shrugged it off.

Yet, there was that one moment in which his infamous vigor had resurfaced, as if all the energy lacking in his general behavior had unleashed itself in a single, volcanic gesture. While Dave was driving his relatives from the funeral home to Greenwood Cemetery, he heard Edward lean over to Karen and whisper, "So, do you mind your grandfather's death?" A dumb silence followed and Karen failed to respond. With sudden swiftness, Edward yanked the headphones off his niece's ears and tossed them out the window. Karen's scream sent Po Po and Debra into a panic; they begged Dave to pull over and retrieve the headphones. He found them on the street, pulverized by the minivan wheels. Karen sat clutching her ears as if to shield herself from the sound of the exterior world and her own screeches. But who would dare to reproach Edward?

Before their father's death, during the yearly drives to visit the tombs of Dave's paternal grandparents, each seat of the vehicle had been filled—and each seat had been filled the day of their father's funeral, too, for Edward had returned and assumed his father's seat. Now, as Dave drove to Riverstone Cemetery, neither their father nor Edward was present, and the seat beside Po Po was unoccupied, despite all Dave's efforts to fill it with an extraneous family member. Dave had even offered to drive a passenger in one of his younger brothers' cars, but his brothers had dismissed Dave's offers as mere effusions of Chinese politeness.

Throughout the drive, Dave turned back now and then to see if his mother had placed any of the dim sum cartons on the empty seat beside her. As if respecting a ghost that sat there, she never touched the seat. This upset Dave; he longed for nothing more than to see his mother absentmindedly place a few char siu bao in the gap. Of course, the empty seat did not bother Dave personally. He only feared to remind his mother of Edward's absence excessively, as if the fact that they were visiting Edward's grave for the Ching Ming festival was not enough of a reminder. The older his mother became, the more he feared for her emotional fragility. He'd always done the mean work to keep his parents protected, and that almost always meant protected from his older brother. When Edward died, for example, Dave had spared his mother from facing what he called in his head "the filth of the situation," by taking full responsibility over the remaining details of Edward's life. For 10 years, Dave had known about Terry but had never seen him, and he'd imagined a skinny white man with dyed black hair who loved tea and dumpster diving. Only on the day Edward had died did Dave finally shake hands with the man. White Terry was, but his handshake was firm and his voice was low in a way that embarrassed Dave.

Edward allowed nobody but this man to enter his hospital room. After Edward died, Dave negotiated with Terry, who maintained that his brother had always wanted to be cremated and spread amid the dust of some hobo's park in the East Village. By that time Terry's baritone voice had shattered into luminous, sharp pieces and his face dripped with tears as he spoke. The higher Terry's voice grew, the more confident Dave was that Terry was making up the stuff about spreading the ashes. His brother's form of burial was specified nowhere in his will. There was very little in the will. Terry's whiteness did not lend him the legal power to enforce his desires, and the Wangs ordered a coffin from Newtown Caskets, their second order within a span of four months.

It was difficult for Dave to recall that first meeting with Terry in the hospital, to remember the smell of waiting-room disinfectant and plastic flowers, while driving a van overwhelmed by the odors of Cantonese dim sum. Thanks to the liveliness of the children, there was enough dialogue in the car that he could steer the wheel and pretend not to notice the empty seat, the missing tooth. Whenever the road didn't demand his concentration, Dave tilted back his head and let his mother feed him a slug of moist tofu. It was not a very comfortable way to eat, but he was under the impression that it pleased his mother to baby him. *If my brother were in the car,* Dave thought, *he would ridicule my behavior until I could no longer call myself a man.* That Edward was what they called in the '60s a "fag" had not altered the dynamic that had existed between them as children. Edward had never ceased to be the testosterone-pumped older brother whose masculine drive ran so hard that other men were feminized before him. Before he'd fallen ill, he'd been a giant red man boasting an expandable stomach with walls tough enough to hold all the food in a refrigerator and a few beers besides. He and Terry had shared a five-bedroom triplex in the city with four other gay men, and his roommates had dubbed him "the Buddha." This nickname set him apart as something even more forbidden than themselves, an Asian "fag" with the strength and pure blubber of a sumo wrestler.

Dave remembered Edward's teeth, the way he bared them like a mobster showing off the rings of the dead, but most of all he remembered how there was something faintly Japanese about his brother's hair. When he thought of Edward, he remembered these features of his brother's youth and didn't think of him as he appeared in the last few years of his life. Dave didn't think about those last years without the feeling of being infected with something like what his brother had died from, a sort of uncontrollable weakness. Near the end, while visiting the triplex, Dave could not help but occasionally say to himself, *I love Edward, too—in a wholesome way.* Somehow he knew that even these words would have provoked his brother's contempt. Edward was the only man who could make Dave feel ashamed of himself. The more he allowed his mother to feed him morsels of pork fat and sticky rice, the more he imagined his brother's disgust.

Dave was relieved when they arrived at Riverstone Cemetery and had plenty to do to keep their hands busy. He parked alongside his younger brothers' cars, ushered and wiped the children through the Port-a-Sans, and began hauling the shovels, potted flowers, and coolers to the grave at the top of the hill. There, the six-foot-long tablet loomed over the grounds like an emperor overseeing his kingdom. Dave had proposed burying his brother at Riverstone, and his siblings had agreed to it, because—although the location required them to make two trips, one to Greenwood Cemetery to pay respects to their father and grandparents, and one to Riverstone—the Riverstone plot's locality was auspicious by the principles of feng shui. Traditionally, unmarried siblings were left flower bouquets and were not accorded the respect of a complete ceremony, but there was no sense in going all the way to Riverstone simply to leave flowers, and so, by no one's direction in particular, the Wangs had prepared to conduct a full ritual. Their visit to Edward's grave for the Ching Ming festival was so belated that there were hardly any other Chinese families in the graveyard.

Dave felt the rituals provided a certain safety, a way to commemorate the life of a person without knowing who the person was, without straining to be inventive. Po Po swept away weeds and dead pine needles from the base of the stone with her willow-leaf broom, and Dave dug holes into the earth she'd cleared. The crust of the ground was hard and took several chops with a shovel to break. Dave feared the job would be difficult and he'd reveal his impotence—it was the one place he couldn't reveal his impotence— and with vigorous effort he forced his muscles to comply; a stream of sweat from his forehead was the only evidence of his struggle. His younger brothers stood around the grave in a circle, crossing their arms and watching him with glazed eyes that concealed their gratitude. To his relief, and theirs, lest he hand the shovel to the next in line, the third and fourth sons, Dave finally cracked the surface of the ground and reached the warm, moist soil below.

Karen shook the daffodils, tulips, and chrysanthemums from their pots and Po Po snuggled them into the holes. Meanwhile, the children roamed the hill in search of branches and leaves to add to Po Po's tin pail. As city-locked children, it was their single chance that year to relish in the primal delight of constructing a bonfire. After they had added enough wood to the can, Dave distributed fake dollar money to some of the kids and red and gold joss to the others. "All you burn goes up to Uncle Edward, so he can enjoy it in the heavens," Dave said to the children, but as soon as he'd spoken he felt he'd told a lie, one that Edward would've hated. The kids accepted the prophecy and with a savage violence tore up the paper offerings and tossed slips into the pail.

Dave's first couple of matches went out among the soggy twigs. Finally, a snatch of joss began to brown, a slip of parchment with the character shao stamped in gold upon the fiber. The crowd of children yelped with excitement as the edges curled and the stationery turned to cinders. They shredded more paper and tossed their offerings into the bucket. Within minutes the flame was so high that it became frightening to drop their paper money. With arms extended, they tossed the stationery clumsily at the pail, allowing shreds to escape through the grass and down the hill. Smoke swam upward but dispersed before reaching the sky. *Hay. Bing soeng. Shao.* Happiness. Honesty. Longevity.

Dave didn't believe the ritual burning would deliver gifts to the heavens, and there was something horrible about the untruth he'd told. He put his hands around his son's shoulders and watched the boy curl his joss paper into an empty coin-wrapper tube to make the traditional boat-shaped offering. Dave felt the warmth of the fire on his cheeks and Edward's acidic breath on the back of his neck. The first time he'd told a lie about Edward, both brothers were attending college and living at home. Edward had brought a young Chinese man to dinner and introduced him as his boyfriend.

The boy was in Dave's year, a freshman, and wore his shirt collar unbuttoned as low as the nipple. During dinner, he spoke in Cantonese about Steve McQueen and sucked the wonton soup broth through his teeth, and when they were not eating, he rested his left hand on Edward's thigh. After that meal, Dave observed his parents sinking into the depths of a nightmare incomprehensible to them. His mother spoke to no one and his father only uttered blunt orders in a voice with sharp, hot inflections, a voice like a wooden beam slapping water. To save them from drowning, Dave resolved he would do everything he could to make denial possible. He built ships out of lies: *American girls say "girlfriend," American guys say "boyfriend," no meaning, it just means* pangjau—*friend—and everyone knows he likes this girl. He's always talking to her.* He believed the white lies would save Edward from embarrassment—and give his parents an excuse to skirt the unapproachable subject.

He'd never anticipated Edward's response. A week later, after their mother had asked Edward about the certain female he was rumored to have eyes on, Edward had entered Dave's room and breathed resentment onto his neck. The intensity of Edward's anger had alarmed Dave but hadn't made him understand why his brother was so determined to disgrace himself, and so Dave had continued to tell the lies. He'd told lies for 20 years until he'd invented a new Edward, a puppet Edward to show his mother and father. This "Edward" did not speak for itself but it lived the decent, employed, heterosexual life of a stereotypical fortysomething-year-old man. *I was trying to protect them*, thought Dave as he took the boat origami from his son's hands and tucked in the paper corners. The ship fell gently into the inferno.

"Dave, Dave!" said Po Po, grabbing her son's arm and pulling him toward the front of the tombstone. Dave saw that she'd filled three shallow glasses with wine and thrust two candles into the earth. "Pour the wine!" she ordered. "And light the candle." Dave folded at the knee before the grave and lit the red tapers. Droplets of wax spilled over the flowers and stained the tombstone with hot red eyes. Although his mother had left to unpack the cooler and his siblings were preoccupied with the arrangement of the feast, he moved as if under close scrutiny. Dave laughed when he saw his own hands shaking. The grave reminded him of the way Edward, as a teenager, would sit in the middle of the couch in such a dominating way that no one else felt comfortable sitting with him and watch television until inappropriate hours of the night. Yes, something about the grave was just like Edward. Dave poured the wine over the roots of the chrysanthemums, his right arm swinging back and forth over the gravestone, his white hands folded branch-like at the wrist. Folded like a boat, shipwrecked on the waves of the unapproachable question. He felt shame creeping into him. Here he was, pretending the stone simply belonged to an extraneous family member, performing rituals that had no meaning to himself or Edward, distracting himself with mechanical activity. He was lying about Edward yet again.

"Dave. Dave. *Bang ngo a*. The incense." In Dave's ear, Po Po's voice was shrill and her Cantonese like the gnawing of an animal. A moment passed before he comprehended; then he lifted himself off the ground and arranged himself to the side of a forming line of family members. He lit three incense sticks and passed them to

Po Po, who, as the current family elder, always exercised the first ceremonial bow. She held the sticks between the-fingers of her entwined hands and took three waist-deep dips. Dave watched her tight figure lower and he feared she would snap in half like straw. Yet on the third dip she lowered to exactly the same place as the first, and the expression on her face was still energized and purposeful, the way it was when she dusted a couch or cooked with her wok. Dave had feared his mother would crack, but she was completely unaffected. He wondered if he would ever see his mother cry for Edward again, cry those silent pearl tears, as she had six months before, the day they buried him. Or had those tears for his brother been as unfelt as these bows to his grave? Had they been merely the beginning of a long ritual that never ended, that, like lies, preserved in memory an Edward who'd never existed?

Po Po inserted her flaming sticks into the earth, smiling the self-satisfied smile of a ballerina curtsying upon the stage, and allowed Debra to step up and take her bows. Dave handed his sister three flaming incense sticks and stood back to watch the dance. One by one, his remaining siblings followed the motion. How much did they know about the real Edward? Everyone, Dave was sure, knew that Edward had died of AIDS, but he doubted his relatives had looked into Edward's personal matters. When Edward had moved out, at the age of 22, it had been after three years of those sharp, hot inflections, those beams slapping water. Edward had seemed determined to drop the gay liberation movement right into the family hot pot, while their parents had been equally resolute about pretending their first son would eventually conform to their ideals. The angrier Edward had grown, the more extensive had grown his mother's dinners. On any weekday night she might serve the bounty of a New Year's meal: brimming bowls of pork fat, shrimp and chestnut soups, steaming jasmine rice. One night Edward had turned over the dining room table, catapulting the china into the walls.

After growing fed up with the battle, he had moved to the Village with the plan of severing communication with the Wangs. Dave, however, had kept in contact with his brother through something like harassment, visiting Edward's apartment uninvited a few times each year. For several years, Dave had relayed false information about his brother's occupation and marital status to his parents and siblings, but after a while they'd stopped asking about Edward, as if they feared testing the bottom of Dave's rescue boat.

Finally, Dave lit his own incense sticks and approached the gravestone with hands pressed together. *And myself?* Without taking his eyes off the vertical line where Edward's name was inscribed in characters, he bent forward. *Why did I keep track of Edward? Why did I lie about him all those years?* He drew his head to his knees; wrists met stomach, and he could see the particles of dust settling around his shoes. He knew the answer to the second question. *Because once you start a lie, you have to keep it going. I was protecting my parents. Filial piety obliged me. After all, it was they who brought Edward into the world. I created an Edward they could be proud of.*

He bowed to the grave a second time, but when he looked up, the tablet, in its throne of candles and flowers, towered above him. He felt like a eunuch appearing before his master. Did Dave think the purpose of his life was to please his parents? Was he such a *kwan goek zai*—mother's boy? Dave bent to the earth a third time, but he was far from submitting. *My life is more than my filial piety. I've stood by my values. I have values. I value a decent life. How was I supposed to throw aside my values and embrace a doctrine of…pleasure?* But when Dave lifted his head, he was not sure if pleasure was the purpose of his brother's life.

The feast began while the children were still finishing their bows. Po Po carved the goose and distributed slices of angel food cake. His siblings were arguing over the quality of various Long Island diners and debating the ills of the most recent dieting fads. For the first time that morning, Dave heard passion in their voices. As Susan passed by them clutching a second puff of angel food cake, Debra caught her daughter around the waist and pulled her close. "Hey, you," she said to Susan. "Once I'm sitting in the sky up there, I better see you in Greenwood Cemetery putting flowers on our family's graves. Promise me?" All the adults watched Susan, waiting for a proper reply. Susan merely laughed as her mother's hands reached down to tickle her belly.

Greenwood Cemetery, thought Dave. He watched Susan wriggle in his sister's arms like a worm surfacing from the rot of graveyard soil. *And Riverstone Cemetery?* After Dave and his siblings were gone and buried, would the children forget to visit their Uncle Edward at Riverstone? What obligation had they to a relative they had met only once, at their grandfather's funeral, a relative with sores on his ashen neck? A man who inspired fear in their parents? What obligation had Karen to the sour skeleton man who'd thrown her headphones out the window? There was nothing to stop them from forgetting Edward; all they had to do was follow their parents' example for him to disappear. Then Dave remembered his son, Richard, and he was suddenly certain that Richard, as the oldest male of his generation, would have the power to choose the graves visited by the children. I will impress upon Rich the importance of visiting Riverstone, he said to himself, *and the sin will be absolved*. Before he realized what was happening, Dave found himself croaking out loud, "Rich will do both, and the rest of these kids better follow."

Debra turned to look at Dave, startled. "Excuse me?"

What pretentious, British-sounding words; *Excuse me* made Dave's throat hot. How long would these people crouch on the decks of their ships? He deepened his voice and whispered, "I know you resented coming here today."

"What?" Debra squinted and released Susan from her arms. Her voice as she replied was high—unnaturally high, Dave thought. "What? No, I—"

"Let's be honest with one another for once."

There was a silence. Dave had spoken loud enough to gain his siblings' attention and even cause his mother to turn her delicate neck, and an odd blend of remorse and savage pride swept through him. Dave peered from brother to brother, as if waiting to be challenged by a traitor. No one replied. His mother gripped her knife and resumed slicing the goose neck.

"Give me a goose breast," someone whispered.

"Where's the beer?"

"They have good beer at that place, too."

Debra sighed and put her hand on Dave's shoulder, as if to lead him aside for a private conversation. He brushed off her arm. "You all know it was right we chose a hilltop location for this grave," he cried at the group, his splintering voice cutting across the renewing exchanges. "You wish we buried him on the edge of the junkyard in Greenwood? And you all know it's right we perform a ceremony here, this year and every year. I don't care how far you're driving. The custom tells us our duty." Breathing heavily, he glanced again at the faces of each of his siblings, but all were looking away, some picking crumbs of angel food cake from their palms. "You all consented to the Riverstone plot. You agreed."

Again, there was silence. Could no words in the world tear off the mask of denial? Dave kneeled and began piling the plastic flowerpots into the garbage bag. He would make Richard understand, and Richard, the oldest son of his generation, would preserve the memory of Edward and answer to no one's complaints—if, of course, the second generation understood family hierarchy. Then, as suddenly as he'd found reassurance in the thought of his son's authority, he found himself rudely awakened: The respect due to the firstborn son had disappeared in the Wang family forever, had disappeared with Edward. Even if he were to tell his son to visit Riverstone Cemetery, what could he tell Richard about his uncle? Could he tell his own son what he'd never told himself?

As his eyes rested on the grave of his brother, he imagined time passing as the tombstone went untended. The earth around his brother's tablet would grow hard and bare, and the soil would never again taste red wax or spilled wine. *The emperor collapses before his kingdom, and the eunuchs bury him on the hill.* Dave saw a ship beating down the ocean. The waves grew ever more still until their gentle throb could not be heard. He lay aside the garbage bag and returned to face his siblings. They'd again made attempts to resume the empty conversation, but he interrupted them.

"My intention was for us all to be buried here."

"What?" someone said, and the group stirred.

"That was my intention." It was his final lie, the culmination of all the other lies. Never had he wished it were the truth more than now. In reality, he'd never imagined himself buried alongside Edward. He'd always imagined his brother alone, because to Dave it had always seemed that his brother was a man who didn't belong close to anyone. Edward had severed communication with his relatives, and they had gratefully accepted the disconnection. Dave did not know if his thought process had been conscious, but he knew that the real reason he'd chosen Riverstone was not to satisfy the requirements of feng shui but to isolate his brother. Dave looked at the faces of his siblings, searching their eyes for shame. They had agreed to bury Edward at Riverstone Cemetery, so they too were guilty of the crime. But rather than shame, he saw the exhaustion of people struggling to put dim sum in the gap left by a missing tooth, trying to forget enigmas they never understood. He'd lied for so long that now he could never disillusion them.

"Someone pass me a fork," said one of his brothers. "I have a lot more to eat before I think about going under."

There was a general laugh in agreement and renewed orders for Coke and soy sauce. Dave tried to smile. He stood at the side and watched his siblings devour their feast with the ignorance of flies encircling a corpse.

The Wangs wrapped up the leftovers, dumped the paper ashes into a garbage bin on the road, and stowed all the remains of the ceremony in the trunks of their cars. Some of the children said goodbye to Edward's grave and were buckled into the backseats of the cars like madmen. While turning on the engine, Dave cast a last glance at the smoky incline and the tombstones protruding from the slope. Dave thought of the crime he'd committed against Edward. What was Edward's crime?

Dave backed out of his parking space and began driving down the hill. *The purpose of Edward's life—it wasn't pleasure.* Debra fiddled with the radio, the children in the backseat howled, Karen turned her Walkman back on, Po Po shuffled through her shopping bags in search of vegetable wontons, and there was the empty seat. *What was it? Was it individuality?* Dave looked in his rearview mirror at the empty seat, and he felt bothered. *Was it privacy?* He felt like a soldier discovering a newly dug wound in his own flesh. *Was it honesty?*

As they neared the gate of Riverstone Cemetery, Po Po placed a bag of pork buns in the empty seat, just as Dave had once hoped she would. The gap was now filled. The wound sealed. Po Po nodded at Dave, smiling her bracket-shaped smile. *They would never return to Riverstone again.*

He slammed on the brakes and pivoted to face the backseat, but the shock and reproach in the faces that returned his gaze held sway over every muscle in his body, and he could not lift his hand. He heard someone call his name, and someone ask why he'd stopped, and some child spout her annoyance. He saw Karen, still plugged into the white headphone cord, and could feel his brother's violence tingling in the repressed muscles of his arm, *but what did it matter? When would Edward ever know?*

"I want that bag," said Dave, trembling. "Those pork buns."

Po Po handed the brown paper bag across the seat and Dave's shaking fingers took hold of the corners. Once he was in possession of it, no one spoke. In the quiet he carefully unrolled its top. At the bottom lay the pink buns, bundled in plastic wrap, and he took one, to prove he hadn't been lying.

Melissa DiJulio, 18
Garnet Valley High School
Glen Mills, PA
Teacher: Heather Arters

Melissa DiJulio will attend Pennsylvania State University, where she will major in English and anthropology. Her writing invites the reader to question the line between reality and fantasy. If she were not able to start a career as a novelist, Melissa would like to work at archaeological dig sites or at museums.

LOTTIE
Short Story

The first time I met Lottie, she blew onto my doorstep with the painted October leaves. She sat there among the dried cornstalks and the stacked bales of hay looking slightly confused. Her eyes were light blue like the cool autumn sky, and her smile was warm, deepening the wrinkles that lined the once beautiful face. I asked her if she was all right, and she said she was, thank you, and picked herself up, smacking the dust off her hands. I asked her if she needed some water or a place to sit for a second, and she said no, thank you, but asked for my hand. In my palm she placed a small pumpkin, though Halloween was weeks away, and then turned on her heel and blew out once more with the autumn leaves. I put the pumpkin on my dresser, but I didn't have the heart to carve a grin onto its face or place a candle inside. I looked at the pumpkin every night before I went to sleep until it was well past the holiday and my mom told me that I had better throw it out. I couldn't bring myself to do this either, though, and, very secretly, I placed it in the back of the top drawer of my desk, where I could still pull it out and look at it from time to time.

I didn't see Lottie again for a while, until she shivered and shook onto my doorstep with the November chill. This time she was wearing a headband with a feather, though Thanksgiving was not until next week, and handed me a knitted scarf. I asked her where she'd been and she said she had been traveling. I asked her if she would come in and stay for a bit, but she said no, thank you, and squeezed my hand before shivering away again into the chilly air. I wore the knitted scarf every day to school and even on the weekends, until the threads began to unravel and I was finally left with just a pile of string, which I placed in my desk drawer, with the tiny pumpkin for company.

But Lottie was carried to my doorstep yet again on the clear, ringing sound of the December carols, covered in lights and ornaments. I invited her in for some hot chocolate and some Christmas cookies, though the holiday was not for a couple of weeks, and asked her if she might stay a while. She smiled, emphasizing the wrinkles at the corners of her light blue eyes, and pulled me close for a quick hug, leaving me holding a green candle when she pulled away. She said no, thank you, and Merry Christmas, and I asked her when she would be back. She said she wasn't sure, but it wouldn't be too long. And then she tumbled away again with the music of Christmas cheer surrounding her. I lit the candle every night before I went to bed and watched the flame dance and sway, until one night I couldn't light the candle anymore, because the wax was too small. I kept the stub, though, to remember her, in the top drawer of my desk for a while.

Lottie didn't come back until January, when she trudged in through the knee-deep snow to my doorstep. She was so wrapped in scarves and hats and jackets that I thought it was a wonder she could move at all. I asked her if she had been traveling and she said she had, thank you. She said she thought of me once when she saw a bracelet, and pushed the small ring of metal with an ivory charm that was white as a snowflake into my hand. I thanked her and asked her if she wouldn't come in out of the cold for a moment and warm up by the fire. She said that she was so bundled that a moment would turn into an hour just to get unwrapped, and then another just to get it all back on. She said she would love to but hadn't the time, and patted my cheek sadly, before trudging back out into the January snow. I wore the bracelet every day, refusing to take it off, until one day the charm fell off and my brother sat on the metal part, bending it in half. But I kept what was left, putting it in the drawer with the candle stub and the rest until I could see Lottie again.

And under the clear, bright February stars, she winked in onto my doorstep again. I asked her what she had been doing since the last time she'd visited and she said she had been seeing the world. I told her that I missed her and had been wanting to write but didn't know where to address the letters. She said she hadn't a clue where the letters should go, since they would probably never reach her, but she said that it was nice that I would want them to. She handed me a tiny pillow that she said she had made for me before she came here. Red, for Valentine's Day, she said, though the pillow was much too small to sleep on and the holiday was still a few days away. I thanked her and asked her if she wouldn't spend the night here and stay for a time. She replied that the nights were her glories and that she must drink as much of them in as she could before the sunrise. She hugged me tight for a moment and then looked back once as she winked away like the February stars. I kept the pillow beside mine every night while I dreamed until my dog got ahold of it somehow and ate all the stuffing out, wearing it like a Santa Claus beard. Even though my mother yelled at him, the pillow was beyond repair, and the stuffing and the case joined the bracelet and the others in my drawer.

But Lottie glided in again on the roaring March winds. She was dressed in green from head to toe, although St. Patrick's Day was not yet upon us. She was smiling as she tucked a four-leaf clover behind my ear, whispering that it would bring me luck until I saw her again. I asked her how her travels had been and she said quite well, thank you, and that she was so enjoying the wind, since it made the journey considerably easier. I asked her if she might come in for a little to tell me a story of one of her adventures. She smiled sadly and said that while the wind was good for journeying, it was also terrible for staying in one place too long, and that if she were to tell me a story it would take quite some time. She kissed my hand, waving goodbye as she glided away on the wind again. I kept the four-leaf clover tucked behind my ear every day until the leaves fell off one by one, and I placed them in the top drawer of my desk for safe keeping.

Although it wasn't too long before Lottie fell onto my doorstep again with the relentless April showers. Her short silver hair was hidden under a shiny, bright yellow hood, and her galoshes squeaked on the welcome mat. I asked her to come in out of the rain to dry off, but she said she had only come to drop off a basket of Easter eggs she had painted for me, though it was already the Tuesday after Easter Sunday. I exclaimed that they were lovely, with their paints running down their sides like raindrops, and I pulled her into a tight embrace. She laughed softly, saying she was sorry she was getting me so wet. I asked her how her holiday was, and she said it was lovely, thank you, and she was sorry she hadn't made it to me beforehand. I told her that I was just glad she had come at all, and that I missed her. She replied that she would stay if she could, but she couldn't, having pressing business in the morning, and waded sadly away again into the April rains. My brother and I saved the eggs for as long as we could, admiring the pictures painted on their fragile surfaces, until our mother told us that if we didn't eat them she was going to have to throw them out. So we ended up making egg salad and had sandwiches for a week straight.

In May she spilled onto my doorstep like the abundance of blooming flowers nearly falling out of her arms. She handed them to me, a collage of colorful pinks, purples, and greens, weaving some into a crown which she placed on my head. She told me I had bloomed like her present since she had last seen me, sneezing as she sniffed one of the brightly colored gems. I thanked her, asking if she would come in for a while to escape the pollen, but she replied that if the bees could handle it, so could she. She kissed my forehead gently, saying that she would be back as soon as she could, before spilling off the doorstep again into the bright May morning. I put the flowers in a vase as soon as she had gone, admiring their beauty every day, until they began to wilt and brown. My mother helped me press a few in our dictionary and in one of her cookbooks. She framed them for me so that we could hang them in my room to look at always.

When the rays of the June sun shone down on the earth, so Lottie returned to me again, radiating in the sunlight on my doorstep, draped in a lovely sundress spotted with sunflowers. I told her how pretty she looked and that it seemed too long since she had last visited. She agreed, apologizing by handing me a small metal box with a tiny latch glinting in the light. I asked her if she would like to come in for some lemonade and to get out of the sun for a bit to cool off. She said that lemonade sounded delicious but that she was well past late for an appointment and had to be leaving. Still, she gazed at me for a long moment, as though trying to memorize my every feature, before radiating off my doorstep again into the brilliant June sun. I looked inside the box when she had left and discovered it was full of buttons. I kept the box by my bed every night to gaze at them, and sewed them onto shirts that didn't need them, stuck them on drawings I drew, and gave them to my little brother to play with until every single one of them was gone. To make sure it wasn't lonely after losing its contents, I placed the empty metal box in my top desk drawer.

Under the crackle of the July fireworks, Lottie exploded onto my doorstep once again, filled with a wild excitement of the night. She was dressed in red, white, and blue from head to toe, an American flag draped over her shoulders like a cape. She saluted me like a soldier, exclaiming every time a shower of sparks erupted overhead. I asked how her appointment had gone, and she said very well, thank you. I asked if she mightn't come in for a bit to celebrate with me, but she said it might kill her to be under a roof on a night like this. From under her patriotic cape, she pulled a jar of fireflies, glowing like the night around them. She pressed the jar into my hands, telling me that they were her eyes to watch over me in the darkness when she herself would not be there to do so. She placed a small kiss on my cheek before exploding off my doorstep again, her awe of the fireworks etched into her aging face. I kept the fireflies in my room for a day, watching them glow as I drifted off to sleep. But it broke my heart to keep them in a jar like that, and besides I had no clue what to feed them, so I ended up letting them go in my backyard, watching them fade into the coming twilight. Still, I couldn't help but keep the jar.

And soon Lottie sauntered lazily onto my doorstep again at the very height of an afternoon in August, slow and content in her measured advance. She hugged me closely, telling me she'd missed me. I told her I had, too, and asked her if she might stay a while and enjoy the afternoon with me. She said she ought not, for she was feeling so lazy that she feared she might never get up again if she sat down. I told her that was fine with me, but she just smiled, studying me with her light blue eyes. She placed a book into my hands, telling me that it was her favorite and she thought that I might like it. She said that reading it made her think of me and that maybe when I read it I might think of her. She promised to come back very soon and hugged me close again before rolling back out into the August afternoon. I read the book a hundred times after she was gone, until I could quote every passage, and the weathered pages were dog-eared and worn. My mother told me that if I read it too much it would not be as fun to read anymore and soon I might not like it at all. So I put it on my shelf next to my other books to make sure that it would always be my favorite.

In September, when the lazy frivolity of the summer had gone and the world of work and duty began anew, Lottie walked up onto my doorstep again. Although the weather was mild and pleasant, she herself seemed sad as a rain shower and tired to her core. I asked her if she was all right, and she said she was, thank you, now that she could see me again. I didn't say anything for a second, letting the silence stretch out between us. She sighed then and asked if she might not come in and rest for a while. Her eyes were the blue of a summer morning, and her smile was cool like crisp autumn air. I couldn't help but smile too, a warm smile that, if I had had wrinkles, would have deepened them on my face, I'm sure. I asked for her hand, in her palm placing my own. Slowly, surely, I led her over the doorstep and into my house. Really, I told her, I would love for her to stay for a while, and it wouldn't have to be too long if she didn't want. She nodded, wearily but hopefully, promising me a story of all her adventures, and saying that, yes, thank you, a rest might just be exactly what she needed.

Haris Durrani, 16
Staples High School
Westport, CT
Teacher: Michael Fulton

Haris Durrani will be a high school senior in Westport, Connecticut. His experience of growing up as the only Pakistani-Dominican-American in a mostly Caucasian environment made him want to share his unique life story and raise awareness about the discrimination faced by various minorities in the U.S. He is inspired by Isaac Asimov.

U.S.-Man and the Gulab Jamin Machine
Short Story

"I think people really need to think what it's like to have all of society arrayed against you."
—Octavia Butler

It took a while to understand that there were subtleties *everywhere* after 9/11, challenging who I am. It was a scary thing when I realized how true it was, what Mom told me all the time about anti-Muslim sentiment—that it's all around us. I always thought she was paranoid. I knew there were people who hated Muslims, but they never really affected me—until they took Baba.

It was like everything was saying "Are you *sure* that is who you are? Are you sure about that?" I was in Fitness Concepts once and this kid was putting his hood on, acting like he was funny. The teacher laughed, said he looked like a Muslim. Earlier that month in health class, we talked about decision making and what parts of our lives help us make good or bad choices. Someone raised their hand to say that religion could be in the "bad" column, "like Muslims, you know?"

People like me call each other, in a friendly and proud kind of way, *desi*. South Asian–American. American. I like pizza and science fiction. My favorite movie is *The Matrix*. I snowboard every winter when I can save enough allowance to do so. I'm not that different from anyone else.

So those other people were ignorant, I guess. Maybe *all* the people who don't like us—maybe they're just *ignorant*. Maybe it's not *real* hate, if you get where I'm going.

It's still hard to be sure of my identity when I'm shut down every five seconds. It's like in Algebra II class. Anytime we tell Mr. Wetzel the answer to a problem, he says, "Are you sure about that?" He laughs because we start saying we were wrong all of a sudden, despite the fact that we happened to have it right all along.

Mr. Wetzel says we need to have more confidence in ourselves.

I remember spending a Sunday afternoon in the storage area at the back of Baba's halal store near our apartment in Brooklyn. Baba's gulab jamin machine was like something from the desi Willy Wonka Factory. I loved to hang out in that tiny room and do homework—or just sit there, to listen to the whir of machinery, to smell the sweet air, to jump-start my brain.

I was writing my history essay—or trying to write it. I wasn't having much success.

Baba came through the door. He was a tall man with broad shoulders and a big head of hair. But Baba was gentle with his hands, an engineer at heart. *He* had invented the gulab jamin machine.

Gulab jamin is the best Indian-Pakistani dessert *ever*. It's like a small, firm matzo ball bathed in warm, sweet syrup. Baba sold them in his halal store. His machine was a giant mechanical octopus with tubes, wires, and metal sprawled out like massive tentacles. At its center stood a dark gray, refrigerator-sized box with control panels and switches. Syrup canisters were dotted across the machine, and little spoons molded each gulab jamin into shape. The tubes shifted, turned to keep the system running. It was—and sounded—like clockwork: the clinking of metal, the crunching of gears, the occasional beep.

But it wasn't just a hunk of machinery; it was my father's prized creation. And its sweet aromas reminded me of my own Pakistani heritage.

But Baba was speaking now.

"Paagal!"—*Crazy!*—"I don't understand, Usman, why you have

to focus on these history essays instead of math and science." He adjusted his glasses. "What's the point of studying history? It's past." Baba spoke in Urdu—he didn't know much English. My little sister Aisha and I are the only ones in the family who know enough to translate for him.

"History repeats itself," I answered in Urdu. "We don't want that." I wanted to go on struggling over my essay, even though nothing was really clicking.

"If history repeats itself, and we have educated leaders," Baba replied, with this real trickster kind of grin, "then why *does* it keep on repeating itself?"

"I don't know." I shrugged, suddenly unsure of myself. I tugged at my hair for a moment... "They're not *all* educated, Baba."

I remember that Sunday night one month after 9/11. We'd both started laughing then. My body shook with the joy of the moment. Baba followed along in his baritone voice—a voice which always seemed to wash over me like the distant rumble of a peculiarly mellifluous auto-rickshaw engine that sang Bollywood musicals as it ran and "La Ilaha Illa Allah" as it rested.

It was the last time I saw Baba laugh like that.

Beside us, the gulab jamin machine hummed its gentle rhythm. Later that night, it too would give its last chuckle—and then die.

The next day, Mom, Aisha, and I waited for Baba to come home. We called his cell, then the store. No one there. Mom got worried, pulling her shawl around herself, as if an intense and ubiquitous cold had curled itself against her.

Aisha kept asking, "Where's Baba? Where's Baba?" Again and again.

I rolled my eyes. "Shut *up*. He's somewhere."

But it was like Algebra II, and Mr. Wetzel was asking if I was sure about something. This time there was nothing to laugh at.

"The FBI picked up some illegals at a halal store," the officer told me once I'd made it to the police station. "Yeah. That was it. The FBI got a tip from a lady in an apartment nearby. She said there were too many Middle Eastern men hanging around. If you're looking for a *Moslem* or whatever, maybe he was one of them."

But Baba was a *legal* immigrant. And, what struck me most, he was actually in trouble. The idea hadn't hit me until now.

I realized that the officer hadn't seen past my fair skin, so I quickly played along with him. "Oh, really?" I choked in a small voice.

"Uh-huh," he said, scratching his chin. "After 9/11, they've got to find the terrorists. Fast. But we don't really know much about them. The only logical action is to follow what we know about the 9/11 people: Middle Eastern, Muslims—"

I coughed. Not loud, but loud enough. I couldn't help it, thinking about what Mom and Baba say all the time, that if they were to judge, they'd say the terrorists weren't *real* Muslims.

"Where did they put them? The illegals?" I said, suppressing my urge to stutter.

"Metropolitan Detention Center. MDC." His answer sounded almost like a question. He seemed suspicious, but not sure about what. I noticed the way he squinted at me as I stumbled out.

I told Mom everything, and she started bawling like crazy. I was sad, definitely, and I hugged her, but I'm not exactly the emotional type. So I went to Baba's halal store, unlocked the door to the back entrance, sat next to the gulab jamin machine, and then wrote like hell.

I soon realized I shouldn't just sit there. I should do something. That's what America was about, why Mom and Baba came. Things get *done* here. There's an unbreakable rule of law.

Isn't there?

I dug into the yellow pages and called up the MDC. No Hamed Khan.

"I want to speak with my father!" I demanded. "I want to speak with him *now*." I almost had a temper tantrum every time I went to the MDC in person, which was about twice a week.

"He's not here, kid," they'd say. "I'm sorry, but he just...ain't... *here*."

I know they thought I was crazy, and maybe I was. Maybe that's what happens when you realize that everyone is, in his or her own little or big kind of way, against you.

I've abandoned countless novels because they made the Arab the bad guy, or because they think we worship a rock in Mecca or something. The latter was Isaac Asimov, who *used* to be my favorite author. That pissed me off. I read it in Urdu to Mom. She said he was ignorant—not malignant. Either way, I didn't like it. Usually, the only time Muslims are introduced in media is to criticize. Kim Stanley Robinson, an author whom I'd been eager to read, tossed an Arab settlement on a Mars colony. He said they were rough men who subdued their women. That type of trash.

I still can't help but cite Asimov now. I remember feeling like the Neanderthal in his short story "The Ugly Little Boy." They extract him from his past, and everybody in the present hates him because he's so freaking *ugly*. I cried, almost. I think the only reason the boy *didn't* go crazy was because he never fully grasped his situation. I bet if he *did*, he would've gone paagal. Definitely paagal.

"Are you sure about that?" Mr. Wetzel asks.

About God? Islam? *Me*? Either way, I say, "Maybe not."

If there is a God, where is he to help me now? He does not answer my prayers.

Six weeks after he disappeared, I managed to get on the telephone with Baba, and with a lawyer from the Center for Constitutional Rights. I told Baba I loved and missed him. He sounded faint.

"My situation disturbs me," he said. He worked for each phrase, fighting to make every syllable happen while still choosing his words carefully, as he always did when he was serious. "Your mother and I moved here because we believed the justice system in the United States would be stronger than in our home countries. It makes me sad to think this faith has been broken."

His "situation" lasted a long time.

And the CCR lady was nice enough, explained it all. She said the Immigration and Naturalization Service detained 1,000 foreign nationals within the first seven weeks after 9/11, and 5,000 in the next two years.

"We need the government to protect us from other countries and from dangerous individuals. "I don't want a terrorist attack"—she pointed to herself—"you don't want one"—to Mom—"and you don't want one"—to me. "None of us do," she said after a moment. Mom's eyes were red, and so were mine. "But it stops becoming protection when we sacrifice some people's human rights because we're all afraid. That's not the way it's supposed to happen in the States. That's not the way it's supposed to happen anywhere. I'm sorry."

They claimed Baba violated immigration laws, and used that as an excuse to arrest and keep him for a while. During that "while," they put him in the Administrative Maximum Special Housing Unit. They hit him and swore at him and didn't let him pray and fed him pork and called him a terrorist. They made him strip, checked him for weapons he couldn't possibly have obtained. They put him in burning hot and freezing cold temperatures, and kept him in solitary confinement. Kept the lights on real bright.

"Always bright," Baba would tell me later, eyes shaded by fatigue. He rubbed them as if he still lay beneath the relentless glare. "So bright."

The freaky thing was, it all happened in the U.S. It wasn't in Cuba or Syria or wherever. It was *here*. That scared the hell out of me.

After a full nine months in the MDC, the government cleared Baba of all terrorist affiliations but deported him and Mom off to Pakistan. Mom forced Aisha and me to stay back, said there were good prospects here. Maybe the lawyers can help my parents return home, to America, but I doubt it.

I won't see Mom and Baba for a long time.

Now I'm where I started—in the small, dingy room in Baba's halal store, beside his gulab jamin machine. It has been cold since it broke down the night before they took him. I pick my laptop up from the table and start to write. Words spill out, one after another. It's hard to get it all down. God, there is just so *much* to remember. Yet, when all the bad memories are exhausted, I begin to recall the happy moments with Mom and Baba.

And then I know why I write. Not only because of love, but *purpose*. I need to write about this kind of stuff. So it doesn't happen again. Paranoia, I realize, might not be so bad. You're more sensitive to times when things get broken; you see when everyone and everything is against you. This is a nation of freedom. If it isn't doing its job, I've got to change it.

That's what it's all about here. *That* is why I write. To fix things.

My eyes rest on the malfunctioned gulab jamin machine. I can rebuild it—rebuild my own life in the U.S., as so many immigrants and sons of immigrants have done. *And daughters*, I add, remembering Aisha.

I asked myself, once, how there can be a God in such turmoil. I have an answer now: Every race, religion, and creed of any goodwill shall be tested. It is merely our time. I consider it an opportunity to be strong in the face of calamity. The greatest strength is not strength itself but hope in the midst of utter despair.

I hear Mr. Wetzel's voice: "Are you *sure*?"

My mouth opens, grins. "I am," I say, over and over again. "I am."

Elizabeth Walker, 18
Deerfield Academy
Deerfield, MA
Teacher: Jaed Coffin

Elizabeth Walker will attend Tulane University, where she plans to major in English and communications with a minor in film studies. In addition to writing, she is an avid runner and a member of the cross-country team. Someday she would like to publish books or screenplays.

HARD TIMES
Short Story

The air is filled with the dull roar of lawn mowers, droning like worker bees through the backyard. Men swarm the perimeter of the monolithic white house, hovering over hydrangea and bustling between leaf blowers and hedge clippers. Every week they come by the truckload with hungry fingers to prune the azaleas and with mendicant hands to turn the soil. For each magnolia there are two men, for each pile of leaves two rakes. Pedro pushes a lawn mower across the glaring green grass, gazing up at the house with a resentment that has hardened with his calluses. He wipes the sweat from his brow in the shadow of the ominous pillars, overcome with anger in knowing that at the end of this long day he will have only half the money he needs.

Pay the rent or buy food? Heat for the apartment or winter clothes for the kids? If only he could find time for night school, maybe he could get a better job. But it's hard to go to classes when he's working the 6-to-midnight shift at the Mobil station, ringing up gas guzzled thoughtlessly into Range Rovers and Mercedes on clement evenings. Every so often, the woman who lives inside the house will roll up to the pump. She sits in her car, drumming her fingers idly on the steering wheel or laughing into her BlackBerry, waiting for him to fill her tank. Every time, she passes over him with a glimmer of nameless recognition, his face faintly memorable among the many other gardeners with dark skin and dark hair. And every time, she rolls down the window, hands him a twenty with an exaggerated "*Gracias!*" and a smile that lets him know how good she feels about her donation to charity, her good deed of the day. He hates the way the money feels in his hand, hates how she drives away thinking about how happy she just made him, how he probably never sees that much money in one place. But he hates more than anything that she is right.

He hardly even knows his kids anymore, but at least there's food on the table. He feels guilty they have to share a cot but knows it is the best he can do. Paying the rent this month should be tough—better walk home instead of taking the bus. Anything is better than that community shelter. Forcing the lawn mower through the stubborn grass, he hopes he is doing what the woman inside asked, but she talks so quickly and his English isn't as good as he would like. She always smiles, always speaks politely, but he sees her lock her car every time he is here working, surreptitiously fumbling for the button on her keys as she slips inside the great, heavy doors. She locks those, too.

But inside, life is crumbling beneath her. Poor Pedro could never understand. The market is a mess and Mr. Big White House made a bad investment. She lies awake at night, terrified at all the money they've lost. They may have to sell a house. She could do without the lodge in Aspen, but please, anything but Nantucket. And what will her friends think? A charity case, that's what she'll be. While she excuses herself at lunch with the girls to answer a quick phone call, she knows what they will say. "Do you think we should pick up the check?" they wonder, glancing at each other with knowing eyes. What generous friends. How fortunate she is to have people looking out for her in her time of need. While the house goes on the market, she takes out her frustration on her credit cards. Some new Manolos will make her feel better, and besides, there will always be a Four Seasons in Aspen.

She glances outside to see a gardener climbing down from an abomination of a hedge clipping. She storms through the garden to where Pedro stands, stooped to rake the fallen branches into a trash bag. He straightens up at the sound of her footsteps and she sees a mixture of fear and hatred harden in his gaze. He will be easily replaceable, and she doesn't have the money for incompetent help anymore.

Merrick Wilson, 17
The Kinkaid School
Houston, TX
Teacher: Carolyn McCarthy

Merrick Wilson was raised in Houston and views the city as a major form of inspiration. He is involved in his school's theatric program and its acting troupe, and he also participates in inter-school debate. He would like to major in a humanities-related field in college.

V-Day
Short Story

The sky is on fire. Beads of light flicker off towers of glass. Red, blue, and green streak across the sky in a dazzling waltz before disappearing into space. With each burst of orchestrated flame, great pillars of smoke and gray contrails are illuminated for an instant against the empty backdrop of the sky. Some things are too good to be true. Tonight defies that statement. Tonight the world is alive once more; everyone will sleep sure of what the next day brings. Yesterday was a day of war, tonight is a night of victory, and tomorrow is a day of peace. This is V-Day: the end and beginning of all things. The old world has been torn down and a new one has taken its place. And although the everyday struggles of life will be there tomorrow, all is right in the world for a few brief hours.

You live in an apartment on the 31st story of the Worchester building; it overlooks First Street and the park. At 10:32 p.m. you lean on the windowpane with your forehead, pressing against the thick glass. Below you are the main launchers, near the fringe of the park. They have been hurling rockets right past your window for two hours now. As each missile flies by, there is a sudden tense vibration, and a dull *thwump*. The next thing you hear is a cracking noise far above your head. You can also see that throngs of celebrators, partyers, and soldiers are still parading through the street, on foot or in "victory cars," which blare loud, rhythmic music and wave the many banners and streamers of the military branches. The city, so coarse and disjointed in nature, is celebrating in a strange harmony.

You, on the other hand, are not celebrating. You are not outside. You are inside because life has not stopped for you. Your mother is in the hospital. She has been diagnosed with some disease you can't pronounce that could compound the effects of the white flu. When you think about your mother or the flu that runs in both of your veins, you begin to sweat and fidget, so you try not to. Your sister, Natalia, is supposed to call you from the hospital in the town you grew up in. She was supposed to call at least thirty minutes ago. To take your mind off things, you decide to boil up some noodles. You always eat too much when you're nervous.

Setting your phone on the marble kitchen counter, you pull out a pot, fill it with water, and set it on the stove. The igniter fires several times before setting the gas stream aflame. About a minute passes before your phone rings. With a degree of panic you rush across the kitchen and bring the phone to your ear. Somehow you are already out of breath.

"Hello?"

"Garin? What's wrong?" It's a man's voice; you sigh in relief.

"Christ, you scared the hell out of me. I was just waiting for my sister to call me. My mom's in the hospital. They think it's the white flu but they don't know how serious it is yet."

"Did she forget to take her shots?"

"No, she wouldn't do that. Forget about it, man. What's up?"

"Are you at your apartment right now?"

"Yeah."

"Can you be at Pauli's in ten minutes?"

"Yeah? Wait, what is this about?"

"Something has come up that I really think you should know."

"What are you talking about? You sound like a crazy person. I can't leave. I need to talk with my sister. Just tell me now." Working for the government makes some people a little too serious about things.

"Garin, your entire family could be in danger." Your heart skips a beat.

"Wha—what?"

"You need to meet me at Pauli's. I'll tell you there."

"Wait, no, why can't you tell me—" He has already hung up.

You put the phone down on the counter and stare at it for a few seconds. Either it could be elaborate bullshit he wants to play on you, or it could be something else. You don't really know which it is, but you have always been on the paranoid side, so at about the same time the water begins to boil, you put out the stove.

You drop your cell phone into your left pocket and pull on the navy jacket you bought a few weeks ago. The plastic mask you pull over your face stifles you at first, but with the flick of a switch, air begins to cycle through. Three clasps secure several elastic bands around the back of your head. You check your watch; it is 10:56.

At 10:59 you step through the revolving glass doors of the Worchester and into the cool night air. A blue headlight on the forehead of your mask automatically switches on. You walk east down First Street. Pauli's is on Alahuac Avenue, about two blocks down and on the right. Tonight is a good night for a walk; being out on the street helps you clear your mind. Your thoughts drift to the towering skyscrapers and the crowds of people streaming in every direction; they all are smiling through their masks. They all are singing. V-Day, just the thought of it makes your skin crawl, in a good way of course. It doesn't seem real, but you know it is. It's V-Day; the world is being given a second chance. You're smiling.

At the turnoff for Alahuac Avenue, there are two men leaning on a beat-up taxi. They are wearing black suits and solid masks with vertical LED strips. You try to ignore them, but as you pass you can feel their eyes tracking behind their blank facade. You know who they are. They are part of the liberation party—a bunch of crazies, in your opinion. They are racists and criminals whom nobody takes seriously; however, you know to keep your distance. They aren't exactly the people you would want to run into in a dark alleyway. Only twenty steps later you have forgotten about them and have resumed your daydreams. If it weren't for an especially loud victory car distracting you, then you would probably have missed Pauli's altogether. It is 11:05; you are five minutes late when you step through the front door. He is sitting in a booth to your far right, taking a sip of his coffee as he sees you. You walk over and sit across from him.

"Well, what's so important?" There is something wrong with his eyes; it bothers you, but you can't look away from him.

"In about one hour you're going to be put on the blacklist."

"I knew you would pull this stupid cop bullshit on me." You laugh, but his eyes are aflame.

"They believe—we believe you have been making calls into the occupation zone."

"This is ridiculous."

"Garin, what stupid shit are you up to?"

"Nothing. I don't even know anyone stationed in the occupation zone."

"They were civilian numbers."

"What? See, that's just—Christ, do you actually believe I did any of that?"

"You tell me." You pause and lean in to whisper.

"I have made no calls to anyone in the occupation zone whatsoever. I don't know anyone stationed or living there. Now you tell me, am I going on the blacklist? Because you better be goddamn serious because this is not the time."

"Garin, you are going on the blacklist, no bullshit. However, I think I can help you out."

"As if things couldn't get worse. What's the plan?"

"You're going to get out of the city, while I try to sort things out. You'll probably need to stay hidden for a day or two."

"No phone calls?"

"From this point onward." You lean your head into your hands; they slip across the front of the mask. "No masks, either. They can track it."

"Well, I would much rather risk getting caught than dying from the white flu. In case you've forgotten, I have Type C."

"Don't worry. I've got you covered." He pulls out a packet and hands it to you; there are three green capsules inside. "These will do fine for a day."

"Are you sure these work? I thought…"

"You think, Garin, but I know. These will work fine for now. I'm already sticking my neck out too far for you, so I'd be a fool to give you the faulty medications."

"I guess you have all this figured out."

"Damn right I do. You need to take these now, but keep wearing your mask. Go to the metro station on Jordan Street." He slides a ticket across the table. "Put your mask on the southbound, and then go northbound until the stop at Fairbanks. Someone will meet you there; you can trust him. He'll take you somewhere safe until I get all of this wrapped up."

"I thought the metros were closed?"

"They just reopened. Have you had your shots today?"

"Yeah."

"Good. Take the pills and get out of here."

"OK." Lifting the mask off your mouth, you open the packet and pour the capsules into your mouth. He hands you a glass of water; you drink it, and the medicine washes down your throat. "I don't know what's going on, but I guess I don't really have a choice."

"It's a bad situation, Garin, but it'll be OK." You stand up and walk to the door. Out of the corner of your eye, you can see he's firing an inhibitor shot into his arm. As the cool night air surrounds you, you break into a fast walk, hiding in the shadows of a nearby alley. You fumble through your pockets, grab your phone, and then hurriedly you dial your sister.

"Pick up, Talia, pick up." The tone sounds several times. "Goddamn, pick up."

"Hello."

"Talia. This is Yuga." It's her answering machine. You swear under your breath and clench your teeth as it grinds on to the recording tone. "Talia, I know you can't talk right now, but you need to know something. I have to leave town. I—I—I don't what's going on, but I have to leave for a couple of days and you won't be able to reach me. Please do not call me. Something bad could—I'll explain later. Tell my mom I love her, and, um, yeah. I'm so sorry, but I can't explain it all right now." Your gaze moves to the other end of the alley. Two men are standing side by side. Are they watching you? "I've got to go."

You slip the phone into your pocket and casually walk the other way. Your heartbeat speeds up. You exit the alley and walk thirty steps before looking behind you. The two men are now standing at the entrance to the alley, clearly facing you. They must be the two liberation guys trying to pull something. You face them. "Listen, guys, I've got no deal with the liberation party, OK? I don't mean any disrespect, but I just want some privacy." They don't move. "You're not with the..." You start backing away. "Christ, guys, I didn't do anything. This is a mistake. Go talk to—" You turn and begin to run. You can't hear if they're following you, but you don't care. Your body is burning up, your head is on fire, and your heart is pumping like mad. Paranoia takes over.

When you reach the metro station, you can barely breathe. Leaning over to catch your breath, you look down the street and see that the two men are gone. What were you thinking? You don't go on the blacklist for another hour. You pull yourself together and walk up the metro station steps. Few people notice that you're breathing heavily or that your eyes are wildly searching the crowd. It's V-Day. They have bigger things on their minds. You scan the ticket at the entrance and move onto the first platform. People are already filling up the southbound train, and you can see through the doors of the metro that the northbound has just arrived on the platform beyond. You step through the metro doors, drop your mask, and calmly walk out.

"Hey, man, you dropped your—" The door shuts and you move onto the second train. You manage to navigate the crowds and sit in a booth at the back of the car. As you get yourself comfortable, you can feel the train begin to move. The train picks up speed and the platform rushes by. Just as the platform disappears, you see something that makes you jump. On the edge of the platform you could swear were two men in solid black masks. They must've followed you; they must be tracking you. You curl into your booth away from the window. The position you find is extremely comfortable. Shuffling to prop your feet up, you relax your neck muscles. You're falling asleep. Funny, you weren't even tired only moments before, but now you can barely keep your eyes open. As your eyes open and shut, you can see several men coughing across from you. You fall asleep.

You jump yourself awake. How long have you been asleep? You can see you're still on the train, but it is no longer moving, and now you are alone. A sudden wave of fear hits you: You slept in an open area without your mask on. You scramble to pull out your inhibitor case. You take off your jacket, and jam one of the needles into your shoulder. For a second it stings as the fluid rushes into your body. Discarding the needle and the jacket, you walk outside the metro car. You are in a suburban neighborhood, one that overlooks the city, and one that you have never seen before. It is dawn now, and the sun is piercing thick clouds with light, engulfing the whole city in shades of red. In the distance you hear a chorus of police sirens, but the place you find yourself standing in is totally silent.

Out of nowhere, a car pulls up beside you: a beat-up old taxi that you remember from a distant nightmare. The driver leans out from the driver's side window.

"Get in, Yugarin." You don't see any point in arguing with him. You are lost, and any hope of getting out of the city is pretty much gone by now. The second man opens up the door to the backseat, and you climb in. The car ride lasts about five minutes. The two men are silent; their black masks reflect your face like a mirror. Seemingly identical houses pass by your window, all cast in horrific red. You don't even think about talking. The car stops at a house that looks just like all the others. You get out and walk to the front door, the two men flanking up the sidewalk. The door is unlocked, and you open it, stepping into the foyer.

You see me standing before you. Of course you want to know who I am, as you have never seen me in your life. In these extraordinary circumstances, the answer to the question is very hard to explain and will lead you to ask another question.

Picture your life as a book, a novel if you will. It is a novel about a very unusual place that doesn't make all that much sense. Naturally you would be in disbelief of this world; you would believe the book to be a silly fantasy. However, as you begin to read it, you are mesmerized. This impossible landscape quickly sucks you in; you can see it, feel it, touch it. This once impossible story becomes reality to you. You believe in it, and cannot disbelieve it. What makes you attached to this world, this fanciful story? The writing, of course; it must be descriptive and convincing. Behind this orchestration of words lies the writer, the unseen narrator. In the simplest terms possible: I am the narrator of your life.

This is truly the simplest way to describe myself, but now you want to know what all I just said means, so I will elaborate.

You were born in the occupation zone. You volunteered to undergo an extensive psychotherapeutic program, which, through multiple waves of drugs and hypnotherapy, would make you believe you were someone else. I made you believe that your name is Yugarin, that you have a sister named Natalia, or that two other mysterious men are standing in this room. This is effectively a lie, but I make it true because I tell you that it is true. After being transplanted into this city, you became our insurance policy for the war that turned against us; you became an undetectable living weapon of mass destruction. Today, this war was lost, and you were turned into a biological factory of a white flu mutagen. This mutagen, spread by your train ride, turned the white flu from an immune deficiency into a killer. Ninety-five percent of this nation is infected with the white flu. Ninety-five percent will die. You are the hero of our people, the unknown warrior who succeeded where our armies failed. You are a wolf playing a sheep.

You think I'm crazy. You think I'm talking lunacy. Turn around. Those men who drove you here are not there anymore. You turn around and they have vanished into thin air. Your name is not Yugarin; it was, but it is no more, because I say it is. I am the narrator and you are the unknowing protagonist.

Now, due to chemicals introduced into your bloodstream several hours ago, you go into cardiac arrest. Your body begins to tremble; you can't feel your left arm. Your legs buckle, and you pound your chest with your right hand, shaking erratically and gasping for air. You eventually collapse to the floor, your glazed eyes staring at the ceiling.

The last thing you see is me, standing over you. Did you really shake erratically? Or did I just tell you that? Did you even go into cardiac arrest? Or did I just make that up? This whole episode could have been the ravings of a madman, and you would never know it. You accept what's in front of your face no matter how unreal or insane it is. Such is the power of the storyteller. Today is V-Day, the end and the beginning. I am smiling.

ACKNOWLEDGMENTS

The Alliance gratefully acknowledges the thousands of teachers who annually encourage students to submit their works to The Scholastic Art & Writing Awards, and the remarkable students who have the courage to put their art and writing before panels of renowned jurors. Our mission is greatly furthered through special partnerships with the National Art Education Association and the Association of Independent Colleges of Art & Design. In addition we would like to specially recognize the National Writing Project for their continued commitment to our program and for their far-reaching effects in the writing community. Our ability to honor creative teens is also made possible through the generosity of our supporters: Scholastic Inc., Maurice R. Robinson Foundation, Command Web Offset, Jack Kent Cooke Foundation, The New York Times, Ovation, Amazon.com, Dick Blick Co. and AMD Foundation.

Regional Affiliate Organizations

The Alliance would like to thank the Regional Affiliates listed for coordinating The Scholastic Art & Writing Awards

ALASKA
Alaska Art Region
MTS Gallery/Alaska Art Education Association

CALIFORNIA
California Art Region
The California Arts Project

California Writing Region
California Writing Project

Los Angeles Art Region
Armory Center for the Arts

COLORADO
Colorado Art Region
Colorado Art Education Association

Southern Colorado Writing Region
Southern Colorado Writing Project

CONNECTICUT
Connecticut Art Region
Connecticut Art Education Association

DISTRICT OF COLUMBIA
DC Metro Writing Region
Writopia Lab DC

DELAWARE
Delaware Art Region
Delaware State University

FLORIDA
Broward Art Region
American Learning Systems

Miami-Dade Art Region
Miami-Dade County Public Schools

Miami-Dade Writing Region
The Miami-Dade County Fair & Exposition

Palm Beach Art Region
Educational Gallery Group (Eg2)

Palm Beach Writing Region
Blue Planet Writers' Room

Pinellas Art Region
Pinellas County Schools

Sarasota Art Region
Sarasota County Schools

GEORGIA
Georgia Art Region
Georgia State University Ernest G. Welch School of Art & Design

HAWAII
Hawai'i Art Region
Hawai'i State Department of Education

ILLINOIS
Chicago Writing Region
Chicago Area Writing Project

Mid-Central Illinois Art Region
The Regional Scholastic Art Awards Council

Southern Illinois Art Region
Cedarhurst Center for the Arts

Suburban Chicago Art Region
Downers Grove North and South High Schools

INDIANA
Central/Southern Indiana Art Region
Clowes Memorial Hall of Butler University

Central/Southern Indiana Writing Region
*Clowes Memorial Hall of Butler University and
  Hoosier Writing Project at IUPUI*

Northeast Indiana and Northwest Ohio Art & Writing Region
Fort Wayne Museum of Art

Northwest Indiana and Lower Southwest Michigan Art Region
The Regional Scholastic Art Awards Advisory Committee

IOWA
Iowa Multi-State Art & Writing Region
The Connie Belin & Jacqueline N. Blank International Center for Gifted
  Education and Talent Development

KANSAS
Eastern Kansas Art Region
The Wichita Center for the Arts

Western Kansas Art Region
The Western Kansas Scholastic Art Awards

KENTUCKY
Louisville Metropolitan Area Art Region
Jefferson County Public Schools

Northern Kentucky Writing Region
Writing Is Art Fund

South Central Kentucky Art Region
Capitol Arts Alliance, Inc.

Southern Ohio, Northern Kentucky, and Southeastern Indiana
  Art Region
Art Machine, Inc.

LOUISIANA
North Central Louisiana Writing Region
Northwestern State University Writing Project

Southeast Louisiana Writing Region
Greater New Orleans Writing Project

MAINE
Maine Art Region
Heartwood College of Art

Southern Maine Writing Region
Southern Maine Writing Project

MASSACHUSETTS
Massachusetts Art & Writing Region
New England Art Education Conference, Inc., and The Boston Globe

MICHIGAN
Macomb, St. Clair, and Lapeer Art Region
College for Creative Studies and Macomb Community College

Southeastern Michigan Art Region
College for Creative Studies

West Central Michigan Art Region
Kendall College of Art and Design of Ferris State University

MINNESOTA
Minnesota Art Region
Minneapolis College of Art and Design

MISSISSIPPI
Mississippi Art Region
Mississippi Museum of Art

Mississippi Writing Region
The Eudora Welty Foundation

MISSOURI
Missouri Writing Region
Prairie Lands Writing Project at Missouri Western State University

NEVADA
Northern Nevada Art Region
The Nevada Museum of Art

Southern Nevada Art & Writing Region
Springs Preserve

Southern Nevada Writing Region
Sierra Arts Foundation

NEBRASKA
Nebraska Art Region
Omaha Public Schools

NEW HAMPSHIRE
New Hampshire Art Region
The New Hampshire Art Educators' Association

New Hampshire Writing Region
Plymouth Writing Project

NEW JERSEY
Northeast New Jersey Art Region
Montclair Art Museum

NEW YORK
Central New York Art Region
Central New York Art Council, Inc.

Hudson Valley Art Region
Hudson Valley Art Awards

Central New York Art Region
Central New York Art Council, Inc.

New York City Art & Writing Region
Casita Maria Center for Arts and Education

Twin Tiers Art Region
Arnot Art Museum

North Carolina
Eastern/Central North Carolina Art Region
Barton College

Mid-Carolina Art Region
The Arts Education Department of the Charlotte-Mecklenburg Schools

Mid-Carolina Writing Region
Charlotte-Mecklenburg Library

Western North Carolina Art Region
Asheville Art Museum

Ohio
Cuyahoga County Art Region
The Cleveland Institute of Art

Lorain County Art Region
Lorain County Scholastic Arts

Northeast Central Ohio Art Region
Kent State University, Stark Campus

Northeastern Ohio Art Region
The McDonough Museum at Youngstown State University

Oklahoma
Oklahoma Art Region
Tulsa Community College Liberal Arts Department

Oklahoma Writing Region
Daniel and Kristen Marangoni

Oregon
Oregon Art Region - Central Oregon Area
The Oregon Art Education Association

Oregon Art Region - Portland Metro Area
The Oregon Art Education Association

Oregon Art Region - Willamette Valley Art Region
The Oregon Art Education Association

PENNSYLVANIA
Berks, Carbon, Lehigh, and Northampton Art Region
The Regional Scholastic Art Awards Council

Lancaster County Art Region
Lancaster Museum of Art

Lancaster County Writing Region
Lancaster Public Library

Northeastern Pennsylvania Art Region
The Times-Tribune

Philadelphia Art Region
Philadelphia Arts in Education Partnership (PAEP)

Philadelphia Writing Region
Philadelphia Writing Project and PAEP

Pittsburgh Art Region
La Roche College

The South Central Pennsylvania Writing Region
Commonwealth Connections Academy

Southwestern Pennsylvania Art & Writing Region
California University of Pennsylvania

RHODE ISLAND
Rhode Island Art Region
Rhode Island Art Education Association

SOUTH CAROLINA
South Carolina Art Region
Lander University

TENNESSEE
East Tennessee Art Region
Maryville College

Middle Tennessee Art Region
Cheekwood Botanical Garden & Museum of Art

Mid-South Art Region
Memphis Brooks Museum of Art

TEXAS
Harris County Art & Writing Region
Harris County Department of Education

San Antonio Art Region
SAY Sí (San Antonio Youth Yes)

Travis County Art Region
St. Stephen's Episcopal School

West Texas Art Region
Wayland Baptist University, Department of Art

VIRGINIA
Arlington County Art Region
Arlington Public Schools

Fairfax County Art Region
Fairfax County Public Schools

Richmond County Art Region
Virginia Museum of the Arts

Southwest Virginia Art Region
The Fine Arts Center for the New River Valley

VERMONT
Vermont Art & Writing Region
Great River Arts Institute

WASHINGTON
Snohomish County Art Region
The Arts Council of Snohomish County

WISCONSIN
Wisconsin Art Region
The Milwaukee Art Museum

Milwaukee Writing Region
Still Waters Collective

S0-BRO-191

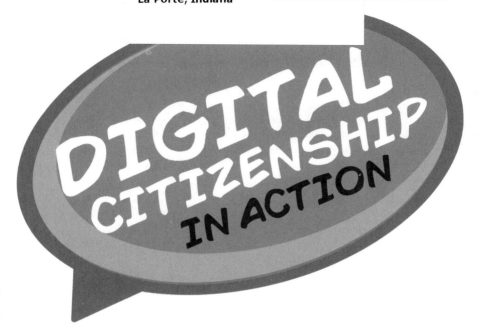

Empowering Students
to Engage in Online Communities

- Kristen Mattson -

International Society for Technology in Education

PORTLAND, OREGON • ARLINGTON, VIRGINIA

Digital Citizenship in Action
Empowering Students to Engage in Online Communities
Kristen Mattson

© 2017 International Society for Technology in Education

Acquisitions Editor: *Valerie Witte*

Copy Editor: *Kristin Ferraioli*

Proofreader: *Linda Laflamme*

Indexer: *Wendy Allex*

Book Design and Production: *Jeff Puda*

Cover Design: *Eddie Ouellette*

Library of Congress Cataloging-in-Publication Data
Names: Mattson, Kristen, author.
Title: Digital citizenship in action : empowering students to engage in online
   communities / Kristen Mattson.
Description: First edition. | Portland, Oregon : International Society for Technology in Education, 2017. | Includes bibliographical references and index.
Identifiers: LCCN 2017030375| ISBN 9781564843937 (paperback) | ISBN
   9781564846433 (mobi) | ISBN 9781564846457 (pdf)
Subjects: LCSH: Online social networks. | Citizenship. | BISAC: EDUCATION /
   Secondary. | EDUCATION / Philosophy & Social Aspects. | EDUCATION /
   Teaching Methods & Materials / General.
Classification: LCC HM742 .M375 2017 | DDC 302.30285–dc23
LC record available at https://lccn.loc.gov/2017030375

First Edition
ISBN: 978-1-56484-393-7

Ebook version available

Printed in the United States of America

ISTE® is a registered trademark of the International Society for Technology in Education.

About ISTE

The International Society for Technology in Education (ISTE) is the premier nonprofit organization serving educators and education leaders committed to empowering connected learners in a connected world. ISTE serves more than 100,000 education stakeholders throughout the world.

ISTE's innovative offerings include the ISTE Conference & Expo, one of the biggest, most comprehensive ed tech events in the world—as well as the widely adopted ISTE Standards for learning, teaching and leading in the digital age and a robust suite of professional learning resources, including webinars, online courses, consulting services for schools and districts, books, and peer-reviewed journals and publications. Visit iste.org to learn more.

Join our community of passionate educators

ISTE members get free year-round professional development opportunities and discounts on ISTE resources and conference registration. Membership also connects you to a network of educators who can instantly help with advice and best practices.

Join or renew your ISTE membership today!
Visit iste.org/membership or call 800.336.5191.

Related ISTE Titles

Digital Citizenship in Schools, Third Edition, by Mike Ribble
To see all books available from ISTE, please visit iste.org/resources.

About the Author

Dr. Kristen Mattson is a wife, mother of three, former English teacher, and current high school Library Media Center Director in Aurora, Illinois. She partners with teachers in all content areas to integrate digital literacy, research skills, creation, and innovation in the classroom. In addition to supporting teachers, Kristen finds joy in supporting fellow librarians by hosting site visits, facilitating professional development, and blogging about her experiences.

Kristen holds a Bachelor's Degree in Education and a Master's Degree in Instructional Design and Technology. She earned her Doctoral Degree in Curriculum and Instruction Leadership from Northern Illinois University in 2016 after conducting a critical discourse analysis on secondary digital citizenship curriculum.

Acknowledgments

I want to thank several individuals who have been instrumental in making this book possible:

My professors, specifically Dr. Joseph Flynn and Dr. Michael Manderino, who saw promise in my work and continued to push my thinking in new and exciting ways.

My #digcit PLN, including (but not limited to!) Nancy Watson and Dr. Marialice Curran, who have always been willing to ideate with me, read drafts of my work, and offer constructive feedback when I needed it.

The team at ISTE, including editor Valerie Witte, who made the process of writing my first book such an enjoyable one.

My husband, children, and parents. Your unwavering support is the reason I am able to continue to do what I love. Thank you for that gift.

My biggest debt of gratitude is to the educators featured throughout the book: Thank you for trusting me to write and share your stories. Thank you for the work you do day in and day out as forward-thinking educators, willing to embrace the messy and unpredictable in order to help students succeed.

Dedication

To Marybeth and Dolores; two strong women in their own right who set the course for generations of strong women to follow.

Thanks for dreaming with me and never doubting that I would grow up to be exactly what I wanted to be.

Contents

Foreword

All of us live in two places at once, at every moment, wherever we go. First, we live in real life, or RL, as we now refer to it. Once simply referred to as "life," we have had to rename it in order to distinguish it from the second place we now live, which I call IR, or immersive reality. Regardless of what name you use, this second reality consists of the ubiquitous, massively interconnected, parallel universe on the other end of our smart devices that provides integrated functionality for every aspect of our lives. Our devices are, to quote MIT's Sherry Turkle, "always on and always on us," immersing us in a secondary source of information and a sense of place, wherever we are. Although we could turn this second reality off anytime we like, the reality is that we are never going to. It is here to stay and will become more indispensable as its power evolves.

We also live in a third world: the world of imagination. It is here that we can dream boldly about how to integrate RL and IR, and how to shape the endless possibilities that living a digital lifestyle presents us. And it's here that we have let ourselves and our students down in terms of an approach to digital citizenship. The education world has imagined mostly fear. And most importantly, it has imagined our new digital world largely without student voice.

In fact, the most important digital citizenship conversations we can have are with our children. If we are looking for a focus for that conversation, let it be the following question: How can we make the internet a positive influence in the lives of our children? Unfortunately, that conversation rarely occurs and when it does it is often one-sided, with adults handing out lists of "don'ts" to students about how to behave online. There are rarely "do's" to go along with the don'ts, and students often have no hand in crafting the internet user agreements that define their virtual lives as they are lived at school.

That's why when I imagine how to approach digital citizenship in schools, in my mind's eye I see an end to adults making all the internet rules for students without their participation. Of course, we should be involved. But when we make all the rules, we rob our students of the opportunities they need and deserve to see the bigger picture and to apply their understanding of that bigger picture to themselves and the digital lifestyles that they live. If we don't ask them to help frame the system, they tend to game the system. That is, when we make the rules, it's "game on" for them in terms of figuring out how to circumvent those rules. But when the rules are their rules, their approach shifts. I have worked with thousands of students using an activity I call "You're in Charge" in which I ask them to create policies about using technology and the internet in their schools that they will have to live by. In every case, students tend to become much more adult and conservative in their perspective than when they are not involved. They want their online spaces to be safe and respectful and look at activities such as cyberbullying as a kind of virtual vandalism. Why don't we know this? Because we often don't involve them in the discussion.

There is another very important reason we need students to actively participate in imagining their digital citizenship identities, which is neurological in nature. The part of the brain that is primarily involved in ethical decision-making is not fully developed until our early 20s. Yet, managing our virtual decision-making requires weighing very sophisticated ethical considerations long before then. My colleagues in the neurological sciences tell me there is only one way to jumpstart the development of those skills earlier in life: practice. But when the adults make all the decisions without student participation, this can't happen. Students need to practice thinking about and acting within the online commons.

Again, the message is clear. We need students' active participation to create the kinds of digital lifestyles we all consider healthy and hopeful. At the end of the day, we want students to be able to strike a balance between outrageous opportunity and informed awareness; between passionate engagement and reflective action; between being absorbed at the keyboard and stepping back from the screen. Achieving this balance lies at the heart of dancing gracefully and purposefully with digital change. And we can't get there without student participation.

Kristen Mattson hits this issue head-on in her timely and articulate book by recasting the digital citizenship landscape as one that values "...possibilities over problems, opportunities over risks, and community successes over personal gain." She offers practical ways to move forward, by creating space for students to practice digital citizenship, and provides examples of school success as guidelines for educators to consider. She deconstructs current digital citizenship practices and methodically updates them to reflect more student involvement and more informed, effective professional practice. Her book is at once practical, but also visionary, calling for a new way of seeing digital citizenship. As Mattson says, "A participatory approach to digital citizenship education recognizes that all members of the digital community are valuable, deserve to have a voice, and can make positive contributions to various groups." This is where we need to head if we want to create the kinds of online communities in which we all want to live.

—Jason Ohler

Professor Emeritus of Educational Technology and Virtual Learning, University of Alaska; and Professor of the Media Psychology PhD Program, Fielding Graduate University

Introduction

1998:
- Don't get in strangers' cars
- Don't meet ppl from internet

2016:
- Literally summon strangers from internet to get in their car

I saw this image on Twitter the other day. It made me chuckle. It made me think. I retweeted it with this accompanying message: "Let's make sure our #digcit stances keep up with the times."

Digital citizenship, commonly shortened to #digcit on Twitter, is a concept that has gained traction with K–12 educators since it was first introduced in 2004 by Dr. Mike Ribble. Ribble's initial "Nine Elements of Digital Citizenship" encouraged educators to provide direct instruction in digital norms and in concepts such as digital law, digital commerce, and digital health and wellness (Ribble, 2015).

Digital citizenship came to mind when I saw the image above Tweeted out because, unfortunately, much of the free, readily available curricula for schools are written as if we were living in 1998: do not talk to strangers; do not post information that would help someone figure out your identity; do not share addresses, phone numbers, or passwords. As Mattson (2016) has noted, the list of "do nots" usually includes language about cyberbullying, safety, security, and privacy. While these lessons have a place in conversations about our digital world, the heavy emphasis on the "do nots" leaves me wondering if our curricula are sometimes met with eye rolls because, to some, the messages sound like outdated tidbits from a generation that is still a little leery of all these new-fangled ride-sharing businesses.

I am not the only educator who has recognized the abundance of "do nots" in the digital citizenship discourse. Like most curriculum in education, the digital citizenship pendulum is starting to swing. Many more voices are emerging to say, "Why aren't we teaching kids the power of social media?" As a result, research has indicated that educators, consultants, and technology companies are ditching the once familiar rhetoric of not posting anything that could get you in trouble, and are attempting to rebrand the term "digital citizenship," teaching students to positively portray themselves online so as to stand out for future scholarships and job opportunities (Couros, 2015; Passeport, 2017; Singer, 2016).

Whether your curriculum falls in line with the "do nots" or has started to shift toward building a desirable online presence, the truth is that both of these stances focus heavily on the individual digital user. The egocentric messages of "protect yourself" or "market yourself" restrict us from digging into one of the most important aspects of what it means to be a citizen—to be in community with others.

 Digital citizenship curricula must strive to show students possibilities over problems, opportunities over risks, and community successes over personal gain.

If we take a moment to look back at citizenship education as it has existed in schools for more than a hundred years, only a very small portion of that education was about rules, morality, and personal betterment. The goal of education was to develop citizens who would stay informed about and contribute to the societies of which they were a part (Dewey 1909, 1916). Today, citizenship education continues in many forms through character education, sure, but also through social studies and civics courses, taken from kindergarten through high school, which introduce students to communities of the family, classroom, school, town, state, nation, and globe. Today we are citizens of digital communities as well—communities that may include people we know and people we've never met face to face.

If your definition of a good citizen is someone who is moral and ethical, a curriculum of "do nots," or even one of "personal branding," makes sense. I see ethics as only a very small aspect of citizenship, however. If you believe that citizens have a responsibility to give back to their communities, the process of contribution looks very different in digital spaces than it does in traditional ones. Being able to connect globally offers a magnitude of possibilities for learning, collaborating, and even working together to change the world, but that means digital citizenship curricula must strive to show students possibilities over problems, opportunities over risks, and community successes over personal gain.

What's in This Book

In this book, I'd like to get you thinking about digital citizenship as more than a conversation about personal responsibility. The ideas put forth in this book will challenge you to create opportunities in the classroom for students to become *participatory citizens*—citizens who actively engage in multiple levels of community and who can develop, as noted by Westheimer and Kahne (2004), "relationships, common understandings, trust, and collective commitments" with other citizens in those spaces (p. 242).

With this in mind, each chapter will include the following:

- Highlights of some of the current approaches to teaching digital citizenship to help you identify easy places to make change

- Suggestions for moving beyond personal responsibility lessons into opportunities for participatory citizenship

- A featured activity to bring into your classroom and try with students

- "Spotlight Stories" that feature one or more communities of teachers and learners that are embracing the notion of participatory digital citizenship and doing amazing things as a result

- A summarizing "You Can Do It!" section with words of encouragement and final advice to get you started

Throughout the book, you will also see references to the ISTE Standards for Students (International Society for Technology in Education [ISTE], 2016). These Student Standards are designed to help teachers purposefully use and thoughtfully integrate technology in the classroom as a vehicle for developing both content knowledge and skill. Where appropriate, I will show you how the Student Standards can support your goal of equipping participatory digital citizens with the skills they need to succeed.

Who This Book Is For

This book is intended for teachers of Grades 6–12, school librarians, administrators, and other adults in the school community who are responsible for developing and delivering digital citizenship lessons.

Digital citizenship conversations should start as soon as students begin using devices, but I have chosen to focus on adolescent digital citizenship in this book for several reasons. First, my own experiences as both a middle school teacher and a high school teacher-librarian coupled with my research into existing digital citizenship curricula for high school students allow me to write about secondary digital citizenship from both a theoretical and a practical perspective.

Additionally, the largest bodies of research on adolescent digital behavior center around students ages 12–17 (boyd, 2014; Gardner & Davis, 2013; Ito et al., 2009; Lenhart et al., 2011). These studies provided vital insights that have informed the ideas you will read in this book. Finally, by the age of 13, students are legally able to join many online communities and will need the skills discussed in this text to help them participate effectively.

If you are ready to take your digital citizenship lessons to the next level and engage your students in productive, supportive digital communities, you've chosen the right book!

Enjoy,

Kristen

1
Creating Space for Digital Citizenship

Imagine this. You enter your child's middle school to volunteer for a few hours in the library. Walking down the halls, you encounter a poster encouraging students to THINK before they post on social media (Shannon, 2014). You smile to yourself knowing that your own 11-year-old is not using most of these apps or websites due to the 13 and up age restrictions to create an account. You also feel relief knowing that most of the social media sites on the poster are blocked at your child's school (Figure 1.1).

You walk a few more feet down the hall, passing an open classroom door. Students are sitting quietly at their desks, which are arranged in straight rows, facing

Figure 1.1
This popular poster encourages students to consider what they say on social media before they press the Post button.

7

the front of the room. They furiously scribble information into their notebooks as the teacher recites important facts and gestures toward bullet points on the PowerPoint slide behind him.

Wow, you think to yourself. This teacher has everything under control. That's just the way I remember school! Before moving on, another poster catches your eye. This one is hanging just outside of the classroom door—visible to all who enter. It reminds students to put away their devices before coming into the room (Figure 1.2).

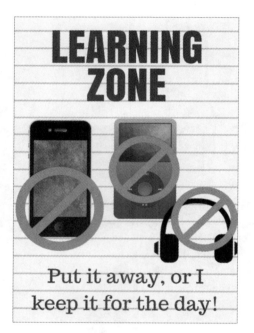

You feel your phone buzz in your pocket, reminding you of your scheduled volunteer time, and hustle away to the library, feeling confident that your child's teachers have this whole technology thing under control.

Figure 1.2
The message this poster sends is that technology is a distraction from learning and does not belong in the classroom.

Current Approaches to Digital Citizenship

If you are a teacher or administrator, you may have posters like those in Figures 1.1 and 1.2 hanging in your school or classroom. You may have also participated in "Digital Citizenship Week," taught lessons about cyberbullying during an advisory period, or attended an assembly where your school resource officer spoke about the legal ramifications of online harassment, sexting, or sharing images of illegal behaviors.

Oftentimes, digital citizenship education is relegated to isolated lessons, events, posters, or messages presented to students outside of the context of their typical, daily learning experiences. Ironically, these messages of online safety are delivered in the same classrooms that may have a "no device" poster hanging on the door. In fact, as Mattson (2016) has pointed out, many free, readily available digital citizenship lessons found online can be completed without students even touching a device.

 How can we ensure that we are teaching all aspects of citizenship, digital citizenship included, through life experiences and not solely through lecture?

Because these lessons, parent nights, posters, and slogans deliver messages outside of authentic digital contexts, they're often relegated to a list of rules and guidelines for students to follow when they *do* enter a digital space. I've come to think of these rules as the personal responsibilities of digital citizens. While online, we all have a responsibility to be respectful to ourselves and others, to follow acceptable use policies, and to make healthy decisions, in the same ways that we must follow laws and respect others in our physical communities.

The difference between the traditional citizenship education our students receive and the digital citizenship lessons they are given is often a difference in contexts—experiential learning as opposed to more abstract, classroom-based techniques. When children are young, for example, they learn about safe ways to cross the street as they walk to school. They learn about sharing, disagreement, and compromise as they argue over toys in their preschool classroom or negotiate the ways to work on a group assignment in the fifth grade.

Our middle school students experience what it means to be a contributing citizen of a school community when they decorate their hallways for a big game, serve as student council volunteers, and navigate their way through changing friendships and social dynamics. By high school, our students are choosing communities of their own as they find clubs, sports, activities, and even places of part-time employment to join, learn from, and contribute to.

Through all of these experiences—whether it's learning that cutting in line is socially unacceptable or it's figuring out how to live in a community of people from a variety of backgrounds and with life experiences different from theirs—students are by and large learning aspects of citizenship, civil life, and community engagement under the tutelage and guidance of adult mentors in the form of parents, religious leaders, coaches, and teachers.

And yet, in online spaces, we have come to accept a mentorship gap between children and adults. As noted by James (2014), we feel an obligation to tell our students the "rules of the road," but policy, fear, expectations, or curricular priorities keep us from jumping in the passenger seat and guiding our students as they navigate new digital terrain.

So how can we close this mentorship gap? How can we ensure that we are teaching all aspects of citizenship, digital citizenship included, through life experiences and not solely through lecture? As educators, part of our responsibility is to create time and space for this type of learning to occur.

Participatory Citizenship Approach

I was at a fairly large educational technology conference earlier this year and sat in a session that required participants to share an edtech success story with other people at our table. When it was my turn, I told the group about a community bulletin board website called Padlet that I enjoy using with students. The tool had enabled my high schoolers to organize their learning collaboratively and through the use of multimedia. Instead of relying on a static notebook filled with information they wrote down, students now had a dynamic, collaborative space for keeping track of information. As the class learned new content, students were able to rearrange information on their digital boards, allowing them to make connections to previous learning and create space for new ideas to come.

The man to my right, however, had not had such a fabulous experience using Padlet in his own high school classroom. He had given it a try, but quickly gave up because the teens could not refrain from posting inappropriate content to the boards. The teacher declared that he would no longer be offering his class opportunities to use this digital tool because students simply could not handle the responsibility of collaborative, online curation and discussion.

So why did one tool work so fabulously with my students while it was a total flop for another group of kids the same age? One possible reason could be attributed to the work I had done with my students earlier in the year. Before even introducing the technology to the class, I modeled the types of posts I wanted to see and demonstrated how this process of community note-taking would be different from the individual note-taking students were used to. During our units, I was also continuously monitoring, mentoring, and providing feedback and redirection as students contributed to the community bulletin boards. After I shared this experience at the conference session, the teacher agreed he could have done a lot more to teach, model, and hold students accountable for the type of interactions he was hoping for.

You see, it's simply not enough to give students a technology tool and ask them to use it while silently hoping for the best. In order for your students to become participatory digital citizens, they are going to need some space to practice under your mentorship. This space does not have to be the most popular social media platform that all the "cool kids" are using. It's perfectly acceptable to help students learn about digital communities in spaces designed for education, such as Google Classroom, Edmodo, Canvas, and a variety of other educational technology tools like the Padlet boards I used with my students.

> **In order for your students to become participatory digital citizens, they are going to need some space to practice under your mentorship.**

Creating a digital space is a start, and maybe you already have an online presence for your class. There are unique aspects, however, that can differentiate a classroom website from a true digital learning community. Classroom websites are often places for one-way communication from teachers to students and parents. On such class websites, the teacher is the only person posting content. A digital learning community, on the other hand, is a space where many voices are invited to contribute, collaborate with one another, and think critically together.

Allowing your students to collaborate with one another in digital communities can be a little scary at first, but remember that when you take this leap in your classroom, you are providing students with an awesome opportunity to participate as digital citizens in spaces that are authentic, purposeful, and guided. The digital space you create will be a safe place for students to try something new, make mistakes they can grow from, and experience successes they can be proud of—all while learning what it takes to be a citizen of many different types of spaces. These digital communities, when designed and executed with these goals in mind, can mimic the types of online spaces that students will share with friends, relatives, and eventually, the world!

> **A digital learning community…is a space where many voices are invited to contribute, collaborate with one another, and think critically together.**

If you are ready to set up a digital learning community for your students, here are some excellent first steps.

Investigate

Talk with your colleagues, the school librarian, and your building administrators about digital tools that you may already have access to through building or district subscriptions. You must also consider the age of your students. If they are under 13, any digital tool you use with them may require parental consent to set up accounts. Again, your school librarian or administrator that handles digital subscriptions should be able to help you with any legalities, permissions forms, and account setups.

Communicate

Talk to your students and their parents. What would they like to use a digital learning community for? What other digital spaces do they already belong to? What skills would they like to practice? Besides one another, is there a larger audience your students would like to connect with? Use the answers to these questions to help you choose a digital platform and develop a space that will meet your class's needs as well as your own curricular goals.

Build a Support Network

Find a "partner in crime" who will support you in your attempt to try something new. Is there another teacher on your team who wants to try this with you? If not, is there a teacher in another building who is already doing some great work with digital communities and might serve as your mentor? Do you have a tech-savvy neighbor, parent, or friend that you could bounce ideas around with? Identifying a person or two who can cheer you on when you hit a bump in the road is vital to your professional growth—as it is to anyone's! It's also important to make sure to communicate your goals with your administrators. Let them know you want to try something new and ask for their support in the process.

Set Learning Targets and Give Direct Instruction

You know the curricular goals you have to meet, but what other life skills might your students gain in a digital community? The following ISTE Standards for Students (2016) can serve as guidelines as you start to develop learning targets for your class:

- **Empowered Learner** (1b): Students build networks and customize their learning environments in ways that support the learning process.

- **Digital Citizen** (2b): Students engage in positive, safe, legal and ethical behavior when using technology, including social interactions online or when using networked devices.

- **Global Collaborator** (7b): Students use collaborative technologies to work with others, including peers, experts or community members, to examine issues and problems from multiple viewpoints.

In the same way that you would model and support content learning, you must also spend time giving direct instruction about and modeling the types of interactions you wish to see in your digital classroom space. Remember that online interaction in a classroom setting might be a new skill for your students. Be patient, flexible, and willing to redirect rather than punish, when one of them makes a mistake.

Start Slow, then Grow

Keep your communities small and slowly expand outward. Let students learn, make mistakes, and grow in the safety of your own classroom community. Once students have learned the ropes and met your expectations, start to expand the community. If you teach multiple sections of a course, consider starting a discussion board that students in all of your class periods can contribute to. Pair up with another teacher in the building and let your students communicate with his or her students. When you're ready to give students an even larger community, try collaborating with a class in another building in the school district. Over time, your students will be ready to join larger, global communities.

Avoid Rookie Mistakes

To help you and your students get the most benefit from a digital learning community regardless of the platform you choose, Table 1.1 lists some common mistakes to avoid and best practices to embrace.

TABLE 1.1 Common Mistakes and Best Practices

Avoid...	Instead...
Getting caught off guard by questions you cannot answer.	Spend time exploring the platform before introducing it to students; consider setting up a phony student account with your personal email address so you can see the platform from your students' perspective in addition to your own.
Using all the bells and whistles built into your digital space (discussion boards, small group spaces, instant message features, etc.) all at once.	Introduce areas of the digital community one by one, model how they work, discuss when they can and should be used, and give students time and space to practice.
Requiring students to express themselves and their ideas in only one format.	Encourage the production and sharing of all types of media, including text, video, audio, and even memes!

Avoid...	Instead...
Dominating conversations or expecting students to deliver a "right answer."	Post thought-provoking questions, articles, images, or video, and allow students to discuss, debate, research, and refute with one another.
Setting up all of the rules and expectations for the digital learning community yourself.	Read Chapter 2 of this book!

FEATURED ACTIVITY:

"Getting to Know You" Digital Citizen Survey

Many teachers start the school year by giving students a "getting to know you" survey that includes questions about favorite books and movies, family life and friends, activities they enjoy outside of school, and goals for the year. The answers to these surveys help teachers know their students a little better and often provide insights that can help start conversation, build rapport, and foster community.

Think of this featured activity as a "getting to know you" survey for the digital citizen. The questions are grouped into categories related to access, online activity, and skill level. It is not recommended that you have students answer every single question listed. The questions you choose to include, perhaps a few from each category, will depend on the age of your students, the digital tools that may or may not be available to them, and the type of digital citizenship work you and your school are already doing.

You can turn these questions into a digital survey by using a tool such as Google Forms, or you could ask students to reflect on paper. Whatever format you choose, ideally you will receive answers that can help you better understand your students' digital experiences, provide you with opportunities to make connections with kids, and identify areas where you have the most opportunity to help them grow as digital citizens.

Questions about Access:

- Do you have a computer or laptop in your home? If so, is it yours or is it shared among family members?

- Do you have internet access at home?

- Do you have a smartphone?

- Are you allowed to use social media? If so, which websites or apps do you use?

- Which adults do you friend or follow on social media? Parents? Teachers? Celebrities? Athletes?

- Who are your social media "role models," and why?

- Are most of your social media friends and followers people you have met offline? If you communicate online with people you have not met in person, what drew you together?

Questions about Online Activity:

- When you are online, what websites do you spend the most time on?

- What are your preferred methods for communicating with friends? Family members? Parents? Teachers? Why do you think those methods of communication are the same or different?

- If you consider all of the time you spend on your device in one week, what percentage of that time is spent reading/researching/learning for school? Reading/researching/learning for your own interests? Watching videos? Playing games? Communicating with friends? Creating something original to share? Doing something else?

- Do you pay attention to local and world news? If so, where do you get your news?

- Have you ever purchased something online? If so, what was it?

- Have you ever been in an online community with a teacher and your classmates? If so, what platform did you use? What were your experiences like?

- What is one thing adults falsely assume about teenagers and technology?

- What is one thing you wish adults knew about teenagers and technology?

Questions about Skill Level:

- Describe how you keep your digital files organized.

- When you are not sure how to do something with technology (inserting a YouTube video into a slideshow, for example), what steps do you usually take to get an answer?

- When someone uses an abbreviation, symbol, gif, emoji, or meme on social media and you're not sure what message the poster is trying to communicate, what steps do you usually take to get clarification?

- Describe how you would handle a situation in which someone publicly insults you on social media.

- What technological skill(s) do you have that you could teach to someone else?

- What is one technical skill that you wish you were better with?

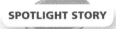

Online Literature Circles

J essica Conlon (@ms_jcon) is a first-year librarian at Still Middle School in Aurora, Illinois, and a former seventh- and eighth-grade English teacher. She transformed her traditional classroom literature circles into an exciting opportunity for students to experience digital community. Jessica provides a unique perspective to the digital citizenship conversation because her own coming of age as a student and educator coincided with the rise of educational technology. As a seventh-grade student in 2001, Jessica's experiences with technology were limited to word processing, online gradebooks, and "stranger danger" conversations. When she entered the other side of the classroom in 2011 as a teacher, technology's role in education had already begun to change.

As a teacher, Jessica found success by giving students time and space to practice their digital citizenship skills while still learning subject

Continued on following page.

Continued from previous page.

area content. In her first year as a middle school English teacher, Jessica and another teacher in her district facilitated cross-building literature circles with their students. The notion of digitally pairing students in two different buildings was overwhelming at first, but ultimately the teachers were excited about what the students would learn. "We wanted to give them an authentic audience for their work, and a chance to practice the communication skills they had been working on all year long in a totally different format."

The teachers developed a three-week long unit that required students to work with peers from both their own school and the middle school across town. In doing so, students were not limited to discussing their reading inside their classroom only; they were able to communicate and collaborate with peers they had never met. Groups were assigned a book to read and a series of tasks to complete using an assigned web platform, including designing websites about their book and participating in online discussion boards.

Modeling Appropriate Interactions

Because Jessica and the other teacher were in two separate buildings, they modeled using the same digital tools and the type of interactions they expected from their students while using those tools.

The colleagues found that students needed a lot of modeling before they became proficient at discussion board conversations. When the teachers posted questions to the board, students had the tendency to simply read the question and type an answer, almost like they were completing an item on a worksheet. In classroom communities, students are expected to listen to what others have to say and take that information into account before crafting their own responses. In the digital space, Jessica and her colleague had to model this behavior, showing students ways that they could acknowledge what others had said and either expand upon those ideas or disagree with them. Kids from both schools had been practicing these skills in the classroom all year, but when the format changed, the students needed adult mentors to help them navigate this new type of conversation.

Student Reflections on the Project

Through the project, students had the chance to practice all the skills that were required by their English curriculum—reading, writing, research, and communication. Because of the format, students learned digital citizenship skills as well. When the project was done, students anonymously shared their reflections with the two teachers:

- "It was a pretty unique and fun project to work with people in another school instead of always being in groups with the students we know."

- "It was really fun to build a website. I never knew how links and pages worked until now!"

- "I learned that online communication is more about planning. When we didn't plan, communication was bad and things didn't get done."

- "Sharing my thoughts on paper was hard. I feel that I was too wordy at times and that the team couldn't understand me."

Curricular and Social-Emotional Growth

Jessica looks back fondly at this project and cannot help but feel proud of the work her students put in. Every group experienced a productive struggle as they grappled with the responsibilities and opportunities that accompany digital learning. Students' growth was both curricular and social-emotional as they practiced reading and writing skills while also learning how to effectively collaborate online.

Witnessing what her students were able to do and create within a digital learning context shed light for Jessica on how binary her own experiences with technology were as a student. Jessica knew that designing and facilitating digital learning experiences for her students were important, so she continued to find small opportunities for collaborating and sharing her work with willing colleagues. Now, as a library media center director, Jessica's experiences have come full circle. Students and teachers with varying levels of experience and interest in technology can venture into the library to create, discover, and most importantly, participate, as digital citizens of our constantly changing world. ●

#LeydenPride

C reating a safe space for students to practice life as digital citizens can certainly happen at the classroom level, but it can also be fostered through schoolwide and districtwide opportunities created by those in educational leadership positions. Jason Markey, principal at East Leyden High School, located in the northwest suburbs of Chicago, Illinois, has been recognized as a pioneer in fostering and supporting school community by allowing his students to demonstrate the positive power of connecting as digital citizens. The successes East Leyden experienced have had a ripple effect, not only to their sister high school, West Leyden, but with school leaders throughout the country. This is the story of the #LeydenPride community.

When East and West Leyden first went 1:1 with Chromebooks back in the 2012–13 school year, Twitter was one social media tool not caught by the school's filters. Students quickly flocked to the platform as the place where they could be social on their school-issued devices. According to student blogger Maja Bulka (2014), the freedom to socialize was short lived: "As Twitter feeds became cluttered by 140-character hate rants on school, homework, teachers, other people and illegal activities, Twitter became a thing of the past on our Chromebooks.... Students abused their powers and didn't heed the warnings, so the administration took action. Gone were the good days of Twitter on Chromebooks."

Changing the Narrative

Jason Markey saw power in social media tools such as Twitter, however. And the possibilities he envisioned went beyond using digital tools to quickly and effectively communicate mass messages to students and parents in his school community. Jason wanted to engage his students in a conversation—one that was authentic and productive. He wanted students and teachers to see that social media posts could be more than just white noise.

Jason set out on several simultaneous endeavors: to connect with other school leaders from around the country for his own personal learning, to gather his school community around a social media hashtag, and to start a crowdsourced blog space to amplify the voices at East Leyden. All of these projects were intended to model the power of being a connected citizen in a digital world.

When Jason's students started the social media #LeydenPride in the winter of 2012, he, the activity director, and a few students were pretty much the only ones using the hashtag to share out the great things they saw happening in the school. Jason remained persistent, though, and over time, the hashtag caught on. As more teachers, clubs, athletic teams, and parents began using the hashtag across multiple social media platforms, Bulka (2014) claimed it really began "redefining what it meant to be a part of our school—a definition that would mesh together exemplary digital citizenship and school pride."

In the years that followed those early attempts to get #LeydenPride off the ground, Jason has seen some amazing things happen. He created an @leydenpride Twitter account, and turned it over to a different student each week, which empowered student voice but also allowed for diversity in the experiences and stories being shared with the larger community.

West Leyden staff and students as well as district administrators also began using the hashtag, and suddenly school district accounts were seen less as a one-way communication tool. Social media became a community space for educators, administrators, parents, and students across the two campuses. Jason watched in awe as students used the hashtag to pressure administrators into an additional school dance, and then used the same hashtag to celebrate and encourage their teachers and peers publicly during Make a Difference Day.

Essentially, "#LeydenPride set the precedent for 1:1 districts everywhere," wrote Bulka (2014). "Instead of repressing Twitter and restricting students from using it, [the] principal steered the use of it away from mindless tweeting and created #LeydenPride....the trend gradually caught on as the use of Twitter became something more than just an outlet for boredom." The community has since used #LeydenPride to do everything from celebrate their academic and athletic

Continued on following page.

Continued from previous page.

achievements to find a safe space to share in their grief, which is what happened when an East Leyden graduate lost her life in a car accident during the summer of 2013.

More Than Just a Hashtag

Jason knew that his students and teachers had more to share than could be captured in 140-character Tweets or in Instagram photos and captions, so he also started the Leyden Learn365 blog. The work of junior Maja Bulka, whose quotes appear in this Spotlight Story, is featured there along with dozens of other posts. The blog is not only a collaboration between the two high schools, but also one among students, teachers, and administrators alike.

On the blog, teachers share their experiences with trying new things in the classroom—everything from rolling out 20% time in a business class to an English teacher bringing her own toddler to school in an effort to reignite the joy of reading in her high schoolers. Another English teacher wrote up her reflections after shadowing a high school freshman for a day, making a plea to her colleagues to remember what high school was like and to have empathy for the pressures their students feel each day. The student blogs are equally, if not more impactful. They write about life as English Language Learners and the importance of kindness in their school culture, as well as celebrate finding their safe spaces in clubs, sports, and school activities.

And while Jason Markey has gotten a lot of national attention for his work in the Leyden community over the last few years, he had some humble reflections on those accomplishments: "Because of Leyden, I've had the good fortune to present all over the continent, as people are endlessly interested in our endeavors. In every trip I make, my goal is not to tell others schools how to mirror Leyden's actions" (2016).

Instead, Jason said that his goal is the same as that of any other educator—to do what is best for kids. But, to do that, we need to be willing to learn and grow from one another and show our students how to do the same. "If chance can favor the connected school then we owe it to our students to give them an environment full of opportunity. It's my goal [to build] a culture in our schools where connection is not accidental, but intentional" (Markey, 2016). ●

You Can Do It!

Setting up your digital space might seem like a daunting task at first, but once you have the digital community in place, there are amazing learning opportunities like the ones Jessica's and Jason's students had waiting for your students too! Consider all the ways you can help foster positive digital citizenship as a mentor, and support students on their learning journey as you enter into online communities together. What are you waiting for?

2

Acknowledging Student Voice in Digital Spaces

After the 2016 U.S. presidential election, something very interesting started happening in my social media feeds. People were posting status updates begging their friends to stop sharing so much political commentary. There were rounds of posts encouraging people to change the tone of their feeds by sharing pictures of cute kittens and tagging and challenging ten of their friends to do the same. My own mother started begging her social media friends to stop talking about the election and start sharing posts of their favorite recipes again. She frequently told me, both in person and online, that it was time to stop talking politics and just move on!

My mom and I certainly did not see eye to eye on the purpose of our social media communities in the days and weeks after the election. While she was eager to return to a feed filled with pictures of her friends' grandchildren, I reveled in the opportunity to engage in dialogue around politics with my peers. Admittedly, I felt that people like my mom, who were taking themselves out of the conversation by posting "no more politics" messages, were engaged in shallow attempts to bury their heads in the sand.

My mom, on the other hand, felt she should not have to be subjected to my political conversations every time she logged in to Facebook. At one point, she even posted on my wall a bright collage called "Make Facebook Fun Again." It looked like a colorful mind map and was filled with the written commands in vibrant bubbles: "Show pictures of your kids & family," "Make me laugh," "Give me a reason to smile," and "No politics!"

So, who was right in this situation? Is it possible that we both were? As I reflected on the debate my mom and I had about the purposes of social media in those weeks after the election, I came away with a few important realizations about how our digital communities work.

Have we given our students the tools to shape their own digital communities in ways that are reasonable, empowering, and valid?

The internet, and social media spaces in particular, are not static sources of information set out for easy consumption. The internet is a mere conglomeration of people with vastly different life experiences, sharing a space together. We make our digital communities what we want them to be, and we have some measure of control over the social media experiences we want to have. My mom, and perhaps others who shared her viewpoint, felt shaken by the change in norms they had come to expect from their online communities in those days after the election. Her posts, begging friends to stop talking about politics and to start sharing recipes again, were simply an attempt to reset the standard operating procedures of the space that she had come to know and rely on.

I found myself frustrated with my mom, though, because it felt as though she wanted me to change my online behaviors for her benefit. Instead of taking simple measures, such as scrolling past my posts without reading them, or more drastic measures, such as unfollowing me, my mom just begged me to post more of what she liked to read. I felt frustrated that she could not see social media as an ideal space for me to engage in political dialogue with others. And as much as I wanted to oblige by her request, I felt that I would have more to lose than gain by doing so.

Naturally, I began thinking about the implication of these reflections for curriculum. Do our students feel like I did when we tell them how to behave online without taking the time to listen to their point of view? Is our curriculum an attempt to manage our own online, and sometimes offline, experiences by telling our students what kind of online lives they can or should lead? Have we given our students the tools to shape their own digital communities in ways that are reasonable, empowering, and valid?

Current Approaches to Digital Citizenship

Many digital citizenship curricula are full of rules and expectations for students to follow. Some are packaged as eye-catching classroom posters such as those in the introduction of this book. As noted by Mattson (2016), others attempt to call out and redirect specific "noncitizen-like" behaviors through the use of scenarios and reflection questions. While posters of expectations and opportunities for discussion and self-assessment are not inherently negative approaches to teaching digital citizenship, they are a packaged set of lessons that have rules and objectives set by outsiders—adult curricula writers who are not in a digital community with the students whose experiences they are trying to shape.

Research shows that as a society, cultural norms—that is, expectations and standards for moral and ethical behavior—and how teens see themselves within these norms are changing. James (2014) has pointed out that, increasingly, conversations about morals and ethics are tied to the idea that what is "right" is in the eye of the beholder, and there is a lesser degree of respect for rules dictated by authority figures, including classroom teachers and institutions such as schools. Young adults today are less likely to determine their identities and moral codes by tradition or inner voice than their parents were. This generation's decision-making and identity development are guided by a mass-created authority with whom they are constantly connected by way of the devices in their pockets (Gardner & Davis, 2013).

In school, however, students are being told how to behave online by teachers and administrators and through curricula that have been designed and developed without students' input. Teens report very little dialogue with adults in their schools about issues related to online behavior, although many report having sat through large group assemblies in which they were lectured to about internet safety. Teens also report that the majority of messages delivered in these assemblies were full of fear-based tactics that focused on the risks, rather than the rewards, associated with participation in digital spaces (James, 2014).

While it is tempting for adults to try to dictate digital behavior from the outside, there is no denying that young adults are the ones leading change in digital spaces. For example, many methods of digital communication, such as text messaging, began as a popular youth behavior and now persist as a standard form of connection that cuts across age groups. Teens also tend to be early adopters of new social media platforms, such as Instagram and Snapchat, using them extensively with their peer groups before

 This generation's decision-making and identity development are guided by a mass-created authority with whom they are constantly connected by way of the devices in their pockets.

the platforms become more mainstream and are adopted by a much broader population (Ito, 2009). While teens may not have the digital superpowers some people allude to by giving them labels such as "digital natives" (Prensky, 2001), adolescents *are* willing to take risks, try new things, explore new media, and help usher in digital change. Research also shows that teens are able to create multiple media identities for themselves, moving fluidly between digital spaces with different group norms, and learning the rules and expectations in those spaces through careful observation and participation in each digital community (Ito et al., 2009).

What this means for curriculum is that we cannot set out a list of rules for digital communities that will be all encompassing. The norms for behavior will change depending upon the space an adolescent is in, and even in those spaces where teens feel comfortable, there may be times when the status quo is challenged and they find themselves facing a changing digital landscape.

While schools may not feel comfortable giving up complete control, there must be some recognition that students—teenagers especially—are already engaging in digital communities with their own sets of norms that are citizen-created, not generated from an outside entity such as a school. When we choose a curriculum of rules created by outsiders that leaves no room for student voice, we do so with blatant disregard for the experiences students are already having in their digital communities. Instead of favoring easy lectures about "right" and "wrong" online behavior, we must be willing to listen to our students' experiences and empower them with a variety of skills to be successful participants in various digital communities.

Participatory Citizenship Approach

The ISTE Standards for Students (2016) recognized that teens are actively participating in online communities. By giving your students voice and ownership in the digital citizenship opportunities they have in your classroom, they will be better equipped to meet the following Student Standards:

- **Digital Citizen** (2a): Cultivate and manage their digital identity and reputation and [be] aware of the permanence of their actions in the digital world.

- **Digital Citizen** (2b): Engage in positive, safe, legal and ethical behavior when using technology, including social interactions online or when using networked devices.

A participatory approach to digital citizenship education recognizes that all members of the digital community are valuable, deserve to have a voice, and can make positive contributions to various groups. Your students may need some guidance, though, to help them see their role as digital citizens and recognize the power of that voice. You can begin by having them set the norms for their digital classroom community.

Helping Students Set Expectations

It might be tempting to approach students with a list of your expectations for using this new space you've created for them. But, instead of telling students how to behave, embrace this perfect opportunity to listen more than you speak, showing students the power they have in shaping the norms and interactions in that space.

To help students collectively create the expectations and norms for their digital classroom, facilitate a whole-class discussion. Here are a few guiding questions that can help you and your students get the conversation started:

- What type of posts do you expect to see in our space? What type of information do you not want to see?

- How formal should our English be? Are abbreviations okay?

- Can anyone begin a discussion thread? Are any topics off-limits?

- Do we need to have a separate space (depending on platform) to discuss different topics?

- Should everyone be required to participate in the online community? Do we need to set a minimum and/or maximum number of posts?

- How will we uphold our community standards?

It is also important to have students discuss and decide how members will hold one another accountable for respecting and upholding the norms they have just set. Ask students to brainstorm ideas for how the community members will respectfully respond if a classmate deviates from the community expectations. Post the newly agreed upon community norms in both the digital classroom and the physical one.

Facilitating Student Reflection

Students should have a voice in creating community norms, but it's also important that they reflect on the ways they've chosen to uphold or disregard those standards, both individually and as a group. After a few weeks of working together in the digital classroom community, set aside time for the students to observe and reflect on the community standards they've collectively set. Pose questions such as these to the class:

- How easy or difficult has it been for you to uphold the community norms?

- Have the community standards changed over time? Were these changes purposeful and deliberate, or did they just start to happen?

- Can you pinpoint instances in which you saw someone deviate from the norms? What happened as a result?

- Do the agreed-upon guidelines need to change to better serve your digital community? If so, how?

- Has our work in the classroom digital community made you reflect at all on your role in other digital communities you belong to? How so?

When students are given time to reflect on their role in the online community, they are not only self-assessing their work as students in your classroom, but also simultaneously exploring the part they play in all digital spaces. You can continue facilitating this metacognitive reflection by allowing your students to consider the roles, responsibilities, and experiences they have as digital citizens in digital communities outside of school.

SPOTLIGHT STORY

Empowering Student Voice through Public Service Announcements

Laura Gardner (@LibrarianMsG) is a library media specialist at Dartmouth Middle School in Dartmouth, Massachusetts. Like many states, Massachusetts law requires schools to have a plan for teaching students about the consequences of cyberbullying. This task has fallen to Laura as well as a health teacher and computer teacher in her building. Even though the law mentions only cyberbullying education, Laura knows that digital citizenship encompasses so much more. She wants her students to have a positive online presence and does her best to model that type of presence with school library accounts across various social media platforms.

Continued on following page.

Continued from previous page.

"I want my students to think, and I want them to be engaged in active learning," Laura says. So instead of lecture-style lessons that tell students how to behave online, Laura prefers giving her sixth graders the opportunity to explore with one another issues such as privacy, reality versus perception, reputation, and community. For a final digital citizenship unit of the year, Laura designed an experience that not only got her kids thinking about the role they play in online communities, but also helped them meet learning targets related to identifying problems and proposing solutions, creating messages for authentic audiences, and using effective persuasion and advertising techniques.

Laura showed her students many public service announcements (PSAs) and introduced them to a variety of persuasion techniques used in the videos. She helped the students see how each PSA identified a problem and proposed a solution to its audience. Then, it was time for Laura's sixth graders to make some PSAs of their own.

Figure 2.1
Students at Dartmouth Middle School enjoy a red carpet premier of their digital citizenship public service announcements.

Students brainstormed problems they had personally seen in online communities or had heard about from their friends and relatives. They then did more research about the problem, brainstormed possible solutions, and chose an audience for their message.

The sixth graders took what they had learned about issues in online communities, wrote scripts that employed at least two persuasive advertising techniques, acted out their PSAs in front of a green screen, and did some editing to bring their messages to life.

To make this unit even more impactful, Laura knew that the students' PSAs had to reach an audience larger than herself. In class, groups of students showed their one-minute messages to one another. The top six videos, as determined by a rubric, were chosen to be part of an extra-special red carpet event attended by students, their families, and even the local newspaper. The students got to see their PSAs on the big screen, played as previews before an evening showing of the documentary *Screenagers* in the school auditorium.

By allowing her students to take ownership in this unit, Laura witnessed them dive deeply into their feelings about "likes" and "followers," cyberbullies, privacy in digital communities, and even norms related to the ways they use their devices in face-to-face meetups with friends. By extending this project into an evening event for families, Laura opened up more opportunities for parents, children, and peers to have honest discussions about what it means to be citizens in a digital age (Figure 2.1). ●

FEATURED ACTIVITY:
Image-Inspired Conversations

It can be difficult to get students talking about their online lives, and if you are not sure how to kick off the conversation, things can get awkward fast! Luckily, there are dozens of artists who are making powerful statements about our lives as digital citizens, and you can employ the power of image to get your students thinking and talking.

In an English, health, or social studies class, use pictures such as the one in Figure 2.2 as bell ringer activities. Project the image and have students spend just five minutes journaling their thoughts about the picture.

If students feel stuck or you think they may need some prompting to get started, you can pose questions along with the image:

- What do you think the artist is trying to say about society through this image?

- Do you agree with the artist's message? Why or why not?

- Can you or any of your friends relate to this message?

- What does the statement made by this image mean for our society?

Once students have had an opportunity to reflect on the image, you can have them share their thoughts with a peer or even with the whole class, if they feel comfortable. As an extension, you can show students

Figure 2.2
Images that make powerful statements can get students talking about their digital lives.

images with opposing viewpoints and have them choose the one they agree with, justifying their answer with some examples from their own experience. Students may also enjoy creating their own thought-provoking images, portraying a piece of their life as a digital citizen.

Note: For an ever-growing collection of images to provoke thinking, writing, discussion, and reflecting on our lives as digital citizens, visit the Dig Cit Discussions Pinterest board (https://www.pinterest.com/kmattson1105/dig-cit-discussions).

Embracing Voice with a Student-Written Curricula

D igital citizenship is often a topic of conversation when school districts make the decision to go 1:1. In Gurnee, Illinois, a team of administrators from Warren Township High School (WTHS) were in the process of developing a series of digital citizenship lessons in preparation for their own rollout when a sexting incident came to their attention. This incident reinforced the need for a future digital citizenship curriculum, but administrators also knew they needed a more immediate message and intervention that would reach all facets of the school community. In response to that immediate need, administrators from WTHS pulled a series of digital citizenship lessons from the internet and required all teachers in the building to deliver the lessons during specified periods of the school day, thus ensuring that all students in the high school were exposed to each lesson.

Cheryl Parmenter (@DrParmenter), a 9th- and 10th-grade social studies teacher at the school, admits that the rollout of these prepackaged lessons was well intended, but not the right fit for the students and staff at WTHS. "Most of the student body was unaware that there had even been a sexting incident. They were so confused about why we were interrupting our classroom lessons to talk about these issues." Some teachers felt uneasy about the lessons, too. Many expressed that they were not adequately prepared to have tough conversations with their students on the first day of school, and they also struggled with the rigid schedule of lessons interrupting the flow of their own curricular goals. To both students and staff, some of the digital citizenship lessons felt inauthentic and outdated.

A digital citizenship committee of administrators and teachers, including Cheryl, recognized the flaws in their approach to digital

Continued on following page.

Continued from previous page.

citizenship education. It was driven by an outside curricula that became one more thing to do, rather than an embedded part of the culture at Warren. There was a huge focus on negative behaviors and rules without a lot of conversation about the power of digital tools. And to many on the committee, one of the biggest issues with their approach is that it did not include student voice. Enough of the teachers and administrators in the building saw a need to modify the approach, and a digital citizenship committee was formed to address those concerns.

Giving Voice to Students

The digital citizenship committee was "founded on the belief that it should empower students in the process of developing and creating digital citizenship lessons with guidance from teachers." In the first student committee meeting, the kids were brutally honest about the digital citizenship lessons they had just received, but also said they were willing to help make the learning experience better. According to Cheryl, the team developed a long-term goal "to successfully integrate digital citizenship into school culture, so that it can be perceived less as a separate program and more as a way of life."

In the early stages of the committee work, the teachers encouraged students to brainstorm. What were the most relevant topics to students at their school? What did teens want to have conversations about with adult mentors? Older students wondered about the impact of social media on the college application process. Other kids wanted to know if technology addiction was a real thing. Together, the team landed on ten topics that they felt were important enough to be addressed schoolwide, and then narrowed those topics down to a list of six.

Toward a Collaboration-Based Curriculum

The committee of students, with guidance from the teachers, went to work developing curricular resources. The teacher team developed the overarching question, "What does it mean to be digitally responsible?" and encouraged the students to tie each lesson back to that essential question. The students created short videos, slideshow presentations, and both large and small group discussion questions for teachers to use in their classrooms. The school administrators set a more flexible schedule for the delivery of the lessons, and the team of both students and teachers met throughout the year to reflect on their work as it was rolled out in the school.

Although the team is still focused on improving the stand-alone nature of the lessons they developed, the schoolwide, student-designed curriculum has received compliments from both teachers and students. The next step for the team now is to identify best fits in the established high school curriculum for their priority topics to be addressed, moving closer to the goal of digital citizenship education as a natural part of the school experience, rather than an isolated monthly event. And, you guessed it, students will be at be at the center of this important work. ●

You Can Do It!

One reason adolescents love being in digital communities with their peers is because their voices can be heard. When you put aside a prepackaged lesson in favor of opportunities for students to self-reflect and share their voices, not only will you be blown away by the depth and complexity of their thinking, but you will help students see the power they have to co-create, enforce, and modify digital norms in the communities they belong to.

In your classroom, regardless of the content you teach, remember that you have the power to do the following:

- Listen to and acknowledge the digital experiences students bring to the classroom.

- Facilitate the co-creation of norms in your digital classroom community.

- Help students thoughtfully reflect on their lives and experiences as digital citizens.

3

Helping Students Understand Their Roles in Digital Communities

A pretty standard question that adults ask kids is "What do you want to be when you grow up?" This question is a fun way to get a glimpse into the mind of a child, but it also carries some assumptions with it. Adults inherently recognize that there are many distinct roles we play in our communities—doctors, teachers, police officers, business owners, parents, spouses. As we grow, we figure out our gifts and talents, and attempt to take on a role that will not only make us happy, but will simultaneously contribute something to the community we live in.

Traditional schooling allows students to explore a variety of roles they might play in society. In elementary school, kids are excited to take turns with classroom jobs such as line leader and paper passer. By middle school, students have the chance to be a band kid, an athlete, a student council member, an honors student, an artist, a gamer. They often jump into and out of different groups as they attempt to figure out where they best fit in the school community. By high school, these roles become less fluid as students settle into areas they enjoy and begin thinking about future roles as employees, college students, or service members to our country.

In the previous two chapters, I discussed how students need a place to practice life in a digital community and that their voices and experiences in those spaces should be both heard and fostered. This chapter is dedicated to helping students explore the roles they currently and will eventually play as digital citizens in global communities.

Current Approaches to Digital Citizenship

Because so much digital citizenship curricula are written from a perspective of individual responsibility, there is not a lot of overt conversation about the ways communities function as a whole. Digital citizenship lessons that are written from a place of behavior management inadvertently, yet consistently, portray adults as having all of the power and control while teens are described as victims that need protecting from abusers, troublemakers that need punishing, or mistake makers who need someone to intervene on their behalf (Mattson, 2016).

Figure 3.1 shows the six roles that teens and adults are given in three of the leading digital citizenship curricular packages written for high school students.

In many digital citizenship lessons, adults are not only the rule makers, they are also portrayed as the internet police when students make mistakes or as the saviors who will swoop in to protect young people when something goes wrong. We tell kids to report cyberbullying to an adult and to tell a parent if they come across online content that makes them feel uncomfortable. While these messages make sense for some of our youngest digital citizens, by the time our students are in their teens, we really should be empowering them with the skills they need to be less dependent on adult intervention, and showing them a more realistic picture of the roles that adults and adolescents take in digital spaces (Gardner & Davis, 2013).

I noticed this overreliance on adult intervention in a recent news story that came out of a high school near my home. A student had taken screenshots of two very racist, very offensive Tweets written

Figure 3.1
Adults and teens are portrayed in one of six ways in the leading digital citizenship curriculum for high school students.

by two different students at the school. The screenshots were put on a poster alongside the Tweeters' profile pictures, full first and last names, their grade levels, and a list of their extracurricular activities. The poster included the phrases "Is this your friend?," "Is this your student?," and "Is this what we will tolerate at our school?" Whoever anonymously created the poster made dozens of copies and hung them all over the hallways of the high school (Martin, 2017).

It did not take long for the poster maker to reveal herself on social media, though. Both the student (who I will call Maya for the sake of her privacy) and her mother were proud to announce that Maya was the one who created and hung the posters around the school. I connected with Maya and she agreed to answer some of my questions through private messaging.

According to Maya, there are students at her school who make racist remarks on social media quite regularly. Although Maya says she has never felt unsafe at school or personally threatened by any of these students, she did take her concerns to the school administration prior to making the posters. Apparently, the school refused to punish the students who had put their offensive opinions online. When more of the same posts appeared, Maya decided it was up to her to make sure the adults in her school were listening.

If Maya's experiences with digital citizenship curriculum mirrored the findings of the Mattson (2016) study (shown in Figure 3.1), it is easy to see why she was frustrated by the perceived lack of action from the adults in her school. Maya felt offended by the posts and was looking for an adult to step in and protect her from seeing more of the same messages. She also anticipated that an adult at her school could act in the role of punisher, making sure that her fellow students received some type of consequence for making racist statements online.

What likely happened in this case was not an uncaring administration, but a gray area where free speech, hate speech, cyberbullying, and school law mingle. When hate speech makes its way into a school building, administration has every right to step in and limit the free speech rights of individuals in order to protect the safety, security, and learning environment for all other students (Warnick, 2013). But, the school's reach can only go so far. School administrators do not have the authority to limit the free speech of students who are communicating on personal devices outside of the school day unless those comments carry over into the school and cause a disruption to the learning environment (Meyer, 2016). This caveat is what Maya was describing when she said she had never felt personally threatened or intimidated at school by her fellow students. Unfortunately, most digital citizenship curricula, with their sweeping generalizations about "being nice" and "not cyberbullying" and "telling a grown-up" are not helping students navigate these legal nuances.

Students must be given opportunities to explore the gray areas of free speech and participation in digital spaces.

Because the school was not legally able to step in and intervene, what other choices did Maya have for dealing with these offensive messages? If you look back at the framework for adult and teen relationships in most digital citizenship curricula, Maya did exactly what traditional digital citizenship lessons conditioned her to do. In them, the only role a teen can take that has any sort of power is the role of the aggressor who acts upon his or her victims. Someone who feels victimized, like Maya did, is shown as powerless.

In considering the curricular implications of Maya's story, it's clear we have a lot of work to do. Students must be given opportunities to explore the gray areas of free speech and participation in digital spaces. High school students, especially, need to be taught ways to intervene respectfully and on their own behalves when they encounter hateful or derogatory remarks.

More importantly, our curricula need to be rewritten to better reflect the roles, relationships, and power dynamics of people in digital communities. When the curriculum narrowly defines teens as troublemakers and victims, and adults as predators or punishers, students have very limited models of what they can be "when they grow up" in a digital space.

Participatory Citizenship Approach

A participatory citizenship approach to digital communities recognizes that all digital citizens, regardless of age, contribute to and consume from digital spaces. When people come together in communities and exchange ideas as both consumers and contributors, dialogue and deliberation happen. Rather than picturing the relationships between teens and adults in online communities as positions of power or weakness, I prefer a model such as the one in Figure 3.2.

Consuming and Contributing

Digital consumers are those who use the internet to gain information or entertainment. In the role of consumer, we enter into digital communities with the intention of taking something away. A digital contributor, on the other hand, is interested in adding his or her voice to a digital space. Contributors may share their opinions in a comments section, put up original content—images, blog posts, videos, etc.—for others to see, or provide feedback to companies by writing reviews of products and services. In online spaces, both teens and adults have the power to determine the value of their digital contributions and the ways they interact with the digital contributions of others. I think it's worth noting that both consumption and contribution can happen in isolation. When I write a blog post, I am contributing content to

Figure 3.2

Digital citizens of all ages play the roles of consumers and contributors in digital communities.

my community of followers. When I read someone else's blog post, I am consuming content they've written. The two roles only overlap when users enter into conversation with one another around a shared piece of content. When I can consume someone else's viewpoint and contribute my own back, I begin a dialogue that moves both me and the other user into a space of conversation, whereby we are simultaneously consuming and contributing.

When students like Maya, whom you met in the opening of this chapter, are taught through a lens of consumption and contribution rather than approached as troublemakers or victims, a teacher's opportunity to grow a variety of student skills sets emerges. Had Maya understood the rights of other community contributors, been taught techniques for controlling the types of information coming her way, and had some practice with digital deliberation and discussion under the mentorship of an adult, her story may have ended very differently.

We can have students explore their roles as consumers and contributors in a variety of ways because digital citizenship conversations fit well in many different content areas. Anywhere in the curriculum that explores people in community with one another is an easy place to extend that conversation into online spaces by simply "hacking" the learning standards.

Hacking the Standards

To "hack" learning standards, simply take the original and add a few words or phrases that will help you consider the ways your curriculum can address the roles of students as citizens in both physical communities and digital ones. Please note that hacking your standards does not mean scrapping parts of the curriculum or completely changing what students will learn. You are simply identifying opportunities in your existing units to extend and deepen what is already happening in your classroom.

> A participatory citizenship approach to digital communities recognizes that all digital citizens, regardless of age, contribute to and consume from digital spaces.

Try hacking a few of your classroom learning targets like I did for the following health standards, giving students more opportunities to explore their roles as digital citizens in ways that are authentically integrated into the curriculum rather than presented to them as stand-alone topics.

These standards were taken from the National Health Education Standards (Joint Committee on National Health Education, 2007), but you can find similar standards in many state and local curricula as well. Whatever set of curricular standards you use will work just fine for a hack as long as you can think about them through a digital citizenship lens.

HEALTH STANDARDS

- 2.12.3   Analyze how peers influence healthy and unhealthy behaviors.

- 5.12.1   Examine barriers that can hinder healthy decision making.

HACKED HEALTH STANDARDS

- 2.12.3 Analyze how peers influence healthy and unhealthy _digital_ behaviors.

- 5.12.1 Examine barriers that can hinder healthy _online_ decision making.

Hacking your learning standards can allow you to cover the content you are required to teach while also helping students explore how those curricular concepts impact their lives as digital citizens. The featured activity that follows can be an excellent fit in a health class unit on relationships.

FEATURED ACTIVITY:

Consume or Contribute

A participatory citizen never acts in isolation, so student behaviors can be personally healthy or unhealthy, but can also impact the larger digital community in positive and negative ways. Help students reflect on their digital behaviors and roles as consumers and contributors with this simple activity.

Before starting the activity, use Table 3.1 "How Do Our Behaviors Impact Digital Communities?" to prepare an index card for each student in the class. On each card, write a behavior from the first column on one side and a behavior from the second column on the other side. Label the cards Side A and Side B so that students can easily tell which side you want them to refer to during the lesson.

Table 3.1 How Do Our Behaviors Impact Digital Communities?

Contribute or Consume?	Contributions: Positive, Negative or Neutral?
Leave a nasty comment on someone's Instagram post.	Reply to a Tweet by calling the person a loser and an idiot.
Read online news articles.	Like a post on Facebook.
Play Xbox Live with others.	Create an anonymous Twitter account to send out compliments.
Use Google Maps to get directions.	

Contribute or Consume?	Contributions: Positive, Negative or Neutral?
Check show times on a movie theater website.	Follow the school library on Instagram.
Listen to a new track on SoundCloud.	Use racial slurs while playing Call of Duty.
Send a text to a friend.	Create a "We Hate Our School" Facebook group.
Share a news article on Twitter.	
Watch videos on YouTube.	Leave a nasty comment on someone's Instagram post.
Create videos and post them on YouTube.	Post how-to videos on YouTube.
Edit incorrect information on an athlete's Wikipedia page.	Create a website to share original poetry.
Listen to podcasts.	Share a picture of a meal on Instagram.
Create a website to promote a personal project.	Edit incorrect information on an athlete's Wikipedia page.
Make a purchase on Amazon.	
Stream a movie from Netflix.	Post thoughts about a book on a class message board.
Write a Tweet that insults someone's religion.	Tweet a picture before a game.
Send a Snap to a boyfriend/girlfriend.	Subtweet a mean comment without mentioning anyone's name.
Post thoughts about a book on a class message board.	Post an Instagram story about a personal accomplishment.
Email a teacher a question about an assignment.	Write a product review on Amazon.
Write a product review on Amazon.	Send 50 texts to a boyfriend or girlfriend in one day.
Like a post on Facebook.	
Share a picture of a meal on Instagram.	Read a book to a kindergarten class over Google Hangouts.
"Check in" to the gym.	Write a blog post about a family vacation.
Share a piece of original artwork on DeviantArt.	
Scroll through Twitter while waiting for a ride.	Retweet the school principal.
Click on an ad inside an article.	Send a Snap of a cat to a friend.
Get interviewed for a school newscast.	Leave derogatory comments about women on a story about equal pay.
Retweet the school principal.	

Contribute or Consume?	Contributions: Positive, Negative or Neutral?
Compliment a friend's new haircut through a text.	Post pictures of a teacher with a caption about her horrible outfit.
Do a Google image search for a prom dress.	Share writing on a fan fiction website.
Design a file on Tinkercad to print on a 3-D printer.	Teach someone how to modify settings on an iPhone.
Play Candy Crush or 8 Ball Pool on a phone.	Start using a schoolwide hashtag to celebrate achievements.
Write a blog post about a family vacation.	Create a phony Facebook account to troll stories put out by the school.
Read a book to a kindergarten class through Google Hangouts.	Make a video of someone changing in the locker room without his or her knowledge and then share it.
Check out an ebook through the public library.	Tweet out a favorite song lyric.
	Post a funny cat video to Facebook.
	Screenshot a Tweet from a protected account and share it publicly.
	Text a friend an animated gif to wish them a happy birthday.
	Connect with a nonprofit organization via LinkedIn.
	Start a petition on Change.org.

To begin, ask students to tell you ways they contribute to their school as well as ways they consume from it. Students may talk about consuming lessons or learning materials and contributing through their involvement in clubs, athletics, and participation in service projects. Once it's clear they understand the difference between consume and contribute, hand out the index cards and ask students to look at Side A.

As students look at the digital behavior on Side A of their card, have them move to one side of the room if they are holding a digital contribution and to the opposite side of the room if they are holding a digital consumption. Some behaviors, such as "Retweeting the school principal," may not have an obvious answer, and that's okay! Allow students to move as they see fit.

While still standing on one side of the room, have students pair up with the classmate closest to them and discuss the behaviors:

- Share the behavior on your card with your discussion partner. Does he or she agree that it is a contribution/consumption?

- Ask your partner these questions: Is this contribution/consumption something that you do or have done? If so, what influences you to adopt that behavior? If not, what influences you to reject that behavior?

Next, ask students to find a discussion partner on the opposite side of the room, so that one contributor is standing with one consumer. Have students answer the same questions listed above with their new discussion partner and then return to their seats.

> **When students are taught through a lens of consumption and contribution rather than approached as troublemakers or victims, a teacher's opportunity to grow a variety of student skills sets emerges.**

Once students are seated, point out that it was pretty easy for them to recognize consumption in digital communities because it typically looked like the user taking something away, whether that something was information or entertainment. The contributions were a little trickier to discern, though.

While we typically think of a contribution as a positive thing, not all contributions are made equally. When someone contributes graffiti to the school bathroom, for example, it actually creates a mess that the maintenance staff has to clean up. Digital contributions are the same way. We all add to digital spaces in many ways, shapes, and forms, but what we add has different levels of value.

At this point, have students turn their index card over to Side B, so that each one is looking at a digital contribution. Instruct students to move to the front of the room if their contribution is positive, the back of the room if it is negative, and the center of the room if it is neutral.

Just as before, have students pair up with someone standing close to them and discuss.

- Share the contribution on your card with your discussion partner. Does he or she agree that it is a positive/negative/neutral contribution?

- Ask your partner these questions: Is this contribution something that you do or have done? If so, what influences you? If not, what influences you to abstain?

- Ask your partner: How does this type of contribution impact the other people in your digital community?

As before, instruct students to find a partner whose contribution is in a different category from their own. A neutral contribution might pair up with a positive one, for example. Have students answer the same questions listed above with their new partner.

When they are finished discussing, students should return to their seats and write a personal reflection on the following statements:

- In my online communities, I play the role of consumer when...

- In my online communities, I play the role of contributor when...

- When considering my own online behaviors, peers influence me by...

- I think people make negative contributions to online communities because...

- Some of the barriers that keep people from positively contributing to digital communities are...

- If I could change something about an online community I belong to, it would be...

- In reflecting on my own online behaviors, I could make healthier decisions by...

Ask students to share out their reflections in a whole-class discussion if time permits and they are comfortable doing so. When students are given time to reflect on the roles they play in their digital communities, they are more likely to see how their choices impact their experiences and the experiences of others.

SPOTLIGHT STORY

Deliberating the Role of Outsiders in Digital Communities

Adam Dyche (@mrdyche) is a social studies department chair at Waubonsie Valley High School in Aurora, Illinois. He hacked his content standards in order to help students explore the roles they play in digital communities while simultaneously considering the impact that outsiders can have.

In addition to their learning the curricular content in his semester-long class, American Government, Adam wanted his high school seniors to have guided practice with the types of learning experiences they would encounter after high school. This meant redesigning his class to include more flexibility in the student schedule, components of online learning, and a purposeful focus on life skills such as digital communication, self-advocacy, decision-making, time management, and adaptability.

The Role of Citizens and Government

The main focus of American Government is learning about and exploring the roles of citizens, the government, and the interactions between the two. Because Adam's class blends face-to-face instruction and digital learning, he wanted to help his students explore their roles as digital citizens as well as traditional ones, and looked for opportunities to extend his curricular goals into the digital realm.

Continued on following page.

Continued from previous page.

One of the traditional curricular expectations for this course is that students explore and deliberate the complex nature of personal liberty and collective security. In the past, to teach his students about the various civil liberties promised to them in the Constitution, Adam gave them examples of times when a governmental agency had to step in and remove those civil liberties in the name of collective security. Students explored Supreme Court cases such as New Jersey v. T.L.O., which ruled that schools can search student belongings if they have probable cause, and Hazelwood School District v. Kuhlmeier, which ruled that schools have the right to censor the student newspaper. While Adam still covered these issues with his students, he also wanted to hear their thoughts about how these same concepts may or may not be pertinent in digital spaces.

One of the most successful examples from the semester was an in-class deliberation over the guiding question: "Should 'outsiders' be able to regulate free speech in digital communities?" Before beginning the deliberation, Adam and his students had to collectively define both "outsiders" and "digital communities." They came to a consensus that a "digital community" was any group of people regularly interacting in a digital space. "Outsiders" were anyone who was not part of the community. These outsiders could include technology companies, parents, teachers, law enforcement, or any government agency.

Students were asked to locate two or three articles that could help them learn about the topic and also serve as support in their deliberation. As long as the articles were credible, students could bring in anything that helped them explore the guiding question. Using this method of inquiry-based instruction, Adam was able to emphasize that he was not looking for students to find a "correct answer" to the question. He merely wanted students to be able to make an argument, recognize competing viewpoints, and draw a consensus when possible.

Students Explore the Issue

Adam was surprised at the complexity of thought students brought to the conversation, and recorded some compelling sound bites in his notes. Many of the teens felt that freedom of speech should extend into digital communities, regardless of what others in or outside of the community felt was appropriate. One student proclaimed, "If you aren't willing to open yourself up for criticism and debate, log off and grab a newspaper."

Another student agreed, wondering if "social media would lose its allure" if strict censorship was the norm by way of community standards or through digital algorithms. A third student pointed out that "censorship on social media can create more of the same thinking instead of allowing us to have more tough conversations."

In any good deliberation, though, there is more than one perspective. A student brought up her younger sibling and wondered aloud if there should be some censorship online in order to protect child users. She worried that as her brother started exploring social media, he would be surprised at what he found there. The class agreed, but then started talking about who should be in charge of that type of censorship anyway. Is it the tech companies? The government? Adults?

Most students agreed that it was up to digital community members to set and uphold group standards. "It's the responsibility of users to flag inappropriate content or bring threats to the attention of company owners or authorities." Another student in the circle agreed: "Flagging social media content is better than a company trying to enforce a written policy because the community shapes the behavior of others in it." And in the end, the class seemed to concede that, "it isn't up to companies to draw a line; it is up to people to choose their social communities wisely."

Adam was pleased with his students' first attempt at an in-class deliberation, and overall he saw that students were engaged in the topic because it was relevant and genuine. "I don't want my messages about online community with students to be limited to 'treat others the way you want to be treated'," Adam said. "In the same ways that aspects of government and citizenship are nuanced, so are aspects of life in digital communities. I do not have all of the answers, but I am happy to provide a space for my students to discuss the subtleties of life in a digital age." ●

CLICK

Nancy Watson (@NancyWTech) is a champion of digital citizenship and digital literacy who is challenging students to take on the role of contributor in a very meaningful way. As a technology specialist and instructional coach for Plano Independent School District in Texas, Nancy helps teachers integrate technology into their instruction in ways that enhance learning and benefit students. Her passion project, though, is one that puts students in the role of experts and helps them see the value of using their voices and skills sets while making contributions to digital communities.

In her role, Nancy recognizes that many students across the grade levels do not have the digital literacy skills necessary to be impactful digital citizens. Nancy says that as adults, "we often ascribe much more knowledge and understanding to our 'digital native' students than what is true. While some students do possess technology understanding, we can't assume that ALL students do."

Unfortunately, some teachers lack these technology skills as well, leaving a gap between what is expected of students through the curriculum and the supports students have at their disposal to help them meet those expectations. During Nancy's varied interactions with teachers and students, a thought lingered in the back of her mind: What if there were a safe, kid-friendly space for students to learn digital literacy skills from one another?

CLICK, which stands for Collaborate, Learn, Instruct, Create, Know, was Nancy's solution to that nagging question. She maintains the website, but all of its content is created by kids, for kids. CLICK is aligned to and organized around the ISTE Standards for Students (2016) and is essentially a library of short videos on various technology topics. In them, students demonstrate how to use applications such as Google Drive, SketchUp, and Photoshop and tackle topics such as texting etiquette, digital privacy, and even appropriate ways to carry a Chromebook.

Reaction to the student-developed CLICK content has been positive. Teachers see it as a place to direct students who have technology questions, and are also finding value in the site for their own learning. One student review, in particular, made Nancy smile: "This is cool! Sometimes we can learn stuff better from another kid."

Nancy invests extra time in CLICK because she believes in its ability to foster digital literacy as well as a sense of digital community. "My hope is that CLICK will empower those students who do have an understanding of technology to use their voices to contribute to a project that will help many others—students, teachers, parents, grandparents. The student creators learn too—not only presentation skills, but also a reassurance that they know stuff, and what they say matters." ●

You Can Do It!

The exciting news is that you do not need a complete curricular overhaul or extra time for stand-alone digital citizenship lessons. You can help your students become amazing digital community members by making small changes to the individual units, lessons, or projects that already exist in your curriculum. As members of a classroom community, you can explore life in digital communities in ways that are purposeful and authentic rather than forced or added-on. For instance:

- Identify opportunities in which your current content standards can be "hacked" to include aspects of digital citizenship.

- Ask students if *they* can make connections between class lessons and their experiences in digital communities.

- Share stories like Maya's, and ask students how they may have responded in her situation.

- Encourage your students to contribute to, not just consume from, their digital communities.

- Celebrate students' digital creations as you would their physical ones: In addition to hanging students' artwork on a bulletin board, showcase a digital contribution, such as a student's original SoundCloud track, on your classroom website.

4

Participating through Respectful Discourse

In October of 2016, I attended the Digital Citizenship Summit at Twitter Headquarters in San Francisco, California. While there, I listened to a college freshman named Timmy Sullivan give a keynote address about his experiences with social media. During his senior year in high school, Timmy gave a fantastic TEDx Talk called "It's MY Education!," in which he advocated for more personalized learning opportunities and student voice in the design of classroom curricula. That same year, Timmy was also freelancing as a blogger, student voice advocate, and guest speaker at educational technology conferences.

During his keynote address at Twitter, Timmy praised the work of his teacher and mentor, Jennifer Scheffer. When Timmy was in her class, Jennifer asked all of the students to Google themselves. Then, in front of the class, Jennifer did the same with her own name. As a connected educator and blogger, Jennifer was able to show her high school students the positive ways that she was connecting with others and contributing ideas to her field through her social media presence, all of which came up in the Google search. Timmy was inspired and knew that he could utilize some of the same tools his teacher had to increase the spread of his own voice and ideas.

While I was impressed with Timmy's extensive resume and work in the fields of education and educational technology, it was his stance on the social media discourse in education that stuck with me the most. He made a bold, yet logical, assertion that if adults continue to frame social media negatively, students will continue that downward spiral in a form of self-fulfilling prophecy. His message to the audience? Stop. Stop talking about all of the mistakes people make with technology, and start encouraging students to emulate the positives that they see.

Timmy challenged all of us to "collectively divorce from the rhetoric of social media's explicitly harmful nature, [and] embrace the challenge to promote positive social media use in schools. Students can learn to leverage Twitter to build a global community of learners, use YouTube to share their content, connect with professionals via LinkedIn, and assert their voice through blogging. Through education, demonstration, and proactive conversation we can abolish cyber bullying—but we must first abolish our negative mentality" (Sullivan, 2016).

In many ways, Timmy's message is spot on. Students cannot be what they cannot see. If digital citizenship curriculum focuses solely on all of the things we do not want students to do in digital spaces, are we leaving them with any suggestions for how to effectively use these powerful tools?

Current Approaches to Digital Citizenship

We have all heard the Golden Rule: Treat others the way you want to be treated. This rule is the center cog that keeps most digital citizenship curricula chugging along. In a 2011 survey by the American Association for School Librarians, the topics listed as most prevalent in digital citizenship curricula were cheating and dishonesty, cyberbullying, harassment, and stalking. In the younger grades especially, students are taught that cyberbullying is bad and that trolls will say mean things just to cause a stir. Students are given a few tactics for dealing with a bully, such as blocking the user or telling an adult.

What these curricula do *not* do well, however, is help students differentiate between true cyberbullying, generic hate speech, drama between peer groups, and simple disagreement of opinion. Many digital citizenship curricula also lack positive examples of what healthy online discussion and deliberation look like (Mattson, 2016).

Unless teens construct a perfect digital echo chamber for themselves, they are going to come across ideas, opinions, and content they do not immediately agree with. Unfortunately, as Timmy pointed out in his keynote, parents and educators spend a lot of time telling kids how *not* to react to opposition—warning teens that if they post inappropriate language, harass other users, say something offensive, or post material deemed threatening they could face punishment from a myriad of authority figures. While this advice is not incorrect, it's very one-sided. When all of our tips come in the form of behaviors to avoid, students are left struggling to navigate that interaction on their own, without a model or guide for *how to* respond instead.

 Stop talking about all of the mistakes people make with technology, and start encouraging students to emulate the positives that they see.

If we want our students to be participatory digital citizens, moving beyond a space of isolated consumption or contribution, they need something more than a list of "do nots," so that they can interact respectfully, intelligently, and fairly—especially when they meet people whose lives may be very different from their own.

Participatory Citizenship Approach

While sound argument and civic deliberation are cornerstones of both the College, Career, and Civic Life (C3) Framework for Social Studies State Standards and the Common Core State Standards for English Language Arts, educators are not required to help students translate these skills into digital communities. An inability to transfer these skills can be problematic, especially when people enter into online conversation without a clear purpose, agreed-upon process, or practiced conversation structure. Because digital conversations can happen across physical and cultural boundaries, oftentimes the participants' norms of offline conversation are not even the same. Unfortunately, these missteps can result in misunderstandings, hurt feelings, insults, and unproductive bickering.

Hacking the Standards

As I suggested in Chapter 3, teachers can hack their standards and learning targets, not to change what is being taught, but to expand the depth of student learning into online communities, making the relationships between offline citizenship and digital citizenship more explicit.

Here are a few examples of social studies and English standards that have been modified to reflect the skills we need to interact with others as both traditional and digital citizens. Whatever set of curricular standards you use will work just fine for a hack as long as you can think about them through a digital citizenship lens.

SOCIAL STUDIES STANDARDS

These standards are taken from the College, Career, and Civic Life (C3) Framework for Social Studies State Standards (National Council for the Social Studies, 2013), but you can find similar standards in many state and local curricula as well.

- D2.Civ.9.9-12. Use appropriate deliberative processes in multiple settings.

- D2.Civ.5.9-12. Evaluate citizens' and institutions' effectiveness in addressing social and political problems at the local, state, tribal, national, and/or international level.

HACKED SOCIAL STUDIES STANDARDS:

- D2.Civ.9.9-12. Use appropriate deliberative processes in multiple settings, _including digital communities_.

- D2.Civ.5.9-12. Evaluate citizens' and institutions' effectiveness in _using digital tools and communications_ for addressing social and political problems at the local, state, tribal, national, and/or international level.

ENGLISH LANGUAGE ARTS STANDARDS

These standards are taken from the Common Core State Standards for English Language Arts (Common Core State Standards Initiative, 2010), but you can find similar standards in many state and local curricula as well.

- CCSS.ELA-Literacy SL.9-10.1.A. Come to discussions prepared, having read and researched material under study; explicitly draw on that preparation by referring to evidence from texts and other research on the topic or issue to stimulate a thoughtful, well-reasoned exchange of ideas.

- CCSS.ELA-Literacy SL.9-10.1.C. Propel conversations by posing and responding to questions that relate the current discussion to broader themes or larger ideas; actively incorporate others into the discussion; and clarify, verify, or challenge ideas and conclusions.

HACKED ENGLISH LANGUAGE ARTS STANDARDS

- CCSS.ELA-Literacy SL.9-10.1.A. Come to _digital_ discussions prepared, having read and researched material under study; explicitly draw on that preparation by referring to evidence from texts and other research on the topic or issue to stimulate a thoughtful, well-reasoned exchange of ideas _in online communities_.

- CCSS.ELA-Literacy SL.9-10.1.C. Propel conversations _in digital spaces_ by posing and responding to questions that relate the current discussion to broader themes or larger ideas; actively incorporate others into the discussion; and clarify, verify, or challenge ideas and conclusions.

ISTE Standards for Students

We can also look to the following ISTE Standards for Students (2016) to further justify the need for explicit teaching of discussion and deliberation in digital communities as part of a comprehensive education for all digital citizens.

- Digital Citizen (2b): Students engage in positive, safe, legal and ethical behavior when using technology, including social interactions online or when using networked devices.

- Creative Communicator (6c): Students communicate complex ideas clearly and effectively by creating or using a variety of digital objects such as visualizations, models or simulations.

- Global Collaborator (7a): Students use digital tools to connect with learners from a variety of backgrounds and cultures, engaging with them in ways that broaden mutual understanding and learning.

FEATURED ACTIVITY:

Effective Versus Ineffective Online Discussions

In many social studies and English classrooms, discussion takes place in face-to-face settings in the form of Socratic seminars. In this type of seminar, students have had time to read a text and prepare notes from it, and the teacher lays out clear guidelines for the discussion, often providing a written protocol for students to refer back to. If the Socratic seminar travels into unproductive territory, the teacher is there to redirect the discussion and correct any major missteps.

When students move into online deliberations, however, we often simply hope that they can carry over what they've learned in class to the digital spaces they visit. Instead, let's give them some guidance and practice with digital discussion as well. Begin by having students examine both effective and ineffective online conversations using an activity similar to the one I've outlined on the pages that follow.

Note: You may wish to compile all group answers into a T-chart of effective and ineffective online discussion strategies. Table 4.1 can serve as a reminder or reference for students as you engage them in further practice.

People converse, share their opinions, and even get into disagreements in online communities all the time, but the effectiveness of those discussion can vary greatly. For this activity, give small groups of students one effective discussion and one ineffective discussion from the samples that follow. Ask students to come up with a list of ways that the discussions are either effective or ineffective.

TABLE 4.1 Effective Versus Ineffective Online Discussions

Effective Online Discussion	Ineffective Online Discussion
Users take the time to read and understand the original post before commenting.	People add to the discussion before reading the original post or any of the other comments.
Ideas are exchanged between two or more users.	One person may dominate the conversation, unwilling to hear new ideas.
People tag one another or mention the name(s) of other community member(s) their thoughts are directed toward.	A user adds his or her thoughts without referencing a particular person, line of thinking, or portion of the original text.
People use an agreed-upon style of language and carefully craft their message so that it's easily understood and interpreted by others.	People make typos, write incomplete thoughts, or use uncommon slang, making it hard for others to understand their message.
Commenters refer back to specifics from the original post and other people's comments.	Commenters stray from the original topic.
People present evidence and personal experiences to support their opinions while also respecting the experiences of others.	Users resort to insults or name-calling, attacking other users who do not agree with their opinion.
The digital community has agreed-upon norms for interaction, and users uphold them in their discussion.	The digital community is unmoderated and users interact without agreed-upon standards.
People consume as much as they contribute, reading with the intention of understanding and learning more.	People argue without any intention of learning something new. Their only goal is to combat other people's opinions.

Effective Discussions

Let's start with some examples of effective discussions.

EFFECTIVE DISCUSSION A

An article called "Dress Code Debate: Is the Fingertips Rule Outdated?" is shared on social media. The article is about a high school girl in Tennessee who started a petition. She convinced her school board to change the dress code from shorts that touch the bottoms of your fingertips to shorts that only need to go to the mid-thigh.

The following exchange was found in the comments section:

Shannon: When you live in a hot climate, common sense dictates that you will probably wear less clothing. Why is it that trying to stay cool in a school building that is not air conditioned becomes a shameful, sexual act? Girls should be able to dress for the weather and not have to cover up so the males are not "distracted." Dress codes in school are an outdated concept in general if you ask me.

Riley: While I agree with your point about not making dress codes just to keep boys from "getting distracted at school," I work in a junior high and see plenty of seventh-grade girls with their butt cheeks hanging out. There has to be some middle ground.

Shannon: Point taken. Butt cheeks hanging out is never a good choice—no matter how old you are!

EFFECTIVE DISCUSSION B

An article called "Social Media Posts Lead to a Suspension for a Texas Firefighter" is shared on social media. The article reports that a firefighter received a thirty-day suspension from his job for breaking the organization's social media policy, which states that obscene language cannot be used to ridicule, belittle, or harass any other person.

The following exchange happened in the comments section:

Robert: Volunteer and career firefighters swear an oath to uphold and support the Constitution. Maybe it's about time for the firefighters, such as myself, to give the fire service higher-ups an ultimatum. They need to accept the fact that firefighters are entitled to free speech, as the Constitution says, or we need to go. This is getting out of hand. This suspension is an attack on free speech.

Alejandro: Ok, does anyone commenting here really understand what freedom of speech means? It means that you can protest against the government without fear of imprisonment. It does not mean that a person whose sworn job is public safety can make a demeaning remark against minorities whom he is expected to help without prejudice. It brings into question whether he would do what's expected of him when dealing with minorities and in turn it brings discredit to the organization.

Lisa: @Robert: The suspension is fair enough. His employment contract says that he cannot use social media to degrade other people or groups, and he did. Therefore, he broke a clause in his contract and deserves a punishment; that's just how it works.

Robert: @Lisa, @Alejandro: I guess I could just throw my hands up and say that my superiors shouldn't have a right to free speech while they are on or off duty either, but I wouldn't do that because I believe in the rights of others. I did swear an oath to uphold and support the Constitution, which means a guy should have the freedom to say what he wants to say on Facebook. Sorry that I'm not sorry.

Heather: @Robert: I swore that same oath...but the freedom of speech never guaranteed that we are free from all consequences. That would mean chaos and anarchy, yes? You do not have to be sorry for your opinion, but you do need to realize that words matter and actions have consequences.

EFFECTIVE DISCUSSION C

A local online newspaper publishes a post about a dog park being built in the center of the community. The post details that the park will be surrounded by a tall fence and have lots of open grass, a few trees, drinking stations, and benches for dog owners. The park is being built on a piece of community-owned land that has been sitting empty for several years.

The following exchange happens in the comments section:

Bill: A dog park? Are you kidding me? How is that supposed to help our community? What we need is business. Business brings in tax dollars and helps all of us out. A lot of people I know don't even have a dog.

Lacey: @Bill We have a lot of businesses in our town already. In fact, we have some empty buildings that businesses could move into tomorrow if they wanted. We do not have a lot of places for people to just come together socially. I think this addition will be an awesome way to get neighbors out interacting and people exercising in a fun way with their pets.

Monica: @Lacey I second your opinion. I like having a place to go and be with friends or neighbors that doesn't cost me any money. Anytime I want to sit in public and chat with friends, I feel like I have to buy a coffee or a lunch to justify our presence there. I can definitely see meeting up with some people at this dog park.

Bill: @Lacey @Monica We have a great park district already. Here is a LINK to a list of all the parks that our community maintains. You and your friends can take your dogs to any of these spaces to walk on the trails, or to sit at a picnic table and chat. Our main downtown area should remain a business center.

Monica: @Bill Wow. Thanks for that LINK. I've only been in this neighborhood for about six months and didn't realize I had so many options. While I still think a designated dog park would be a good addition, I appreciate you sharing more choices with me.

Effective Discussion Review

Students may have lots of ideas about what made the discussions effective. Here are a few points students should consider:

EFFECTIVE DISCUSSION A

In this discussion, Riley was able to respectfully affirm Shannon's opinion about school dress codes before challenging her to consider an alternative one. Shannon is able to see that her views may have been limited, and thanks Riley for her respectful counterargument. Riley and Shannon both walked away from the exchange better understanding a viewpoint other than their own.

EFFECTIVE DISCUSSION B

This discussion is a good example of a conversation among several users in which there's an exchange of ideas, not just a stream of contributions. The commenters tag one another in their replies to indicate who they're addressing. While this conversation doesn't end with any of the users changing his or her opinion, everyone involved exchanges ideas in a respectful manner—no one resorts to name-calling, personal attacks, or belittling.

EFFECTIVE DISCUSSION C

This discussion is an example of community members using a digital tool to engage with one another as an extension of their local community. While the people in the conversation have different opinions, they are able to back up their reasoning with authentic experiences and examples. Bill also sees an opportunity to share a hyperlink with a member of his community, thus helping her see his point of view more clearly and gain new information that will benefit her.

Ineffective Discussions

The following exchanges should be given to students as examples of ineffective discussions. The digital citizens in these examples have chosen to move from a space of independent consumption or contribution into a place of dialogue, but the results are not very valuable. Ask students to list the characteristics of ineffective discussion that they see in these three samples.

INEFFECTIVE DISCUSSION A

An article about a police officer who gave himself a speeding ticket is posted on social media. A private citizen filmed the officer traveling at speeds near 80 miles per hour. When the citizen sent the video into the station, the officer admitted his guilt, issued a public apology, and stated that he was writing himself a $300 speeding ticket. The article also says that people in the community are thanking the officer for doing the right thing by leaving comments on the police station's social media page.

The following discussion happened in the comments section:

Kyle: What an idiot. Did he stop himself on the roadway or did he wait until he got back into his comfortable office to write it up?

Spencer: @Kyle You are the idiot. Did you even read the article?

Maya: He probably feels guilty for all the free donuts and coffee he gets around town.

Amjest: This is not doing the right thing. The right thing would be not speeding in the first place.

Steve: He looks kind of fat in this picture. Aren't there health requirements to be a cop?

INEFFECTIVE DISCUSSION B

A local newspaper shared a story on its Facebook page. The article was about an armed robbery at a video game store in the center of town. According to employees, two men in ski masks entered the store around 8:45 p.m. and demanded money from the register. They fled in a car that witnesses could not give a description of. People with information or leads were encouraged to call the county crime stopper hotline.

The following discussion happens in the comments section:

Tyler: That store is terrible anyway. They only gave me $15 for the ten used games I brought in.

Sam: @Tyler What kind of games? I know a guy who is always looking to buy and he is willing to give a lot more cash than that.

Tyler: @Sam Mostly old stuff, but still....

Melissa: This is craziness. I moved into this town because I thought it was safe. I cannot believe I have to worry about armed robberies so close to home.

Harold: Oh boy. Can't wait for all of the crazies on this thread to start yelling about the need for more gun control! It's called the 2nd amendment. Let people have their guns!

Suzanne: These boys need some religion in their lives. All are welcome to come to my church on 3rd Street. We have a 9 a.m. and an 11 a.m. service.

Someone posts an opinion piece entitled "Many Ways Technology Is Interrupting Our Lives." The piece talks about ways that technology can make it hard to focus on tasks, can be a distraction when we are with friends and loved ones, and can make it harder for people to break away from work once they leave the office.

The following is posted in the comments section:

Pablo: Isn't it ironic that we are all reading this on our phones?

Sarah: Isn't it ironic a guy named Pablo can actually read?

Don: It would be nice if this article would also talk about nine ways technology is helping us. I feel like too often technology articles focus on the bad, when there are so many awesome ways technology helps us too. It's all about balance, really.

Sarah: It would be really great if technology could make you less ugly, Don.

Todd: Wow, Sarah. Your a real peach. Maybe you should take a little technology break.

Sarah: *you're

Sarah: The only bad thing about technology is that I have to deal with morons like you making idiotic comments all day. It's tough to combat stupidity, but someone has to try....

Ineffective Discussion Review

Students may have lots of ideas about what made these discussions ineffective. Here are a few key points for you to reinforce:

INEFFECTIVE DISCUSSION A

This is not even a discussion. Various people are contributing, but no one is listening. The only back and forth exchange between people is to name call. Nothing productive results from these posts—they are simply opinions and white noise that do nothing to further the knowledge or experience of other users.

INEFFECTIVE DISCUSSION B

This thread is an example of how people can get away from a topic and try to forward their own agendas. After time, the comments are not even related to the original article. No one is conversing—everyone is posting their own random thoughts.

INEFFECTIVE DISCUSSION C

This thread is an example of one person making negative contributions just for the sake of it. Sarah seems to want to pick a fight with anyone who comments on the article. It's unlikely that a meaningful dialogue will happen on this thread because Sarah is busy derailing anyone's attempt to start a conversation.

There are both productive and unproductive ways to engage in online discussion, as these examples show. Hopefully your class is able to come up with a pretty exhaustive list after this activity, but if students are struggling to articulate their ideas, or you would like to have a comprehensive list to refer back to, you can use Table 4.1.

Once students understand that effective online discussion is a respectful, purposeful exchange of ideas, they will need more examples, your modeling and guidance, as well as reference tools to help them engage in this way.

Sample Sentence Frames

One tool that your students can use, both in class and online, is a set of sample sentence structures that can help them organize their ideas for thoughtful, respectful, and productive discussion. The following sentence frames are based on ideas from the book *They Say, I Say: The Moves That Matter in Academic Writing* (Graff, Birkenstein, & Durst, 2006) but have been modified to better reflect the types of discussion students may have in digital communities (Figure 4.1).

Figure 4.1 (opposite)
Sentence frames can help students develop thoughtful, respectful responses in online conversations.

To **Introduce an Idea** Rooted in Evidence or Experience

Reading about _____ led me to think about _____.

According to _____, we should consider _____.

Because of my experience with _____, I believe _____.

This article defines _____ as _____.

Some important historical/contextual facts to consider are _____.

To **Acknowledge and Further** Someone Else's Viewpoint

The ideas presented by _____ are also seen in _____.

Thank you, _____, for presenting your viewpoint. I agree because _____.

The facts presented by _____ are also supported through _____.

To **Present** an Opposing Idea

_____ said _____, but the evidence I found says _____.

While _____ said _____, I think it is important to remember _____ because____.

I appreciate the experiences shared by _____, but in my experience _____.

To **Ask Questions** and Involve Others

I realize my views on _____ are limited. Does anyone here have experience with ____?

I am curious how others in the group view the notion of _____.

This article says _____. What are the group's thoughts about the quote?

_____, I am not sure what you meant by _____. Can you elaborate?

To **Demonstrate Understanding**

I have never thought about _____ in this way until _____.

I used to think _____, but now I understand _____.

The ideas mentioned in _____ helped me to see _____.

I appreciate the perspectives of _____ because _____.

Respectful Dialogue Starts with Empathy

A ndrea Trudeau (@Andrea_Trudeau) is a library media specialist at Alan B. Shepard Middle School in Deerfield, Illinois. Like many school librarians, Andrea is responsible for delivering her district's agreed-upon scope and sequence of digital citizenship lessons, mostly through partnerships with other teachers in her building. Her formal lessons cover most of the topics we've come to expect from digital citizenship curricula: password management, the permanence of online posts, copyright, fair use, and cyberbullying. But Andrea also includes the definition of a digital citizen as someone who is "respectful, empathetic, and willing to contribute to the world around them."

It's easy to tell students they must respect the people they meet online and in person, but what can we do to help students feel empathy for people they've never met or for someone who may be living in a situation very different from their own? Andrea and the teachers she partners with are making a concerted effort to do just that.

Enriching Lessons through AR/VR

Through the use of augmented reality (AR) and virtual reality (VR), Andrea has transported her students to places around the world—from a dirt-floored schoolhouse in South Africa to the underground remains of the Paris Catacombs. Using one of her favorite virtual reality apps, Andrea has taken her students to the shores of a Greek island where they watch Syrian refugees arrive by boat. The students hear the sounds of the waves, look up and down the coastline, and literally stand in the middle of refugee camps littered with tents and discarded life vests. "Virtual reality is such a fantastic way to help a student 'walk in someone else's shoes,'" says Andrea. "It is even more powerful than reading an article, viewing a photo, or watching a 2-D video. There's something about seeing a 360-degree view that brings the experience to life for a student" (Figure 4.2).

In Andrea's school, teachers from all curricular areas have been able to connect the virtual field trips with their content. Social studies teachers, in particular, are using the virtual reality experiences to enrich lessons on human rights as well as to bring current events to life in the classroom. After the virtual experiences, students' organic class discussions—often driven by the students themselves—reveal that their previously held viewpoints are being challenged, their perceptions of the world are being stretched, and their compassion and appreciation for varied human experiences are growing.

Empathy to Drive Change

Andrea's empathy work recently translated into a genuine opportunity for her students to make change in their corner of the world. A temple in Andrea's community supports a Syrian refugee family from Aleppo. Of course, the family struggles with resources, but it is also trying to quickly acclimate to American culture. When the family's two young children, ages 6 and 8, found they had a lot to learn about going to school in the United States, two social studies teachers, backed by Andrea's support, connected with the temple and asked if their students could help. Now, the eighth graders at Shepard Middle School are making short videos that welcome the family to the community, introduce aspects of American culture, and help them adapt to their new life here. The videos are housed in a Facebook group that can be easily accessed at any time. As Andrea points out, it can be easy for many of us to simply make

Figure 4.2
Shepard Middle School students Grace Friedman and Brady Fisher learn what life is like for other people through a virtual reality experience in their school library.

Continued on following page.

Continued from previous page.

a cash donation to someone in need, but the videos her eighth graders are making are done from the heart.

There are times when Andrea must deliver a stand-alone digital citizenship lesson or two, but she finds that when her messages are integrated seamlessly into everyday learning experiences, the students are more receptive to what she has to say about life in a digital space. Through the learning opportunities Andrea has given to students, both by introducing them to various cultures, viewpoints, and experiences and by modeling ways to contribute back through digital means, students are more apt to see how technology can teach us, connect us, and help us understand one another as citizens of a global society. ●

Encouraging Observation and Reflection

When students practice both in-person and online discussions in your classroom community, they are in a safe space that has some agreed-upon expectations, structures, and guidance from you. As they move into unmoderated digital communities, though, students have to consider whether or not to engage in discussion with various digital citizens, many of whom they have not met face to face. While we can all learn a lot from people whose life experiences are different from our own, we also run the risk of meeting digital citizens who are not in our communities for the same purposes we are.

As students consider their roles in digital communities and whether to move into a space of digital discussion and interaction with other community members, their powers of observation and self-reflection will be important. Encourage students to consider some of the following questions before making the leap from isolated consumers or contributors into a space of dialogue and deliberation:

- Am I willing to engage in an open-minded discussion with these community members, even if their opinions are different from my own?

- By engaging in this discussion, do I have the possibility of learning something new?

- By joining this discussion, do I have a different perspective to respectfully offer?

- Do these community members seem willing to learn and grow with me or do they have a history of negative contributions?

- Is the topic of conversation one I have personal experience with?

The more "yes" answers students can give to these questions, the more likely they are to have a positive interaction in their digital communities. You can model this questioning process for students by pulling up any article on social media or even looking through the comments section on a YouTube video. As you read through the comments, ask yourself some of the questions and answer them aloud, in front of the class. The students will witness your deliberation and see your thought process for deciding whether to stop at consumption or to join the discussion.

Let students know that even when we make thoughtful choices about when to engage in dialogue, we may still be confronted with ineffective, or even derogatory, online contributions from other digital

 As students consider their roles in digital communities and whether to move into a space of digital discussion and interaction with other community members, their powers of observation and self-reflection will be important.

citizens. Of course, when this happens, students can inform a trusted adult, but we can also teach them to do the following:

- Consider the digital community itself: Is the community worth staying in? Do the norms of acceptable behavior and dialogue in that space match your own? If you find yourself constantly upset by others in the community, it may be time to leave it altogether.

- Remind others of community standards: When a community member makes comments that do not fit in with the standards of the space, approach that member about it. This does not need to be done in a mean, confrontational way. Contact the user through a private message, if possible. Remind the member that there are agreed-upon rules to follow if he or she wants to remain in the community. Express that you appreciate the user's presence in the community and that you would hate to see him or her removed from the space.

- Report it, when necessary: If someone is breaking the agreed-upon rules of a community and has not responded well to your polite reminder, it's probably time to report that user to either the community moderator or the technology company itself. You can also block or remove this person from your own circles so that you do not need to interact with him or her again.

Additional classroom ideas to help students recognize, practice, and promote respectful discussion in online communities include the following:

- Have students find examples of effective and ineffective online discussions in their own digital communities. Students can bring in the examples along with a description of what makes the discussions effective or ineffective.

- Have students read an argument from the *New York Times* Room for Debate website (www.nytimes.com/roomfordebate). Ask them to judge the effectiveness of the conversations that follow in the comments section.

- Use the Writing Prompts section on the *New York Times* Learning Network website (www.nytimes.com/section/learning) to connect students, ages 13 and up, with middle and high school students around the country. The Learning Network website provides new writing prompts each week and encourages students to engage in conversation in their moderated comments section.

- Use your own digital classroom community as a space to practice respectful dialogue by posting articles, images, or video prompts that will incite discussion about your content.

Remember, students learn best from modeling, guided practice, and a gradual release of responsibility. The more opportunities your students have to converse with people both known and unknown to them in digital spaces, the more likely they are to develop the skills of responsible, respectful digital citizens.

THINK BIG

E laine McDonald, a third-year teacher at White River High School in Buckley, Washington, has one overarching expectation in her World History and AP Government classes: THINK BIG. This mantra applies to all sorts of learning opportunities, but when Elaine engages her students in conversation about digital citizenship, the motto is easy to reinforce.

Elaine teaches her students that in both physical and digital communities, it is easy for humans to get caught up in silos of thinking. People are naturally drawn into friendships with those who have similar life experiences. Online, we make conscious decisions about what to read and who to follow, and are unconsciously trapped into echo chambers through the digital algorithms that feed us more of the content we interact with most.

Learning to Engage with Others

Elaine helps her students see how easy it is to get caught up in a space of "us versus them," especially when we join conversations online and are suddenly confronted by ideas very different from our own. Instead of sheltering her students from conflict or simply reminding them to be nice online, Elaine challenges teens to THINK BIG; that is, to engage in conversations that might be outside of their comfort zones and to explore complex topics and problems that do not have easy answers.

So how does Elaine accomplish this monumental task? Not with a single mini-lesson. Not with one major assignment or assessment. In Elaine's classroom, relevant deliberation through research and the

Continued on following page.

Continued from previous page.

challenging of one another's ideas is part of the classroom culture she fosters from day one.

All year, students practice generating authentic research questions, evaluating the credibility and relevance of the information they find to answer those questions, and presenting claims to one another that are backed by solid evidence. It isn't uncommon to hear students ask each other, "Where did you find that source?" or "Are you sure those statistics are reliable?" as they present their ideas to one another. In whole-class Socratic seminars, students wrestle with questions such as, "Can a biased article or piece of evidence still be credible?" Elaine finds herself having these types of challenging conversations with her students while supporting them through daily opportunities for interaction and deliberation.

Applying Authentic Learning in the Community

After a full year of practicing these skills in the classroom, Elaine gives her students an authentic assignment requiring them to THINK BIG and use the skills they have acquired to make a contribution in both the local community and in a digital one.

Students in Elaine's class, as well as students in two other teachers' classrooms, are instructed to go out into the community and gather questions people have about history. They then bring the questions back to their class, research answers, and write articles to present answers back out to the community through publication on Google Sites.

Before the articles go live, however, students are expected to digitally critique the articles written by students in another class. The three teachers model how to make value-added comments, as well as how to respectfully leave feedback that is specific and meaningful, something the students innately struggle with. Elaine helps students make connections between the digital community and the physical one by inviting them to reflect on the ways their comments and suggestions would be helpful or meaningless in face-to-face collaboration. At the conclusion of the project, each group's final articles are published and shared with the community members who originally asked the question.

Elaine feels that in the end, it is the job of educators to challenge all students to THINK BIG—to realize they are part of an interconnected, global community full of people with varied viewpoints, experiences, and perspectives. Students must be given opportunities to recognize their biases, thoughtfully consider what they see, and contribute to larger societal conversations in ways that add value to their physical and digital communities. ●

You Can Do It!

While students need to understand some of the realistic consequences that can result from making poor choices online, they also need to see models of respectful online deliberation—just like they need to see models of any new skill you teach. Make it a point to extend the digital citizenship conversation with your students past a list of "do nots" and provide them with the following tools:

- Samples of effective and ineffective online discussion

- Sentence frames to help them craft their own respectful responses

- Opportunities to practice debating and deliberating various viewpoints, both in the classroom and online

5

Networking to Make Meaningful Connections

In October of 2016, I had the pleasure of meeting a very bubbly, sweet, intelligent, 9-year-old girl named Olivia Van Ledtje (@thelivbits). Olivia, better known as LivBit to her 25,000 Twitter followers, is a champion of reading and uses her Vimeo channel, mom-moderated Twitter and Instagram accounts, and a smartphone to film "The LivBits"—a series of one- to three-minute videos in which she shares her reading and thinking about the world around her.

Olivia and her mom started the project after Olivia's looping experience at school left her in the classroom with the same group of cliquish girls two years in a row. These girls did not share her passions for science, sharks, books, and ballet, and were purposefully leaving Olivia out and picking on her. Even though Olivia was feeling bad, her mom, Cyndi, knew that she was an amazing girl with an important voice that should be heard. So she and Olivia started making videos about Olivia's reading and thinking, and together they used social media to connect Olivia with others who shared her passions (Van Ledtje, 2017).

Just twelve short months after her first video, The LivBits has grown tremendously! Olivia has created over seventy videos and interviewed some of her favorite authors, such as Mo Willems. Her work has been featured all over the world, including at educational conferences in Taiwan, Singapore, and England, and she has presented with accomplished authors at national conferences and conventions, including those for NCTE (National Council of Teachers of English), ASCD (Association for Supervision and Curriculum Development), ISTE, and ILA (International Literacy Association). Olivia also visits elementary schools to share her bullying story, her love of reading, and to model positive uses of technology for her peers. Her work inspires both kids and their teachers to share their voices and to make connections that matter.

Traditional Approaches to Digital Citizenship

Traditional approaches to digital citizenship focus on connections forged for entertainment, socialization, or even ill intent, such as harassment or hacking. Lessons about cyberbullying, sexting, and internet addiction reinforce the notion that the internet is mainly a place for inherently negative or shallow, unimportant interactions. When school district policies and web filters restrict students from popular platforms for connecting, such as Facebook and Twitter, it's often because these spaces are considered distractions from, rather than tools for, learning.

Digital citizenship messages that discourage participation by inducing fear—focusing on the negative uses of social media and the consequences of breaking rules or making mistakes—miss the mark in helping students understand how they can make connections that matter.

Participatory Citizenship Approach

If digital citizenship curriculum is designed from a place of assumed participation, we can show our students the value of connecting for reasons other than entertainment and socialization, and help them see the possibilities for unhindered learning, collaborative problem solving, and even opportunities to change the world with the devices in their pockets.

The first step in making this idea a reality is to change the ways we talk about social media in schools. When educators get tired of lessons that focus negatively on social media, they often flip the message and begin talking to students about the value of social media for personal branding and getting noticed. For example, instead of telling students not to post derogatory remarks that a scholarship committee might see, they teach students to post examples of their best self. That way, when students are Googled by a college admissions officer or future employer, all of the amazing things they've done will shine.

While discussions about personal branding are certainly an improvement over messages that focus on what not to post, branding is also not a participatory concept. Branding is a very personal activity that can happen in isolation and does not necessarily result in learning, growth, or valuable connections for the individual using social media to gain attention. In order to move students from independent branders of their own worth to digital citizens seeking valuable connections, we must also teach them how to network.

A network is generally defined as a group or system of interconnected people or things. As educators, we can help students build a network of people they can learn from, offer ideas to, and work with on common interests, much as Oliva from the opening vignette has done.

Table 5.1 helps further differentiate the concepts of branding and networking mindsets.

TABLE 5.1 Branding Mindset Versus Networking Mindset

Branding Mindset	Networking Mindset
How can I get noticed?	How can I become connected with a community?
How can I be visible on every social media platform?	Which social media platforms are used by people in the field?
How can I create an impressive "look" and "feel" to increase my followers?	How can I create ongoing relationships through technology?
What will people offer me because of my brand?	What can I offer to the community?

There are five simple steps you can give students to help them find and connect with personal learning networks:

1. **Reflect.** Spend time considering what types of networks you want to join. Do you wish to perfect a new skill? Learn more about a career field you've considered? Do you want to connect with others who have similar talents? What about finding other people who want to tackle the same problems you do?

2. **Research.** Once you have a purpose for finding a network, it's time to do a little research. Where are people with interests like yours connecting? Many educators, for example, use Twitter as a place to collaborate and share. Crafters flock to Pinterest and Etsy. Artists share their work on DeviantArt. Business professionals follow one another on LinkedIn. Although you have preferred social networks for connecting with friends, you may need to seek out additional platforms that will connect you with a broader network of individuals that you can learn from.

3. **Connect.** Once you have figured out where to connect with others, it's time to get started! Create an account on the appropriate platform(s), if you have not done so already. Search for and follow some of the major people, companies, and accounts in your area of interest.

4. **Observe.** Pay careful attention to the norms of behavior and interaction in the community. How formal is the language? How do people show approval and disapproval of ideas? Who is allowed to start conversations? Is there a community moderator? Spend a sufficient amount of time watching how others in the network interact so that when you are ready to, you will be able to engage thoughtfully and respectfully within the norms of the community.

5. **Contribute.** Networking means learning from others, but also giving some of your experiences and expertise to others in the community as well. Encourage other people's ideas, watch for opportunities to help someone grow, and offer up new ideas where appropriate.

Before long, student will find themselves connected with a network of individuals, building mutually beneficial relationships and using technology to learn and grow in ways they could have never imagined!

Connecting with the Broader Community

One of the most rewarding ways to use the internet is to connect your students with people outside of your physical community. Whether you are teaching a foreign language course, a social studies class, or a piece of literature from a different part of the world, there is value in helping students connect on a personal level with people from the regions of the world they are studying, and there are plenty of platforms and tools to use. Here are a few to help you get started.

Mystery Skype

A Mystery Skype is best described as a game of twenty questions between two classrooms in different parts of the world. The classrooms might be 30 or 3,000 miles apart, but they are linked together via Skype. Students in the classrooms take turns asking one another yes or no questions, attempting to guess the location of their opponent before their own location is guessed.

As students engage in the game, they use their communication skills as well as their abilities in geography and deductive reasoning. Once the game is over, teachers typically give students time to ask one another more personal questions about their schools, lifestyles, and cultures. To get started with Mystery Skype, just head on over to the Skype in the Classroom website (https://education.microsoft.com/skype-in-the-classroom/overview) to learn more. You can also connect with fellow educators who are interested in Skype experiences through the Mystery Skype Facebook group and on Twitter by searching for #MysterySkype.

PenPal Schools

If you and your students are interested in making more in-depth, longer lasting connections, PenPal Schools could be a perfect platform for you! Teachers create a free account at the PenPal Schools website (penpalschools.com) and search for projects to join. Projects are designed to help students grow in world knowledge and build skills for empathizing and perspective-taking while also practicing skills in digital and traditional literacy.

PenPal Schools does all of the difficult work of pairing your students with from one to four pen pals from around the globe. Pen pals log in to the platform asynchronously and learn from various media, including texts, images, and video. Pen pals are also given discussion question on the content to help them start a dialogue about what they've just learned. These projects range from short, one-week opportunities for students to connect, share, and reflect on cultural similarities and differences, to in-depth, six-week-long collaborations that help students dig deeply into topics such as discrimination, immigration, and social justice.

Global Read Aloud

One way to help students learn about varied cultures and parts of the world is to help them explore what makes people unique. Another approach to global collaboration is connecting over shared experiences. The Global Read Aloud began with one teacher making a few connections with others via social media and deciding to share a reading experience among their classrooms. Today, the Global Read Aloud is an opportunity to connect your students with students in other parts of the country around a shared book.

Since its inception seven years ago, the project has continued to grow, and to date, nearly two million students have taken part (Ripp, n.d.). Every year, multiple books are selected for the Global Read Aloud so that students of all ages can participate. During the six-week window for the project, students and their teachers read one or more of the selected books for that year. At the same time, teachers make as many or as few connections as they desire with other participating classrooms. Students are able to share their experiences with the text and hear the perspectives of other readers.

You can learn more and sign up to get started by visiting the Global Read Aloud website (theglobalreadaloud.com). There is also a Global Read Aloud Facebook page and you can connect with the founder of the project, Pernille Ripp on Twitter (@pernilleripp).

Connect with Experts

Skype in the Classroom (https://education.microsoft.com/skype-in-the-classroom/overview) has a whole library of guest experts from around the globe who are available to connect with schools, share their stories, and answer questions from students. Guest speakers include authors and poets, business leaders, scientists, pilots, and even zoo keepers. They are ready and excited to connect with your students, free of charge. Bringing experts into your classroom is an easy way to model what it means to make connections that matter and show your students that learning extends beyond the walls of your classroom.

SPOTLIGHT STORY

From Rural to Global

Ali Schilpp (@AliSchilpp) is a library media specialist at Northern Middle School in Accident, Maryland, a small rural ski town in Garrett County, with a population of less than 500 residents. Ali doesn't let the size of her community stop her students from making connections with people all around the world, though! Ali believes digital citizens should be able to use the tools available to them to learn and grow by connecting with information and experts from around the world.

Ali and her middle school students have reached out to and connected with numerous children's authors thanks to the power of Skype. Her students have been able to have conversations with Tom Angleberger, author of *Origami Yoda*; Margaret Peterson Haddix, author of two famous series—the Shadow Children and The Missing; Gennifer Choldenko, Newberry Award–winning author of *Al Capone Does My Shirts*; and Chris Grabenstein, the hilarious mind behind the series Mr. Lemoncello's Library.

Students thought it was pretty amazing to hear their principal converse with Chris Grabenstein about both growing up in Western Maryland. Through a series of questions and answers, the two determined

Continued on following page.

Continued from previous page.

that their families had both lived on the same street in Cumberland, Maryland! Margaret Peterson Haddix shared funny stories about growing up in rural Ohio; stories that were very relatable to the students in rural Accident. Making these connections helped Ali's middle schoolers realize that not only are best-selling and award-winning authors just a click away, but it's also very possible for rural kids like themselves to grow up and achieve amazing things.

Connecting for Common Goals

While it is certainly fun to connect with famous authors, Ali also wants her students to see how everyday people can use the internet to connect and collaborate around a common goal or problem. Using a web-conferencing tool and some makerspace materials, students from Northern Middle School collaborated with nearly 3,000 other students around the state of Maryland in a "catapult challenge" for Digital Learning Day, a nationwide event promoted by the Alliance for Excellent Education. Students collaborated on teams to build a pom-pom catapult from basic materials like cardboard, plastic spoons, rubber bands, string, and tape. By accessing the webcam, kids in Ali's school were able to share ideas about their innovations and learn from other students all over the state. The students had fun, and teachers were pleased at their ability to work collaboratively in groups, to create and innovate, and to share their ideas with peers they had only met online.

Sharing Life Experiences and Culture

Finally, Ali wants her students to see how they can use the internet to learn about people whose life experiences, backgrounds, cultures, and beliefs may be different from their own. In collaboration with a social studies teacher in her school as well as other school librarians Ali had connected with through a Future Ready Librarians Facebook group, sixth graders at Northern Middle had the opportunity to be "Travel Pals" with other sixth graders from around the country. Students connected via Edmodo and Seesaw to learn more about life in each other's hometowns. By the end of the project, the Northern Middle sixth graders had connected with students from four different states. In addition to learning about geography and practicing their communication skills in very authentic ways, students were visibly excited to connect and correspond in the online forum. -

Being a digital citizen brings so many exciting opportunities for learning, growing, connecting, and collaborating with other digital citizens around the world. Ali, in reflecting on her unique experiences in various public schools, both urban and suburban, and now rural, says that her "goal has always been to provide the most memorable learning experience and to make the library a highly innovative and engaging space, regardless of location. I have found that living in a remote area, though, has been the best incentive to provide new learning opportunities for my students, and feel it has made me a better educator. Making these digital connections with my students has been life-changing." ●

You Can Do It!

One of the most amazing aspects of the internet is the ability to connect with so many different people who all have stories, experiences, and knowledge to share. I have grown tremendously as an educator and scholar because of the connections the internet has allowed me to make with others in my field. Who wouldn't want their students to have exciting learning opportunities, such as the ones Olivia and her mom are carving out with a smartphone and an internet connection? How excited would your students be if you were able to open up new parts of the world to them, the way Ali in rural Maryland did?

The best way to get started is to start small and reflect on your own curricular goals by asking these questions:

- Whom might my students benefit from networking with?

- What one unit, lesson, or project might be even better with the help of a guest expert?

- What might my students be able to contribute to a network of other learners?

6

Making Contributions That Matter

Back in 2009, I was a young second-year teacher at a middle school in Oswego, Illinois. I was teaching three sections of eighth-grade English language arts, and after having been through a year of the curriculum already, I was feeling a little more confident about ways to get creative in my teaching.

One of the assignments that had been passed down over time was how to write a business letter. Students were expected to use proper grammar, spelling, punctuation, and formatting to write a formal business letter to a celebrity or athlete they admired. We used a few websites to look up addresses and sent the letters off in the mail. Throughout my first year of teaching, a few students received mail back, but most of the letters went unanswered.

As I was planning to roll out the business letter assignment for year two, I got a flyer in the mail from Scholastic Reading Club. Scholastic announced that it was partnering with a nonprofit organization called the Pajama Program, which collects brand-new pairs of pajamas for children in foster care and homeless shelters. Scholastic was offering to donate a bedtime story to go along with every pair of brand-new pajamas that schools could raise during a designated window of time.

Something about that flyer made a lightbulb go off in my head, and the business letter assignment got a major makeover! Instead of writing letters to celebrities, my students wrote letters to businesses in our community asking for their support to collect 100 pairs of new pajamas to donate to the Pajama Program. In addition, students wrote friendly letters asking for support from family members and friends.

My classes got incredibly excited when the first few letters came back from our community. Local clothing stores sent gift cards, inviting us to come in and choose some pajamas for our project. A few restaurants in town offered to be designated drop-off locations for community members who wanted to donate. Several parents wrote back saying that they were excited about the project and wanted to spread the word in their own workplaces.

> When students are given authentic audiences for their work, genuine opportunities to make positive contributions to their communities, and the support and guidance of adult mentors, they can do some truly amazing things!

The project took much longer than I anticipated, because it just kept growing! Eventually, the students made commercials to share with other students in the school, created a website to update the community on our progress, and wrote dozens of thank-you notes and emails to companies and community members alike. The students smashed their goal of 100 pairs of pajamas, covering my classroom in nearly 750 pairs.

I was so proud of my students and loved seeing their excitement as the piles of pajamas continued to grow. As a young teacher, I thought I was just taking advantage of a cool opportunity to get my students interested in writing. As a more veteran teacher, I can look back now and see that the success of this project was not an accident.

When students are given authentic audiences for their work, genuine opportunities to make positive contributions to their communities, and the support and guidance of adult mentors, they can do some truly amazing things!

Traditional Approaches to Digital Citizenship

As discussed in Chapter 3, not all contributions are considered equal, and unfortunately, most digital citizenship curricula focus more heavily on behavior management than on positive, productive skill development.

Only 8% of the lessons reviewed in the Mattson (2016) study were designed to teach skills that students would need to make positive contributions in their online communities. This is because lessons about community participation are typically scenario based, whereby a student is given an example of an irresponsible or inappropriate contribution, and is then told what the consequences of such contributions could be. As participants, students are simply told they have a responsibility to avoid behavior that would harm others or ruin their own reputations. While these messages seem logical, the lessons are not introducing students to any alternative forms of contribution.

Imagine how less memorable my business letter unit would have been if I had merely collected papers from students, marked them up with red ink, and handed them back with a reminder not to make the same grammar, spelling, or punctuation errors again. Instead, I chose to show my students a brand-new possibility for their writing—an opportunity to have their voices heard in a way they never had been before. Of course, I was there to support students on each step of the journey as they discovered positive ways to contribute to their community.

Participatory Citizenship Approach

Aside from the opportunities to interact with others in a digital space, digital citizens need a myriad of skills that will allow them to move beyond consumption or connection into meaningful contribution.

In order to help students learn beyond boundaries, engage in meaningful dialogue, and make contributions to digital communities that matter, we have an obligation to foster particular skills through the ways we structure our classrooms and the opportunities we present to our students as digital citizens.

Leveraging Media Literacy to Drive Meaningful Contributions

Many educators use the terms *technological literacy, digital literacy, media literacy,* and sometimes *digital citizenship,* almost interchangeably. It's important to understand the differences between these literacies, however, so that you can see how each one lends itself to a student's ability to make meaningful contribution, and then purposefully foster each one in your own classroom. Here, I'll define each of these areas and explain how media literacy, in particular, can help in the development of participatory citizens.

> Digital citizens need a myriad of skills that will allow them to move beyond consumption or connection into meaningful contribution.

Technological literacy is the ability to operate a device, set up accounts, move around a particular platform or interface, and troubleshoot problems when necessary. It's the most basic of the literacies that students need to possess before gaining entry into a digital community.

Digital literacy includes more than the ability to operate a device. While a variety of definitions and frameworks for digital literacy exist, the most commonly agreed-upon competencies are 1) the ability to decipher meaning from a variety of contexts including audio, images, and video; 2) the ability to match medium, purpose, and audience when communicating; and 3) the ability to locate, analyze, and use reliable sources of information online.

Media literacy is a set of key concepts that help students become critical consumers and intelligent contributors of media in a networked world. While traditional and digital literacies help students access and understand digital information, media literacy helps students critically think about the information they find. Essentially, media literacy is the set of abilities and skills where aural, visual, and digital literacy overlap. These include the ability to understand the power of images and sounds, to recognize and use that power, to manipulate and transform digital media, to distribute them pervasively, and to easily adapt them to new forms (New Media Consortium, 2005, p. 8).

A curriculum rich in media literacy has benefits that are clearly tied to the development of participatory digital citizens who can make meaningful contributions. According to research, media literacy education achieves the following:

- Teaches individuals to become active, engaged media producers and users rather than passive consumers (MediaSmarts, 2015)

- Engages students in real-world issues that allow them to be active citizens and make contributions to civil debate (Jenkins, et.al, 2009; MediaSmarts, 2015)

- Deepens young people's understanding of diversity, identity, perception, and the connections between popular culture, their choices, self-image, and role in their community (MediaSmarts, 2015)

Taking Action to Make a Difference

Meaningful, participatory digital citizenship can be cultivated through direct instruction in technological, digital, and media literacies and by engaging students in participatory, online cultures, encouraging them to explore local and global issues and to use the collaborative technologies at their disposal to work with others and investigate solutions.

These learning opportunities can happen across the curriculum. For example, students in a technology class could give basic computer lessons to senior citizens in a local nursing home. Students could use science classes to identify problems in the local community, such as a littered park, and then use social media to rally support and organize volunteers for a cleanup event. Students in mathematics courses could offer online office hours to help students in their feeder elementary or middle schools with evening homework.

There is also a natural fit for action-based, participatory digital citizenship in social studies education. "Social studies is the ideal staging ground for taking informed action because of its unique role in preparing students for civic life. In social studies, students use disciplinary knowledge, skills, and perspectives to inquire about problems involved in public issues; deliberate with other people about how to define and address issues; take constructive, independent, and collaborative action; reflect on their actions; and create and sustain groups" (National Council for the Social Studies, 2013, pg. 62).

So how can we get students excited about and involved in this type of action-based, participatory work, allowing them to see how their digital contributions can actually make a difference in the world?

- **Give Examples.** Students cannot be what they cannot see, so make sure to show them plenty of examples of citizens coming together to make a positive impact in their local and digital communities. An example of a growing list of young digital citizens who are making a difference can be found on the DigCitUtah website (digcitutah.com/digital-citizenship-kids).

- **Identify Injustices.** Encourage students to brainstorm about injustices they see around them. What are some local issues they feel passionate about? Are there global problems they want to solve? Show students the United Nations 17 Sustainable Development Goals website (www.un.org/sustainabledevelopment) and have them read about various ways to improve the world.

- **Connect.** Use technological connections to find others who are passionate about the work. Are there Facebook groups to join or Twitter accounts to follow? What nonprofit organizations already exist for this type of work?

- **Research.** Have students investigate ways they can contribute to the work that's already being done by others. If they find that no one is taking action yet, have them start digging into the reasons why. As students read, connect, and learn about issues that are most important to them, they should consider what gifts, talents, and ideas they have to offer to the cause and how they can begin to make a difference.

- **Take Action.** Action will look different depending on the work to be done. Your students' first step might be to build a larger network of people to help them. They may need to craft messages for varied audiences, such as lawmakers and legislators as well as the general public. Students may decide a fundraising campaign is necessary or that they need to organize a protest or petition. Whatever the case may be, taking informed action is the only way to truly make a difference.

FEATURED ACTIVITY:
Is Slacktivism Equal to Activism?

Saturday Night Live recently aired a sketch entitled "Thank You, Scott" (C. K., 2017), a tongue-in-cheek nod to a man named Scott who champions the underprivileged, the marginalized, and the oppressed through his witty Tweets, Facebook comments, likes, and shares on social media—all from the comfort of his couch.

People like Scott are sometimes referred to as "armchair activists" or "slacktivists," and there is a lot of debate about the impact, or lack of impact, that social media can have on a particular issue or cause (Seay, 2014). Proponents claim that social media sharing can raise awareness about important issues and spur people toward action. Others say that social media posts are nothing more than token displays of support intended to make users feel good about themselves, and that these tokens do not lead to more meaningful contributions offline (Kristofferson, White, & Peloza, 2014).

In this featured activity, you and your students will explore the ideas of activism and slacktivism in an attempt to answer this essential question: "Is slacktivism a valid form of activism?"

First, preview the *Saturday Night Live* sketch, "Thank You Scott" (C. K., 2017), which can be found on YouTube. If you find it's appropriate for the grade level you teach, show it to your students to get them engaged in the topic. Explain that this satirical piece is one portrayal of the ways people attempt to use social media to bring about change. While the writers of this sketch poked fun at Scott's contributions, others might argue that his posts were worthwhile. Tell students it will be up to them to decide just how meaningful slacktivism is.

Define the following terms for your students:

- **Activism:** "A practice that emphasizes direct, vigorous action especially in support of or opposition to one side of a controversial issue" (Merriam-Webster, 2017).

- **Slacktivism:** "Actions performed via the Internet in support of a political or social cause but regarded as requiring little time or involvement, for example signing an online petition or joining a campaign group on social media" (Oxford Dictionary, 2017).

Allow students to do some research, either independently or in small groups. They should locate articles and examples that will allow them to develop a claim about the value of slacktivism and support it. Please note that there is no one correct answer to the essential question, "Is slacktivism a valid form of activism?" The purpose of this activity is to simply get students exploring the issues and forming a conclusion that they can back with evidence.

Student claims might include (but are not limited to) the following:

- Slacktivism is not a valid form of activism.

- Slacktivism is an important form of activism.

- Slacktivism can lead to tangible change.

- Activism can be enhanced by the work of slacktivists.

- Slacktivism had a huge impact on _____.

For students who need additional support while exploring the issues of activism and slacktivism, you can encourage them to conduct internet searches on:

- ALS Ice Bucket Challenge

- GoFundMe success stories

- Hashtags and social justice

- Activism vs. slacktivism

For students who can be challenged to go deeper with this assignment, ask them to find information on the following:

- Any correlation between a person's social media slacktivism and their offline contributions

- The components of a successful social media campaign for change

- Simple steps people can take to move beyond slacktivism, if they so desire

After students have completed their research and developed a claim about slacktivism and activism that can be supported, there are many ways that they can show what they've learned. Students could write a short essay, stating their claim and then providing examples to support it. You could facilitate a whole-class deliberation, allowing students to talk out their ideas and evidence in a large group setting. Students could also choose to film a persuasive video, either encouraging or discouraging engagement through slacktivism. The final product is up to you!

Whether your students are determined to change the world or are just dipping their toes into the waters of community contribution, this research activity can allow them to see the relationships between their online and offline contributions.

SPOTLIGHT STORY

Open World Cause

The story of Open World Cause is a long, but inspiring one that started with a teacher's challenge and a student willing to take up the call to action in a very real way. In 2010, Benjamin Honeycutt was starting his senior year of high school in Kansas. He anticipated an easy year, but when his senior class was challenged by one of their English teachers to "leave behind a legacy," Ben felt compelled to act (Open World Cause, 2015a).

Ben's father put him in touch with an educator in Nepal named Govinda, who was committed to providing an affordable education to the students in his community of Bageswori. During his senior year, Ben raised enough awareness and money to send the Shantideep Adarsh Vidhyasadan (SAV) School two laptops, internet access, and a small library. In April, 2011, Ben had his first successful Skype call with Govinda and his students (Open World Cause, 2013). Ben pulled up a chair to his webcam along with his dad and his friend Connor Janzen, and the three of them exchanged hellos and waves with the smiling faces at the SAV School that they had been able to support from halfway around the world.

The summer after Ben and Connor's senior year, monsoon season destroyed two of the classrooms in the SAV School. The boys knew they could not simply turn their backs on Govinda and his students now that their senior year was complete. Together, they committed to keeping the project going. Connor built a new website for the project, and the boys raised enough money to rebuild the demolished classrooms. That fall, the boys took the Open World Cause with them to the University of Kansas as a student organization (Open World Cause, 2015a).

The work that Ben and Connor did to help the SAV School during and just after their senior year is only the beginning of this inspiring story. Just as their senior English teacher ignited a spark of passion in the boys, their work has influenced many others to take up the torch for global collaboration and social justice, too.

Growing a Team of Helping Hands

In August of 2013, third-grade teacher Wendi Pillars had the opportunity to spend three weeks at the SAV School as a visiting teacher and representative of Open World Cause. Before she left her third-grade students in North Carolina, she showed them some photos of the school. Wendi's students, from low-income homes themselves, were stunned by the generally poor classroom conditions including a lack of electricity and running water. By lunchtime, four of Wendi's students had started a fundraising campaign to support the students in Nepal. Over the weeks that followed, the students decorated donation boxes, partnered with fifth graders to put a message on the school's morning news broadcast, and sacrificed their own spare change as they watched their total grow (Open World Cause, 2015c). Wendi's third graders got to Skype with Govinda too, which further fueled their interest in the country of Nepal and the SAV School. By the time Wendi left for SAV, her students had raised $248, enough to sponsor a Pre–K classroom for an entire year (Pillars, 2013).

Connor and Ben also inspired another classroom teacher, Kim Herron, who was teaching sixth grade in Kansas in 2013. With the support of Open World Cause, Kim's students partnered with Govinda's to design a dream school. The students in Nepal drew pictures of their ideal school building, and Kim's students turned those drawings into 3-D images using Google SketchUp (Open World Cause, 2015b). The Google SketchUp designs were printed on the 3-D printer at Kim's school and shown to Govinda's students through blog postings and a Skype call between the schools (Herron, 2013). The collaboration gave Kim's students an opportunity to use a variety of skills for an authentic purpose and gave Govinda's students a chance to see their dream school drawings realized. Both groups of students benefitted from the opportunity to interact and learn from and about one another as well.

One of the most remarkable pieces of this story is that Ben and Connor really did leave a legacy at their high school, the way their senior English teacher challenged them to. Little did the boys know, but there was a freshman paying attention to the work Ben and Connor were doing, and he felt inspired by it. When Garrett Wilkinson started his senior year and was challenged with the same legacy project, he knew he wanted to contribute to the work Ben and Connor had started three years earlier. Garrett's dream was to provide clean water to populations that lacked access to it. He learned that water-borne illnesses were a serious threat to students from Govinda's SAV School, with at least one student a day missing out on classes because of sickness (Open World Cause, 2015a).

Garrett joined the Open World Cause team in 2014 as the executive director of their clean water outreach known as Project Purus. Garrett's work has helped Open World Cause distribute Sawyer PointONE™ water filtration systems to families through partnerships with SAV School, Trika School, Child Protection Centers, the Umbrella Foundation, and Next Generation Nepal in Nepal. Recently, the work of

Project Purus has extended to churches and community centers in Haiti as well (Open World Cause, 2015b).

The Power at Our Fingertips

In 2015, Ben, Connor, and Garrett had the opportunity to travel to Nepal for the first time, meeting Govinda and working in the community. Later that year, Open World Cause transitioned into an official nonprofit organization. The trio has brought on a team of dedicated volunteers and continues to look for partnerships in the United States and abroad. Open World Cause is currently serving communities in multiple countries, including Nepal, Haiti, and Kenya.

What started as a challenge from a high school teacher has turned into a full-fledged mission with digital citizenship as just one of its guiding principles: "the power of globalization through digital resources has utterly changed the way humans see and interact with the world. We do our part to seek out common tools that can change a person's life for the better. Immense power rests within our fingertips and in our devices, so what's stopping us?" (Open World Cause, 2015d).

You Can Do It!

Changing the world isn't easy, but the internet can help us find people who share our passions and care about the same causes. And, as cliché as it sounds, two heads are better than one when it comes to making a difference! Try the following activities with your students to help inspire them to make contributions that matter:

- Share stories of other teens that are making a difference.

- Collaborate as a class on a service project that aligns with your curriculum.

- Help your students use digital tools to connect with causes they care about.

Conclusion

For far too long, adults have talked about digital citizenship as a list of rules for students to follow. I propose that we expand our conceptual understanding of the term and begin thinking about well-rounded digital citizens as an outcome goal of a future-ready education.

The citizens of today are not only members of their physical communities, but are also members of digital ones. Just as social studies and civics education is intended to create well-rounded members of our physical societies, digital citizenship education should equip students with the skills and competencies to be intelligent consumers, meaningful contributors, and thoughtful collaborators in online spaces.

My challenge to educators is to find opportunities to be in digital community with your students. Use those opportunities to encourage student voice, empower students as members of the community, model meaningful dialogue, and allow students to reflect upon the roles they play in our global society. Help students see that the connections they forge online can help them learn and grow, but can also lead to opportunities for changing the world.

I certainly cannot flip the script on the perceived value of digital citizenship education overnight, but my hope is that the ideas presented in this book will allow you to start a conversation with a colleague, an administrator, or even your students about the ways our definitions of community and citizenship are ever-evolving.

References

Activism. (2017). In *Merriam-Webster.com*. Retrieved May 15, 2017, from https://www.merriam-webster.com/dictionary/activism

American Association of School Librarians. (2011). School libraries count: Supplemental report on digital citizenship. Retrieved from: www.ala.org/aasl/sites/ala.org.aasl/files/content/researchandstatistics/slcsurvey/2011/AASL-SLC-2011-DIGITAL-FINALweb.pdf

boyd, d. (2014). *It's complicated: The networked social lives of teens.* New Haven, CT: Yale University Press.

Bulka, M. (2014, February 26). #leydenpride: A student perspective. [Blog post]. Retrieved from http://leydenlearn365.blogspot.com/2014/02/leydenpride-student-perspective.html

C. K., Louis (Guest host). (2017, April 8). Louis C. K./The chainsmokers [Television series episode]. In L. Michaels (Executive producer), *Saturday night live.* New York, NY: NBC.

Common Core State Standards Initiative. (2010). *Common core state standards for English language arts & literacy in history/social studies, science, and technical subjects.* Washington, DC: National Governors Association Center for Best Practices and Council of Chief State School Officers.

Couros, G. (2015, January 17). *3 things students should have before they leave high school.* Retrieved from The Principal of Change website: georgecouros.ca/blog/archives/5025

Dewey, J. (1909). *Moral principles in education.* Boston, MA: Houghton Mifflin Company.

Dewey, J. (1916). *Democracy and education: An introduction to the philosophy of education.* New York: Macmillan.

Gardner, H., & Davis, K. (2013). *The App generation: How today's youth navigate identity, intimacy, and imagination in a digital world*. New Haven, CT: Yale University Press.

Graff, G., Birkenstein, C., & Durst, R. (2006). *They say, I say: The moves that matter in academic writing, with readings*. New York: W. W. Norton.

Herron, K. (2013). *Design discussions*. Retrieved from www.usd448. com/herronshappenings/OpenWorldProject2013/Blog/Blog.html

International Society for Technology in Education. (2016). *ISTE Standards for Students*. Retrieved from https://www.iste.org/ standards/standards/for-students

Ito, M. (2009). Introduction. In M. Ito (Ed.), *Hanging out, messing around, and geeking out: Kids living and learning with new media*. (pp. 1–28). Cambridge, MA: MIT Press.

Ito, M., Baumer, S., Bittanti, M., boyd, d., Cody, R., Herr-Stephenson, B., Horst, H. A. ... & Tripp, L. (2009). *Hanging out, messing around, and geeking out: Kids living and learning with new media*. Cambridge, MA: MIT Press.

James, C. (2014). *Disconnected: Youth, new media, and the ethics gap*. Cambridge, MA: MIT Press.

Jenkins, H., Purushotma, R., Weigel, M., Clinton, K., & Robison, A. J. (2009). *Confronting the challenges of participatory culture: Media education for the 21st century*. Cambridge, MA: MIT Press.

Joint Committee on National Health Education Standards. (2007). *National health education standards: Achieving excellence* (2nd ed.). Atlanta, GA: American Cancer Society.

Kristofferson, K., White, K., & Peloza, J. (2014). The nature of slacktivism: How the social observability of an initial act of token support affects subsequent prosocial action. *Journal of Consumer Research, 40*(6), 1149–1166.

Lenhart, A., Madden, M., Smith, A., Purcell, K., Zickuhr, K., & Rainie, L. (2011, November 9). *Teens, kindness and cruelty on social network sites: How American teens navigate the new world of digital citizenship*. Retrieved from Pew Research Center's Internet & American Life Project website: pewinternet.org/Reports/2011/ Teens-and-social-media.aspx

Long, Shannon Perrilloux. (2014, October 8). BEFORE you post: Think [Image]. Retrieved from www.technologyrocksseriously. com/2014/10/before-you-post-think.html#.WNl5-28rKpZ

Markey, J. (2016, August 3). Chance favors the connected school [Blog post]. Retrieved from jmarkeyap.blogspot.com/2016/08/chance-favors-connected-school.html

Martin, P. (2017, February 23). Yorkville High School responds to students' racist tweets. Retrieved from Yorkville Patch website: patch.com/illinois/naperville/ yorkville-high-school-responds-students-racist-tweets

Mattson, K. (2016). *Moving beyond personal responsibility: A critical discourse analysis of digital citizenship curricula* (Doctoral dissertation). Northern Illinois University, DeKalb, IL.

MediaSmarts. (2015). *Media literacy fundamentals*. Retrieved from MediaSmarts website: mediasmarts.ca/digital-media-literacy/ general-information/digital-media-literacy-fundamentals/ media-literacy-fundamentals

Meyer, E. J. (2016, December 5). Free speech vs. hate speech: What's the difference and what can schools do? [Blog post]. Retrieved from https://www.psychologytoday.com/blog/ gender-and-schooling/201612/free-speech-vs-hate-speech

Meyer, E. J. (2010, December 30). Cyberbullying, sexual harassment vs. free speech—where's the line? [Blog post]. Retrieved from https:// www.psychologytoday.com/blog/gender-and-schooling/201012/ cyberbullying-sexual-harassment-vs-free-speech-where-s-the-line

National Council for the Social Studies (2013). *College, career, and civic life (C3) framework for social studies state standards: Guidance for enhancing the rigor of K-12 civics, economics, geography, and history*. Silver Spring, MD: National Council for the Social Studies.

New Media Consortium (2005). *A global imperative: The report of the 21st century literacy summit.* Retrieved from the New Media Consortium website: www.nmc.org/pdf/Global_Imperative.pdf

Open World Cause (2013, July 16). *First Skype call with the SAV students.* [Video file]. Retrieved from https://www.youtube.com/watch?v=ft2RU1D3tTA

Open World Cause. (2015a). *Our story.* Retrieved from the Open World Cause website: https://openworldcause.org/our-story

Open World Cause. (2015b). *Project: Purus.* Retrieved from the Open World Cause website: https://openworldcause.org/causes/project-purus

Open World Cause. (2015c). *Teach.* Retrieved from the Open World Cause website: https://openworldcause.org/causes/teach

Open World Cause. (2015d). *Who we are.* Retrieved from the Open World Cause website: https://openworldcause.org/who-we-are

Passeport, F. (2017, February 1). *How do we get our teenagers to develop a positive digital footprint?* Retrieved from EdTechReview website: http://edtechreview.in/trends-insights/insights/2646-positive-digital-footprint-and-reputation

Pillars, W. (2013, August 15). *From North Carolina to Nepal: Connecting students to make an impact.* Retrieved from GOOD website: https://www.good.is/articles/from-north-carolina-to-nepal-connecting-students-to-make-an-impact

Prensky, M. (2001, September/October). Digital natives, digital immigrants, part 1. *On the Horizon, 9*(5), 1–6.

Ribble, M. (2015). *Digital citizenship in schools: Nine elements all students should know* (3rd ed.). Arlington, VA: International Society for Technology in Education.

Ripp, P. (n.d.) *About the GRA.* Retrieved from Global Read Aloud website: https://theglobalreadaloud.com

Seay, L. (2014, March 12). Does slacktivism work? *Washington Post.* Retrieved from https://www.washingtonpost.com/news/monkey-cage/wp/2014/03/12/does-slacktivism-work/?utm_term=.a7ccbd730ada

Singer, N. (2016, November 5). New item on the college admission checklist: LinkedIn profile. *New York Times.* Retrieved from https://www.nytimes.com/2016/11/06/technology/new-item-on-the-college-admission-checklist-linkedin-profile.html?smid=tw-share&_r=0

Slacktivism. (2017). In *OxfordDictionaries.com.* Retrieved May 11, 2017, from https://en.oxforddictionaries.com/definition/slacktivism

Sullivan, T. (2016, September 3). Digital citizenship: Why is the social media conversation so negative? [Blog post]. Retrieved from https://timmysullivan.com/tag/digital-citizenship

Van Ledtje, O. (2017). #NeverLetAnyoneDullYourSunshine. [Video blog]. Retrieved from www.thelivbits.com/videos.html

Warnick, Bryan R. (2013). *Understanding student rights in schools: Speech, religion, and privacy in educational settings.* New York: Teachers College Press.

Westheimer, J., & Kahne, J. (2004). What kind of citizen? The politics of educating for democracy. *American educational research journal, 41*(2), 237–269.

Index

Bring Dr. Kristen Mattson to your school, university, or conference!

Dr. Kristen Mattson is an award-winning writer, experienced teacher, talented speaker, and exciting workshop facilitator. Dr. Mattson balances every learning experience with the most current and relevant research, personal experiences from the field, and opportunities for participants to engage, reflect, interact, and apply.

Her popular workshop topics* include:

- Digital Citizenship: Moving Beyond Personal Responsibility
- Digital, Media, and Critical Media Literacies as Avenues to Digital Citizenship
- Digital Citizenship and Media Literacy Across the Content Areas
- The Intersection of Social Media and Social Justice
- School Librarians as Instructional Partners
- Embracing the Modern School Library

These topics, and many more, can all be personalized to fit your organization's needs.

Connect with her at **www.DrKMattson.com**
or on Twitter **@DrKMattson**